The Cultural Landscape

The Cultural Landscape

Christopher L. Salter

University of California,
Los Angeles

Duxbury Press
A Division of Wadsworth Publishing Company, Inc.
Belmont, California

Dedication

The Cultural Landscape is dedicated to

> James J. Parsons
>
> Clarence J. Glacken
>
> Paul Wheatley

The sage Shun appointed See to be the minister of instruction and said to him, "Encourage them; help them; give them wings:—thus causing them to become possessors of themselves. Then follow this up by stimulating them. . . ."

from *Mencius*

> and so it has been.

Duxbury Press
A Division of Wadsworth Publishing Company, Inc.

L. C. Cat. Card No.: 75-144141

Printed in the United States of America

1 2 3 4 5 6 7 8 9 10 — 75 74 73 72 71

Foreword

Geographers often are wont to claim as fellow professionals a great many of those persons who once spoke clearly or wrote well about the ways in which mankind has explored, exploited, organized, and marked up the Earth. Thus, Herodotus, Alexander von Humboldt, and Lewis Mumford have been adopted into our ranks, although other disciplines have also laid claim to all three. Geographers have no monopoly on the consideration of how man lives and performs on the Earth, even though geography is the original and central discipline dealing with manifestations of physical, biotic, and cultural processes shaping the surface of our globe. In the tremendous growth of modern knowledge about the Earth, many new disciplines have spun off the mother subject, each dealing with a specialized order of developments.

Nonetheless, far too many geography books appear to have been compounded out of materials published in professional geography journals alone. For that reason, the present volume is a refreshing and valuable departure. It incorporates materials from such fields as literature, economics, and biology, thus revealing geography to be the central discipline that it truly is.

Christopher Salter's interests in the cultural landscapes of the Earth are catholic in nature, and his awareness of sources is wide and varied, for he did not begin his learning career within the restrictive confines of a particular school of geographic thought. This volume is the raw stuff of cultural geography in most explicit terms, emphasizing the human action of peoples who have helped create the actual world in which we now live.

Salter has expressed his own conceptual framework about the cultural development of the Earth by grouping the selections in four basic categories. Exploration of territories and landscapes, usage of resources discovered therein, and organization of peoples, space, and resources are sound basic elements for any geographic presentation. The fourth category is fittingly comprised of various discussions of just where man's use of the Earth is leading him. That the materials for such a presentation come from a wide range of literatures is less important than the fact that they make it possible to understand the rounded process of the making of the contemporary Earth.

J. E. Spencer

Introduction: A Note on Focus

The cultural landscape is the artificial landscape man creates, remaking nature to better provide himself with his short-term needs of food, shelter, clothing, and entertainment. He has, however, seldom focused on the long-range ramifications of such change, nor acknowledged his immense power as an agent of change. Not until the last several years, in fact, has alarm developed over our patterns of landscape modification. It has engendered critical and urgent interest in the cultural landscape.

This anthology is intended to give some structure to the study of man's reshaping of his environment. Three major factors stand out in this transformation process. One is man's mobility, the second is his husbandry of the earth, and the third is his organization of space, each being an effort toward maximizing his ability to draw from the land. This triad describes what has created the contemporary cultural landscape, which we consider at the end of this collection.

As one becomes involved with these readings, he cannot help but sharpen his own landscape appreciation. A ghetto alleyway calls to mind the problems faced by migrants to hostile new environments; an open air produce market adjacent to a new supermarket suggests the variety of man's production of food and its packaging and how this all relates to his need for sustenance; the negotiation of a freeway interchange makes one aware of man's curious patterns of spatial organization. All these prove that the student of the cultural landscape is as much in need of an inquisitive eye as he is of the library.

Understanding the genesis, growth, and morphology of a given landscape, then, is the primary goal of this book. By considering the evidences of man's mobility, husbandry, and spatial organization, one may better understand the nature of the landscape which surrounds him today. Such is the justification for studying cultural geography and, hopefully, for reading *The Cultural Landscape*.

Acknowledgments

An anthology is not unlike a man's library. And a library grows through contact with many and varied people. This collection is the product of shared readings, conversations and arguments with numerous students, teachers and friends. To them I give thanks for suggestions and criticism. People who have been particularly helpful in bringing this collection to publication have been William Thomas, Jr., J. E. Spencer, Susan Rustin, Robert Roundy, Jack Mrowka, Dawn Wheeler, Peggy Burbank Schwieger, Maxine Feifer, Aaron Gallup, Susan Trevitt, and cool-headed Linda.

Contents

The Mobility of Man 1

Husbandry of the Earth 63

The Organization of Space 143

The Contemporary Cultural Landscape   *221*

The mobility of man

Most people never travel beyond the territorial limits of their villages. Before the domestication of plants, when man had to gather and hunt to garner the evening meal, his wanderings were still generally restricted to a familiar, intensively harvested region. The radius of this world and the village world which followed after plant domestication extended no more than five miles in most cases. Far-flung migration and continued long-range mobility, in other words, have not been typical characteristics of man.

But some men have moved—and moved great distances. These peoples represent only a minority, but they have generated much of the complexity and variation in cultural patterns which characterize our Earth. This quality of mobility, expressive of man's exceptional tolerance of varied environments and diet, is the dominant theme in the first section of this anthology.

Myth and man's migration

What qualities characterize the men and the movements that have done so much to bring change in their goal areas (the areas to which they migrate)? Individual giants such as Captain James Cook, folk such as those described in the Steinbeck selection from The Grapes of Wrath, the Africans flocking to urban fringes, the peasants moving into the Peruvian montane hinterland—all possess common qualities which explain their departure from hearth and tradition. Closer consideration of these diverse peoples and their mobility reveals themes intrinsic to migration, exploration, and discovery. These recurring elements provide the unity underlying the events described in these sections.

In any migration there must be a sense of hope and anticipation, or there would be no decision to move. Such hope is invariably a combination of reality and desire, with the latter frequently dominating in significant migrations. Moreover, the mixture is frequently influenced by myth, so that the gap between what migrants expected and what was actually available to them was never bridged; the "hard reality" of the goal area seldom coincides with the migrants' preconceptions.

For the Joads and thousands of their Okie counterparts, the myth was fair wage labor and some chance for land; for Captain Cook, the myth was the sea passage across the top of North America which would link the Atlantic and the Pacific. For the Africans forsaking traditional rural hearths in their migration to the cities, the myth is a more complex collage of wage labor, urban entertainments, and hopes of rising to some affluence. To Christopher Columbus, the myth of the New World (to him nothing more than an island festoon off the eastern shores of China) justified his giving the last 14 years of his life to continued exploration in the Antilles. In virtually all cases of significant explorations and subsequent migrations, the catalyst for the movement has contained mythical elements. In the case of the Dust Bowl migrants, the myth was very consciously generated, in part for an economic reason. The handbills that proliferated across the dust-choked states depicted a seductively easy alternative to the nonproductivity of the dry farms. Financed by railroad and agricultural interests, this California myth effectively recruited cheap labor for labor-intensive agricultural pursuits. The resulting influx utterly changed the complexion of California.

The character of the migration myth, of course, affects the character of the migration. People who migrate in quest of a city of gold are going to have a different cultural influence on the goal area than those who migrate because they are promised a section of land to own and farm themselves. Families who leave the security and relative comfort of their hearth areas because of the promise of religious freedom are going to have a more marked cultural influence on the goal area than those who are moving for short-term employment. (However, the changes brought upon people in the actual process of migration tend to blur this initial cultural distinction.)

Perhaps the most stunning characteristic of myth-stimulated migration, however, is the inertia which it has overcome in prompting man to move—an act which for most of man's history has been discouraged by tradition. Whether the initial migrants came in quest of the land of the Great Khan, the discovery of the water passage between the Atlantic and Pacific Oceans, or the ever-distant cities of gold, the main fact is that they were stimulated to come. This is what has created ever-changing cultural landscapes all over man's world.

In the migration to a marginal region, the information that the potential migrants in the hearth area have about the goal area is focused on its inhospitality. Here, clearly, the "myth" is not so alluring; but still they migrate. Obviously, then, some migrations take place because of intolerable conditions in the hearth area. Even knowledge of vigorous environmental challenge and reported failures of previous migrants does not stop the migration stream if there is at least some possibility of success. (Perhaps myth serves as a rationalization for migrating only as long as man needs such an excuse.)

Thus migration can be stimulated by a full range of things—from mythical goals to unpleasant reality in the hearth area. The changes generated by migration, however, are what concern us here.

The act of mobility as an agent of change in itself

The process of migration itself brings about change. In the Steinbeck selection, the people tend to mellow and become more socially cohesive in response to the stress of the journey. The histories of virtually all far-flung migrations make apparent the increasing importance of physical endurance and psychological flexibility as the journey goes on. Initial social status and racial stock, then, naturally become less important.

The reception in the goal area further changes the migrant. The Queenslanders gave no welcome to the Kanaka unless they performed their explicit economic tasks well and cheaply. The people of California basically saw the arrival of the Okies with alarm. The warm response which Columbus was given by the timid and unlearned Arawaks was soon to change as the second, third, and fourth voyages brought many more intruders and as the Caribs were threatened for the first time by a people more militant than themselves. Such responses to immigrants work a change upon a migrating group as well as upon the goal area population.

Distance or length of time enroute does not necessarily define the magnitude of change experienced by the mobile human. The city-bound Africans from rural hearths, depicted in Stanley Meisler's article, undergo more profound change because of the great dissimilarity of hearth and goal areas than do the serranos of

Stewart's Peruvian example, who have crossed more spatial distance but have minimized the psychological distance through maintaining rural customs.

Migration and the importance of diffusion

If man's mobility and migration were to offer no new techniques or material goods to peoples of the goal area, such movement would affect nothing more than the dots on population maps. In fact, however, all migration generates an evaluation in the goal area of introduced customs and goods, as well as a reevaluation of traditional customs and goods. Migration may be seen as a method of uniting two cultures, and the cultural geographer is interested in studying the effects.

In the first section, for example, Mark Twain bitterly satirizes the Kanaka for the thin veneer of "civilization" they bring back to the New Hebrides. These people serve well as an example of primarily unilateral cultural change with little or no influence upon the society of the goal area. The men who followed Columbus and peopled the New World served as agents of a basically unilateral cultural change, with the change focused upon the goal area, with a massive obliteration, or at least eclipsing, of native cultures.

The cultural transformation generated by an inflow of migrants can be interpreted as having both positive and negative value to the goal area. The Spanish economic control of the New World brought sugar cane, coffee, and rice to European society. The underemployed rural African population flowing so actively toward the urban centers, affords a reservoir of cheap labor while it places heavy strains upon municipal services. Even the lowland farmers who are seeking new homes in the Apurimac Valley in montane Peru provide labor for the hacendados while they develop their own farm sites on the margins of the river.

To the cultural geographer the economic benefits gained from the migration are complementary to the physical and biotic changes wrought by such movement. For example, Captain James Cook felt it his responsibility to transport the English farm pig to "the islands in the South Seas where the English had been treated with so much hospitality." His point in bringing these animals to the islands was not to

afford feastmeats for the welcome of the English but rather to introduce stock to the islands which would grub in the forests, slowly become a part of the local fauna, and subsequently be part of the diet of the islands.

Some of the settlers who constituted a portion of the poorly prepared migrants chronicled by Dunbar, brought with them crops that had been a part of their traditional planting systems. Though misconceptions about the climate rendered many of the species either fruitless or less productive in the American Northeast, new plant breeds were introduced which survived or even flourished. The reverse direction flow of maize (though it was already initiated by the earlier Columbian voyages), changed not only European but also Asian agriculture as it diffused to hill lands and moist lands in the Eastern Hemisphere.

In the articles mentioned above, the identities of the interacting cultures were known, and the effects of interaction were the object of study. Sometimes, however, it is the effect which is known and the origin of the effect which is in question. Such is the case in Edwin Doran's pursuit of the genesis and diffusion of the leeboard as a navigational aid. The very fact that Doran is unable to pinpoint with final certainty the genesis of the leeboard points up the difficulty in knowing exact paths of diffusion. But the actual phenomenon of diffusion is at times not as important as the resultant use pattern upon the cultural landscape. The avenues of movement are of interest, but the dominant concern is the reshaping of the area of adoption. Ian Matley demonstrates another tool of the cultural geographer in tracing the diffusion of a landscape feature. Through careful examination of linguistic evidence he offers the tentative conclusion that the infield-outfield pattern of agricultural land use originated in Scotland. Matley, like Doran, concludes his article with an admission that the full sequence of diffusion is not totally comprehended, but both articles show the progress toward the definition of areas of genesis which cultural geographers can make by use of a wide variety of primary sources.

Conclusions

The cultural geographer views man's mobility with a triparte perspective: the catalyst for movement, the effect of movement on trait or people in motion, and the consequences of such movement. In any migration, cultural changes are likely to be evident in both the hearth and goal area, causing modification of the landscape, which is the cultural geographer's central concern. Alterations of people, flora, fauna, and traits during the trek leave their imprint both on the paths traveled and the ultimate goal. The arrival may generate new campaigns of exploration and discovery, or it may stimulate the out-migration of resident population of the goal area who find that the arrival of the new people and new culture makes their hearth less desirable. In any case, there are the patterns of change and adaptation which produce new cultural landscapes. And man's mobility is the catalyst for the entire process.

A letter written by Columbus following the completion of his first voyage to the New World

CHRISTOPHER COLUMBUS

1

When Columbus wrote this first letter in February and March of 1493, he was eager to gain two ends. The first was to secure his place in both history and the eyes of the court at Seville as a man of daring and foresight. The second, and the one which renders this letter less accurate as a description of the Greater Antilles in the late fifteenth century, was to assure the court that enough potential wealth existed in the islands to justify not only continued but expanded exploration in this archipelago. The initial concept of exploration was hence changed to a plan of conquest and settlement.

To this end we find a number of references to gold and to the willingness of the local inhabitants to exchange it carelessly for things of little or no value to the Spanish. Cathay is suggested as being on the margin of this cluster of islands, while exotics such as rhubarb and cinnamon are spoken of as existing in abundance. Even the name given to the island first landed on, Guanaham, was later represented by Columbus as referring to Kublai Khan, *explaining in part his lifelong belief that he had in fact found sea passage to the Orient.*

On the other hand, Columbus was correct in his perception of the distinction between the timorous Arawaks and the more militant Caribs, and his noting of the winter verdance is part of what initiated the first European migration. He was successful in creating interest in the prizes he had gained, for he was in command of not three ships but 17 when he returned in September of 1493 for his second of

four voyages to the Caribbean in quest of the "land of the Great Khan."

A Letter sent by Columbus to [Luis de Santangel] Chancellor of the Exchequer [of Aragon], respecting the Islands found in the Indies, enclosing another for their Highnesses.

Sir,—Believing that you will take pleasure in hearing of the great success which our Lord has granted me in my voyage, I write you this letter, whereby you will learn how in thirty-three days' time I reached the Indies with the fleet which the most illustrious King and Queen, our Sovereigns, gave to me, where I found very many islands thickly peopled, of all which I took possession without resistance, for their Highnesses by proclamation made and with the royal standard unfurled. To the first island that I found I gave the name of *San Salvador*, in remembrance of His High Majesty, who hath marvellously brought all these things to pass; the Indians call it *Guanaham*. To the second island I gave the name of *Santa-Maria de Concepcion*; the third I called *Fernandina*; the fourth, *Isabella*; the fifth, *Juana* [Cuba]; and so to each one I gave a new name. When I reached *Juana*, I followed its coast to the westward, and found it so large that I thought it must be the mainland,—the province of *Cathay;* and, as I found neither towns nor villages on the sea-coast, but only a few hamlets, with the inhabitants, of which I could not hold conversation, because they all immediately fled, I kept on the same route, thinking that I could not fail to light upon some large cities and towns. At length, after the proceeding of many leagues [league = three miles] and finding that nothing

R. H. Major, ed. and trans., *Selected Letters of Christopher Columbus* (London: The Hakluyt Society, 1870), pp. 1–18.

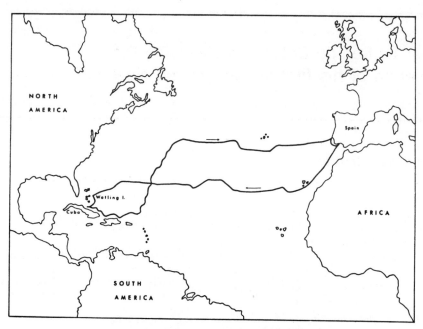

The first voyage of Christopher Columbus 1492–1493

new presented itself, and that the coast was leading me northwards (which I wished to avoid, because winter had already set in, and it was my intention to move southwards; and because moreover the winds were contrary), I resolved not to wait for a change in the weather, but returned to a certain harbour which I had remarked, and from which I sent two men ashore to ascertain whether there was any king or large cities in that part. They journeyed for three days and found countless small hamlets with numberless inhabitants, but with nothing like order; they therefore returned. In the meantime I had learned from some other Indians whom I had seized, that this land was certainly an island; accordingly, I followed the coast eastward for a distance of one hundred and seven leagues, where it ended in a cape. From this cape, I saw another island to the eastward at a distance of eighteen leagues from the former to which I gave the name of *La Española* [the island of Hispaniola]. Thither I went, and followed its northern coast to the eastward (just as I had done with the coast of *Juana*), one hundred and seventy-eight full leagues due east. This island, like all the others, is extraordinarily large, and this one extremely so. In it are many seaports with which none

that I know in Christendom can bear comparison, so good and capacious that it is wonder to see. The lands are high, and there are many very lofty mountains with which the island of *Cetefrey* cannot be compared. They are all most beautiful, of a thousand different shapes, accessible, and covered with trees of a thousand kinds of such great height that they seemed to reach the skies. I am told that the trees never lose their foliage, and I can well understand it, for I observed that they were as green and luxuriant as in Spain in the month of May. Some were in bloom, others bearing fruit, and others otherwise according to their nature. The nightingale was singing as well as other birds of a thousand different kinds; and that, in November, the month in which I myself was roaming amongst them. There are palm-trees of six or eight kinds, wonderful in their beautiful variety; but this is the case with all the other trees and fruits and grasses; trees, plants, or fruits filled us with admiration. It contains extraordinary pine groves, and very extensive plains. There is also honey, a great variety of birds, and many different kinds of fruits. In the interior there are many mines of metals and a population innumerable. *Española* is a wonder. Its mountains and plains, and meadows, and fields, are so beautiful and rich for planting and sowing, and rearing cattle of all kinds, and for building towns and villages. The harbours on the coast, and the number and size and wholesomeness of the rivers, most of them bearing gold, surpass anything that would be believed by one who had not seen them. There is a great difference between the trees, fruits, and plants of this island and those of *Juana*. In this island there are many spices and extensive mines of gold and other metals. The inhabitants of this and of all the other islands I have found or gained intelligence of, both men and women, go as naked as they were born, with the exception that some of the women cover one part only with a single leaf of grass or with a piece of cotton, made for that purpose. They have neither iron, nor steel, nor arms, nor are they competent to use them, not that they are not well-formed and of handsome stature, but because they are timid to a surprising degree. Their only arms are reeds cut in the seeding time, to which they fasten small sharpened sticks, and even these they dare not use; for on several occasions it has happened that I have sent ashore two or three men to some village to hold a parley, and the people have come out in countless numbers, but, as soon as they saw our men approach, would flee with such precipitation that a father would not even stop to protect his son; and this not because any harm had been done to any of them, for, from the first, wherever I went and got speech with them, I gave them all that I had, such as cloth and many other things, without receiving anything in return, but they are, as I have described, incurably timid. It is true that when they are reassured and have thrown off this fear, they are guileless, and so liberal of all they have that no one would believe it who had not seen it. They never refuse anything that they possess when it is asked of them; on the contrary, they offer it themselves, and they exhibit so much loving kindness that they would even give their hearts; and, whether it be something of value or of little worth that is offered to them, they are satisfied. I forbade that worthless things, such as pieces of broken porringers and broken glass, and ends of straps, should be given to them; although, when they succeeded in obtaining them, they thought they possessed the finest jewel in the world. It was ascertained that a sailor received for a leather strap a piece of gold weighing two *castellanos* and a half, and others received for other objects of far less value, much more. For new *blancas* [a copper coin of little value] they would give all that they had, whether it was two or three *castellanos* in gold or one or two arrobas [arroba = 25 pounds] of spun cotton. They took even bits of the broken hoops of the wine barrels, and gave, like fools, all that they possessed in exchange, insomuch that I thought it was wrong, and forbade it. I gave away a thousand good and pretty articles which I had brought with me in order to win their affection; and that they might be led to become Christians, and be well inclined to love and serve their Highnesses and the whole Spanish nation, and that they might aid us by giving us things of which we stand in need, but which they possess in abundance. They are not acquainted with any kind of worship, and are not idolaters; but believe that all power and, indeed, all good things are in heaven; and they are firmly convinced that I, with my vessels and crews, came from heaven, and with this belief received me at every place at which I touched, after they had overcome their apprehension. And this does not spring from ignorance, for they are very intelligent, and navigate all these seas, and relate everything to us, so that it is astonishing what a good account they are able to give of everything; but they have never seen men with clothes on, nor vessels like ours. On my reaching the Indies, I took by force, in the first island that I discovered, some of these natives, that they might learn our language and give me information in regard to what existed in these parts; and it so happened that they soon understood us and we them, either by words or signs, and they have been 'very serviceable to us. They are still with me, and, from conversations that I have had with them, I find that they still believe that I come from heaven. And they were the first to say this wherever I went, and the others ran from house to house and to the neighbouring villages, crying with a loud voice: "Come, come, and see the people from heaven!" And thus they all, men as well as women, after their minds were at rest about us, came, both large and small, and brought us something to eat and drink, which they gave us with extraordinary kindness. They have in all these islands very many canoes like our row-boats: some larger, some smaller, but most of them larger than a barge of eighteen seats. They are not so wide, because they are made of one single piece of timber, but a barge could not keep up with them in rowing, because they go with incredible speed, and with these canoes they navigate among these islands, which are innumerable, and carry on their traffic. I have seen in some of these canoes seventy and eighty men, each with his oar. In all these islands I did not notice much difference in the appearance of the inhabitants, nor in their manners nor language, except that they all understand each other, which is very singular, and leads me to hope that their Highnesses will take means for their conversion to our holy faith, towards which they are very well disposed. I have already said how I had gone one hundred and seven leagues in following the sea-coast of *Juana* in a straight line from west to east: and from that survey I can state that the island is larger than England and Scotland together, because, beyond these one hundred and seven leagues, there lie to the west two provinces which I have not yet visited, one of which is called *Avan,* where the people are born with a tail. These two provinces cannot be less in length than from fifty to sixty leagues, from what can be learned from the Indians that I have with me, and who are acquainted with all these islands. The other, *Española,* has a greater circumference than all Spain, from Catalonia by the sea-coast to Fuenterabia in Biscay, since on one of its four sides I made one hundred and eighty-eight great leagues in a straight line from west to east. This is something to covet, and when found not to be lost sight of. Although I have taken possession of all these islands in the name of their Highnesses, and they are all more abundant in wealth than I am able to express; and although I hold them all for their Highnesses, so that they can dispose of them quite as absolutely as they can of the kingdoms of Castile, yet there was one large town in *Española* of which especially I took possession, situated in a locality well adapted for the working of the gold mines, and for all kinds of commerce, either with the main land on this side, or with that beyond which is the land of the great Khan, with which there will be vast commerce and great profit. To that city I gave the name of *Villa de Navidad,* and fortified it with a fortress, which by this time will be quite completed, and I have left in it a sufficient number

of men with arms, artillery, and provisions for more than a year, a barge, and a sailing master skilful in the arts necessary for building others. I have also established the greatest friendship with the king of that country, so much so that he took pride in calling me his brother, and treating me as such. Even should these people change their intentions towards us and become hostile, they do not know what arms are, but, as I have said, go naked, and are the most timid people in the world; so that the men I have left could, alone, destroy the whole country, and this island has no danger for them, if they only know how to conduct themselves. In all those islands it seems to me that the men are content with one wife, except their chief or king, to whom they give twenty. The women seem to me to work more than the men. I have not been able to learn whether they have any property of their own. It seemed to me that what one possessed belonged to all, especially in the matter of eatables. I have not found in those islands any monsters, as many imagined; but, on the contrary, the whole race is very well-formed, nor are they black, as in Guinea, but their hair is flowing, for they do not dwell in that part where the force of the sun's rays is too powerful. It is true that the sun has very great power there, for the country is distant only twenty-six degrees from the equinoctial line. In the islands where there are high mountains, the cold this winter was very great, but they endure it, not only from being habituated to it, but by eating meat with a variety of excessively hot spices. As to savages, I did not even hear of any, except at an island which lies the second in one's way in coming to the Indies. It is inhabited by a race which is regarded throughout these islands as extremely ferocious, and eaters of human flesh. [These were the Caribs whom Columbus met on his second voyage.] These possess many canoes, in which they visit all the Indian islands, and rob and plunder whatever they can. They are no worse formed than the rest, except that they are in the habit of wearing their hair long, like women, and use bows and arrows made of reeds, with a small stick at the end, for want of iron, which they do not possess. They are ferocious amongst these exceedingly timid people; but I think no more of them than of the rest. These are they which have intercourse with the women of Matenmo [Martinique], the first island one comes to on the way from Spain to the Indies, and in which there are no men. These women employ themselves in no labour suitable to their sex; but use bows and arrows made of reeds like those above described, and arm and cover themselves with plates of copper, of which metal they have a great quantity. They assure me that there is another island larger than *Española,* in which the inhabitants have no hair. It is extremely rich in gold; and I bring with me Indians taken from these different islands, who will testify to all these things. Finally, and speaking only of what has taken place in this voyage, which has been so hasty, their Highnesses may see that I shall give them all the gold they require, if they will give me but a very little assistance; spices also, and cotton, as much as their Highnesses shall command to be shipped; and mastic, hitherto found only in Greece, in the island of Chios, and which the Signoria sells at its own price, as much as their Highnesses shall command to be shipped; lign aloes, as much as their Highnesses shall command to be shipped; slaves, as many of these idolators as their Highnesses shall command to be shipped. I think also I have found rhubarb and cinnamon, and I shall find a thousand other valuable things by means of the men that I have left behind me, for I tarried at no point so long as the wind allowed me to proceed, except in the town of *Navidad,* where I took the necessary precautions for the security and settlement of the men I left there. Much more I would have done if my vessels had been in as good a condition as by rights they ought to have been. This is much, and praised be the eternal God, our Lord, who gives to all those who walk in his ways victory over things which seem impossible; of which this is signally one, for, although others may have spoken or written concerning these countries, it was all mere conjecture, as no

one could say that he had seen them—it amounting only to this, that those who heard listened the more, and regarded the matter rather as a fable than anything else. But our Redeemer hath granted this victory to our illustrious King and Queen and their kingdoms, which have acquired great fame by an event of such high importance, in which all Christendom ought to rejoice, and which it ought to celebrate with great festivals and the offering of solemn thanks to the Holy Trinity with many solemn prayers, both for the great exaltation which may accrue to them in turning so many nations to our holy faith, and also for the temporal benefits which will bring great refreshment and gain, not only to Spain, but to all Christians. This, thus briefly, in accordance with the events.

Done on board the caravel, off the Canary Islands, on the fifteenth of February, fourteen hundred and ninety-three.

At your orders.

The Admiral.

After this letter was written, as I was in the sea of Castille, there arose a south-west wind, which compelled me to lighten my vessels and run this day into this port of Lisbon, an event which I consider the most marvellous thing in the world, and whence I resolved to write to their Highnesses. In all the Indies I have always found the weather like that in the month of May. I reached them in thirty-three days, and returned in twenty-eight, with the exception that these storms detained me fourteen days knocking about in this sea. All seamen say that they have never seen such a severe winter nor so many vessels lost.

Done on the fourteenth day of March.

Captain Cook's third voyage of discovery

2

In mid-July of 1776, Captain James Cook departed from the English Channel in command of the two ships Resolution *and* Discovery. *The primary goal of this voyage, the third and final one for Captain Cook (who was killed in the Hawaiian Islands in 1779), was to search out the Strait of Anian, or sea passage to northern North America, which supposedly linked the Atlantic and Pacific Oceans. Though the passageway had been given great credibility by its inclusion on the world-famous Mercator Map of 1569, no crew had ever been successful in negotiating the strait.*

Cook was obviously not successful in this quest, but the power of this myth to generate exploration and plant and animal dispersal is shown in this selection from the journals of his voyage. Of particular interest is the role Cook and his crews played in transporting European animal stock to the South Seas. Note also the inventories of flora and fauna as well as the ethnography which so richly characterize the journals of many of the seventeenth through nineteenth century explorers.

Third voyage of discovery to the Pacific Ocean, and for exploring the northern hemisphere in H.M. ships "Resolution," 462 tons, and "Discovery," 300 tons, in the years 1776–7–8–9–80.

In the preceding voyage, the question respecting the existence of a southern continent was for the time set at rest, but the practicability of a northern passage to the Pacific Ocean was still an object of so vast importance to England as

Ernest Rhys, ed., *Captain Cook's Voyages of Discovery* (London: J. M. Dent & Co.; New York: E. P. Dutton & Co., 1906), pp. 229–243.

to excite an earnest desire for the most diligent investigation.

It had long been a favourite scheme with the most celebrated navigators, and with the learned men of the day, to discover a shorter and more commodious course to the Oriental regions than by the Cape of Good Hope. This had been attempted in various directions for two centuries and upwards, but the completion of this favourite object was as distant as ever, and the problem of a junction of the two great oceans, the Atlantic and Pacific, by the northern shores of America, was left to be solved in our own time by the several voyages and discoveries of Sir Edward Parry, Ross, Sir John Franklin, Collinson, M'Clure, Sir Leonard M'Clintock, Dease, Simpson, Back, Richardson, and Rae—Franklin being now proved, beyond all doubt, to be the *first* discoverer of a northwest passage.

For the conduct of such an enterprise, it was evident that great skill, perseverance, and abilities, were required; and though, by the universal voice of mankind, Captain Cook was the best qualified, no one could venture to solicit him on the subject. The services he had already rendered to his country, the labours he had sustained, and the dangers he had encountered, were so many and so various, that it was deemed unreasonable to urge him to engage in fresh perils.

As an honourable testimony, however, to his merit and knowledge, it was resolved to ask his advice respecting the most proper person to be intrusted with the conduct of this voyage; and to determine this point, some of the most distinguished naval characters were invited to meet Captain Cook at the house of Lord Sandwich, who then presided over the Board of Admiralty.

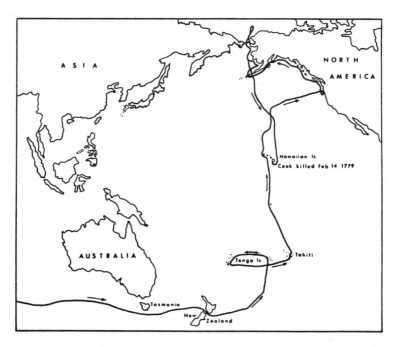

The third voyage of Captain James
Cook 1776–1779

While the conversation became animated on the subject, Cook's mind was fired with the magnitude of the design, and the consequences likely to result from it. He suddenly started up, under the impression of a noble enthusiasm, and offered his best services to direct the important objects in view. No proposal could have been more grateful. Captain Cook was immediately invested with the command.[1]

---

[1] The following letter, dated at the Admiralty, 10th Feb. 1776, formally offers his services:—

Admiralty Office, 10th February 1776.

Sir,—Having understood that their Lordships have ordered two ships to be fitted out for the purpose of making further discoveries in the Pacific Ocean, I take the liberty, as their Lordships, when they were pleased to appoint me a captain in Greenwich Hospital, were at the same time pleased also to say, it should not be in prejudice to any further offer which I might make of my service, to submit myself to their directions, if they think fit to appoint me to the command on the said intended voyage; relying, if they condescend to accept this offer, they will on my return, either restore me to my appointment in the Hospital, or procure for me such other mark of the royal favour as their Lordships, upon the review

This preliminary step settled, the exact plan of the undertaking was next taken into serious consideration. All former navigators round the globe, had returned by the Cape of Good Hope; but to Captain Cook was assigned the arduous task of attempting the same thing by reaching the high northern latitudes between Asia and America; and, it appears that this plan was adopted in consequence of his own suggestions. His instructions were, to proceed to the Pacific Ocean, and through that cluster of islands he had before visited within the southern tropic, and thence, if practicable, to make his way into the Atlantic, along the northern coast of America, in whatever latitude it might be found to lie; for nothing whatever was known at that time respecting it.

To give every stimulus to the prosecution of this great design, motives of interest were superadded to the obligations of duty. An act of parliament, which passed in 1745, offering a

---

of my past services, shall think me deserving of. I am, sir, your most humble servant,

To George Jackson, Esq.   *James Cook.*

—Admiralty Records.

reward of £20,000 to such as should discover a passage through Hudson's Bay, was enlarged and explained; and it was now enacted, that if any ship belonging to his majesty, or his subjects, should find and sail through any passage by sea, between the Atlantic and Pacific Oceans, in any direction or parallel of the northern hemisphere, to the northward of the 52d deg. of northern latitude, the sum of £20,000 was to reward such discovery.

The vessels destined for this service were the Resolution and the Discovery. The command of the former was given to Captain Cook, and that of the latter to Captain Clerke, who had been second lieutenant on the former voyage. Nearly the same complement of men and officers was assigned to each as before. The following is the list of the principal officers appointed to the two ships:—

Resolution.

John Gore, James King, John Williamson, lieutenants.
William Bligh, master.
William Anderson, surgeon.
Molesworth Philips, lieutenant, royal marines.

Discovery.

James Burney, John Rickman, lieutenants.
Thomas Edgar, master.
John Law, surgeon.

Several months were spent in the equipment and preparation of the ships, that the health of the seamen, and the success of the expedition might have every advantage which a liberal and enlightened attention could bestow. In order that the inhabitants of Otaheite, and other islands in the South Seas where the English had been treated with so much hospitality, might be benefited by the voyage, his Majesty was graciously pleased to order some of the most useful European animals to be put on board for those countries.

Besides these, Captain Cook was furnished with a quantity of garden seeds, and the Board of Admiralty added such articles of commerce as were most likely to promote a friendly intercourse with the natives and to induce them to open a traffic with the English.

Omai, who has been mentioned in the preceding voyage, was likewise to be carried back to his native country. He left his friends in London with a mixture of regret and satisfaction. When he reflected on the kindnesses he had received, he could not refrain from tears; but the pleasing idea of revisiting his original connections, soon made his eyes sparkle with joy.

As the original voyage, from which this historical account is abstracted, is written in the words of Captain Cook, till his lamented death, and afterwards in those of Captain King, who published the whole, we have preferred giving the narrative in the same person, with occasional remarks; the propriety and advantage of which will be obvious to our readers. Some of the general descriptions were furnished by Mr. Anderson, the surgeon of the Resolution; a man of distinguished abilities, and to whose talents Captain Cook acknowledged himself much indebted for many interesting parts of his voyage.

Contrary winds, and other circumstances prevented the ships from clearing the Channel till the 14th of July 1776. On board both vessels were one hundred and ninety-two persons, officers included. "Nothing material happened," says Captain Cook, "till the 1st of August, when we arrived off Teneriffe, one of the Canaries, where several of the gentlemen landed. It is said, that none of the aboriginal inhabitants remain here as a distinct people; but that the produce of their intermarriages with the Spaniards may still be traced in a strong and muscular race, dispersed over the islands.

"On the 4th, we weighed anchor and proceeded on our voyage. At nine o'clock in the evening of the 10th, we saw the island of Bonavista, bearing south, distant little more than a league, though, at this time, we thought ourselves much farther off; but this proved a mistake. For, after hauling to the eastward till twelve o'clock, to clear the sunken rocks that lie about a league from the south-east point of the island, we found ourselves at that time close upon them, and did but just weather the breakers. Our situation, for a few minutes, was very alarming. I did not choose to sound, as that might have heightened the danger, without any possibility of lessening it.

"We had, for some days preceding the 6th of October, seen albatrosses, pintadoes, and other peterels; and now we saw three penguins, which occasioned us to sound; but we found no ground with a line of one hundred and fifty fathoms.

"On the 8th, in the evening, one of those

birds which sailors call noddies, settled on our rigging, and was caught.

"On the 18th of October, we arrived at the Cape of Good Hope, and found in the bay two French East India ships; the one outward, and the other homeward bound. And two or three days before our arrival, another homeward-bound ship of the same nation had parted from her cable and was driven on shore at the head of the bay, where she was lost. The crew were saved; but the greatest part of the cargo shared the fate of the ship.

"As soon as we had saluted, I went on shore, accompanied by some of my officers, and waited on the governor, the lieutenant governor, the fiscal, and the commander of the troops. These gentlemen received me with the greatest civility; and the governor, in particular, promised me every assistance that the place afforded. At the same time, I obtained his leave to set up our observatory, to pitch tents for the sailmakers and coopers, and to bring the cattle on shore, to graze near our encampment. Before I returned on board, I ordered soft bread, fresh meat, and greens, to be provided every day for the ship's company.

"Nothing remarkable happened till the evening of the 31st, when it began to blow excessively hard at south-east, and continued for three days; during which time there was no communication between the ship and the shore. The Resolution was the only ship in the bay that rode out the gale without dragging her anchors. We felt its effects as sensibly on shore. Our tents and observatory were torn to pieces, and our astronomical quadrant narrowly escaped irreparable damage. On the 3d of November the storm ceased.

"The Discovery, having been detained some days at Plymouth, did not arrive here till the 10th. Captain Clerke informed me that he had sailed from Plymouth on the 1st of August, and should have been with us here a week sooner, if the late gale of wind had not blown him off the coast. Upon the whole, he was seven days longer in his passage from England than we had been. He had the misfortune to lose one of his marines, by falling overboard; but there had been no other mortality amongst his people, and they now arrived well and healthy.

"While the ships were getting ready, some of our officers made an excursion into the neighbouring country. Mr. Anderson, my surgeon, who was one of the party, gave me the following relation of their proceedings:—

" 'On the 16th, in the forenoon, I set out in a waggon, with five more, to take a view of some part of the country. We crossed the large plain that lies to the eastward of the town, which is entirely a white sand, like that commonly found on beaches, and produces only heath, and other small plants of various sorts. At five in the afternoon we passed a large farm-house, with some corn-fields and vineyards, situated beyond the plain, near the foot of some low hills, where the soil becomes worth cultivating. Between six and seven we arrived at Stellenbosh, the colony next to that of the Cape for its importance.

" 'The village does not consist of more than thirty houses, and stands at the foot of the range of lofty mountains, above twenty miles to the eastward of the Cape Town. The houses are neat; and, with the advantage of a rivulet which runs near, and the shelter of some large oaks, planted at its first settling, forms a rural prospect in this desert country. There are some vineyards and orchards, which, from their thriving appearance, indicate an excellent soil; though, perhaps, they owe much to climate, as the air has an uncommon serenity.

" 'I employed the next day in searching for plants and insects, but had little success. Few plants are in flower here at this season, and insects scarce. I examined the soil in several places, and found it to consist of yellowish clay, mixed with a good deal of sand.

" 'We left Stellenbosh next morning, and arrived at the house we had passed on Saturday; the owner, Mr. Cloeder, had sent us an invitation to visit him. This gentleman entertained us with the greatest hospitality. He received us with music, and a band also played while we were at dinner; which, considering the situation of the place, might be reckoned elegant. He showed us his wine-cellars, orchards, and vineyards; all which inspired me with a wish to know how these industrious people could create such plenty, where, I believe, no other European nation would have attempted to settle.

" 'In the afternoon we crossed the country, and passed a few plantations, one of which seemed very considerable, and was laid out in a taste somewhat different from any other we saw. In the evening we arrived at a farm-house, which is the first in the cultivated tract, called the Pearl. We had, at the same time, a view of Drakenstein, the third colony, which lies by the foot of the lofty hills already mentioned, and contains several farms or plantations, not very extensive.

" 'On the morning of the 20th, we set out from the Pearl; and going a different road from that by which we came, passed through a country wholly uncultivated, till we got to the Tyger Hills, when some tolerable corn-fields appeared. At noon, we stopped in a hollow for refreshment; but, in walking about here, were plagued with a vast number of mosquitoes or sand-flies, which were the first I saw in the country.' "

Here Captain Cook added to his original stock of live animals, by purchasing two young bulls, two heifers, two young stone horses, two mares, two rams, several ewes and goats, and some rabbits and poultry. All of them were intended for New Zealand, Otaheite, and the neighbouring islands, or any other places, in the course of their voyage, where there might be a prospect that leaving any of them would be useful to posterity.

The following is an extract from Captain Cook's letter on this subject:—

Cape of Good Hope, 28th November 1776.

I am now ready to put to sea with the first wind, having filled the sloops with provisions, and made some considerable addition to the live stock on board the Resolution intended to be sent to Otaheite. As I have taken the liberty to do this with a view to serving posterity, by having some to spare to leave on the lands I may touch at before I arrive at that island, I hope it will meet their Lordships' approbation, and that they will order the bill to be honoured, which I have taken the liberty to draw on you of this date in favour of Mr. Christoffel Brand, or order, for the sum of two hundred and fourteen pounds ten shillings and sixpence sterling, in a set of bills of exchange of the same time and date, and payable at thirty days' sight, it being for the purchase and keeping the live stock, supporting Omai, and for defraying Mr. Webber's expenses, all of which will appear by the enclosed vouchers. A painting which he made of St. Cruz, in the island of Teneriffe, I have left with Mr. Brand, of this place, to be forwarded to their Lordships by the first safe opportunity.[2]

Having given Captain Clerke a copy of his instructions, and an order directing him how to proceed in case of separation, in the morning of the 30th they repaired on board, and at five in the afternoon weighed, and stood out of the bay.

"We steered a south-east course, with a very strong gale from the westward, followed by a mountainous sea, which made the ship roll and tumble exceedingly, and gave us much trouble to preserve the cattle we had on board. Notwithstanding our care, several goats, especially the males, died, and some sheep. This misfortune was, in a great measure, owing to the cold, which we now began most sensibly to feel."

Nothing of interest happened from the 5th of December till the 26th of January, when they arrived at Van Diemen's Land; where, as soon as they had anchored in Adventure Bay, Captain Cook ordered the boats to be hoisted out. In one of them he went himself, to look for the most commodious place for furnishing themselves with the necessary supplies; and Captain Clerke went in his own boat upon the same service.

"Next morning early," says Captain Cook, "I sent Lieutenant King to the east side of the bay, with two parties, one to cut wood and the other grass, under the protection of the marines. For although, as yet, none of the natives had appeared, there could be no doubt that some were in our neighbourhood. I also sent the launch for water; and afterwards visited all the parties myself. In the evening, we drew the seine at the head of the bay, and, at one haul, caught a great quantity of fish. Most of them were of that sort known to seamen by the name of elephant fish.

"In the afternoon, next day, we were agreeably surprised, at the place where we were cutting wood, with a visit from some of the natives—eight men and a boy. They approached us from the woods, without betraying any marks of fear, for none of them had any weapons except one, who held in his hand a stick about two feet long, and pointed at one end.

"They were of common stature, but rather slender. Their skin was black, and also their hair, which was as woolly as that of any native of Guinea; but they were not distinguished by remarkably thick lips, nor flat noses. . . . Most of them had their hair and beards smeared with

---

[2] Records, Admiralty, Whitehall.

a red ointment; and some had their faces also painted with the same composition.

"They received every present we made to them without the least appearance of satisfaction. When some bread was given, as soon as they understood that it was to be eaten, they either returned it or threw it away, without even tasting it. They also refused some elephant fish, both raw and dressed, which we offered to them. But upon giving them some birds, they did not return these, and easily made us comprehend that they were fond of such food. I had brought two pigs ashore, with a view to leave them in the woods. The instant these came within their reach, they seized them as a dog would have done, by the ears, and were for carrying them off immediately, with no other intention, as we could perceive, but to kill them.

"Being desirous of knowing the use of the stick which one of our visitors carried in his hand, I made signs to them to show me; and so far succeeded, that one of them set up a piece of wood as a mark, and threw at it, at the distance of about twenty yards. But we had little reason to commend his dexterity; for, after repeated trials, he was still very wide from the object. Omai, to show them how much superior our weapons were to theirs, then fired his musket at it, which alarmed them so much, that, notwithstanding all we could do or say, they ran instantly into the woods.

"Thus ended our first interview with the natives. Immediately after their final retreat, I ordered the two pigs, being a boar and a sow, to be carried about a mile within the woods, at the head of the bay. I saw them left there, by the side of a fresh water brook. A young bull and a cow, and some sheep and goats, were also, at first, intended to have been left by me as an additional present to Van Diemen's Land. But I soon laid aside all thought of this, from a persuasion that the natives, incapable of entering into my views of improving their country, would destroy them.

"The morning of the 29th we had a dead calm, which continued all day, and effectually prevented our sailing. I therefore sent a party over to the east point of the bay to cut grass, and another to cut wood. I accompanied the latter. We had observed several of the natives this morning sauntering along the shore, which assured us that though their consternation had

made them leave us so abruptly the day before, they were convinced that we intended them no mischief, and were desirous of renewing the intercourse. It was natural that I should wish to be present on the occasion.

"We had not been long landed before about twenty of them, men and boys, joined us, without expressing the least sign of fear or distrust. There was one of this company conspicuously deformed; and who was not more distinguishable by the hump on his back, than by the drollery of his gestures, and the seeming humour of his speeches; which he was very fond of exhibiting, as we supposed, for our entertainment. His language appeared to me to be different from that spoken by the inhabitants of the more northern parts of this country, whom I met with in my first voyage, which is not extraordinary, since those we now saw, and those we then visited, differ in many other respects.

"Some of our present group wore, loose, round their necks, three or four folds of small cord, made of the fur of some animal; and others of them had a narrow slip of the kangaroo skin tied round their ankles. I gave to each of them a string of beads and a medal, which I thought they received with some satisfaction. They seemed to set no value on iron or on iron tools. They were even ignorant of the use of fish-hooks, if we might judge from their manner of looking at some of ours which we showed to them—though it is certain they derive no inconsiderable part of their subsistence from the sea. We saw, however, no vessel in which they could go on the water. Their habitations were little sheds or hovels built of sticks, and covered with bark.

"After staying about an hour with the wooding party and the natives, I went over to the grass-cutters. Having seen the boats loaded, I returned on board to dinner, where, some time after, Lieutenant King arrived.

"From him I learnt that I had but just left the shore when several women and children made their appearance. These females wore a kangaroo skin tied over the shoulders, and round the waist. But its only use seemed to be to support their children when carried on their backs, for it did not cover their persons, being in all other respects as naked as the men, and as black, and their bodies tattooed in the same manner. But in this they differed from the men, that though their hair was of the same colour, some of them had their heads completely shorn, in others this operation had been performed only on one side, while the rest of them had all the upper part of the head shorn close, leaving a circle of hair all round, somewhat like the tonsure of the Romish ecclesiastics. Many of the children had fine features, and were thought pretty; but of the persons of the women, especially those advanced in years, a less favourable report was made.

"The only animal of the quadruped kind we got, was a sort of opossum, about twice the size of a large rat. It is of a dusky colour above, tinged with a brown or rusty cast, and whitish below. About a third of the tail towards its tip is white, and bare underneath, by which it probably hangs on the branches of trees, as it climbs these, and lives on berries. The kangaroo, another animal found farther northward in New Holland, without doubt also inhabits here, as the natives we met with had some pieces of their skins; and we several times saw an animal, though indistinctly, run from the thickets when we walked in the woods, which, from the size, could be no other.

"There are several sorts of birds, but all so scarce and shy, that they are evidently harassed by the natives, who perhaps draw much of their subsistence from them. In the woods the principal sorts are large brown hawks or eagles, crows nearly the same as ours in England, yellowish paroquets, and large pigeons. There are also three or four small birds, one of which is of the thrush kind. On the shore were several common and sea-gulls, a few black oyster-catchers or sea-pies, and a pretty plover of a stone colour, with a black hood. About the lake behind the beach, a few wild ducks were seen; and some shags used to perch upon the high leafless trees near the shore.

"The sea affords a much greater plenty, and at least as great a variety, as the land. Of these the elephant fish, or pejegallo, mentioned in Frezier's Voyage, are the most numerous; and though inferior to many other fish, were very palatable food. Next in number, and superior in goodness, to the elephant fish, was a sort none of us recollected to have seen before. It partakes of the nature both of a round and of a flat fish, having the eyes placed very near each other, the forepart of the body very much flattened or depressed, and the rest rounded. It is of a brownish sandy colour, with rusty spots

on the upper part and below. From the quantity of slime it was always covered with, it seems to live after the manner of flat fish, at the bottom. Upon the rocks are plenty of mussels, and some other small shell-fish There are also great numbers of sea-stars, some small limpets, and large quantities of sponge—one sort of which, that is thrown on shore by the sea, but not very common, has a most delicate texture.

"Insects, though not numerous, are here in considerable variety. Among them are grasshoppers, butterflies, and several sorts of small moths, finely variegated. There are two sorts of dragon-flies, gad-flies, camel-flies, several sorts of spiders; and some scorpions; but the last are rather rare. The most troublesome, though not very numerous tribe of insects, are the mosquitoes; and a large black ant, the pain of whose bite is almost intolerable, during the short time it lasts.

"The inhabitants, whom we met here, had little of that fierce or wild appearance common to people in their situation; but, on the contrary, seemed mild and cheerful, without reserve or jealousy of strangers. This, however, may arise from their having little to lose or care for. With respect to personal activity or genius, we can say but little of either. They do not seem to possess the first in any remarkable degree; and as for the last, they have, to appearance, less than even the half-animated inhabitans of Terra del Fuego, who have not invention sufficient to make clothing for defending themselves from the rigour of their climate, though furnished with the materials. Their colour is a dull black, and not quite so deep as that of the African negroes. Their hair, however, is perfectly woolly, and it is clotted or divided into small parcels, like that of the Hottentots, with the use of some sort of grease, mixed with a red paint or ochre, which they smear in great abundance over their heads; and they wear their beards long, and clotted with paint, in the same manner as the hair on their heads. At eight o-clock in the morning of the 30th of January, a light breeze springing up at west, we weighed anchor and put to sea from Adventure Bay. We pursued our course to the eastward, without meeting with any thing worthy of note, till the night between the 6th and 7th of February, when a marine belonging to the Discovery fell overboard, and was never seen afterward.

"On the 12th of February, at four in the

afternoon, we discovered the land of New Zealand; and soon after came to an anchor in Queen Charlotte Sound. Here several canoes, filled with natives, came alongside of the ships; but very few of them would venture on board; which appeared the more extraordinary, as I was well known by them all. There was one man in particular amongst them, whom I had treated with remarkable kindness during the whole of my stay when I was last here. Yet now, neither professions of friendship nor presents could prevail upon him to come into the ship. This shyness was to be accounted for only on this supposition, that they were apprehensive we had revisited their country in order to revenge the death of Captain Furneaux's people.

"On the 13th we set up two tents, one from each ship, on the same spot where we had pitched them formerly. The observatories were at the same time erected; and Messrs. King and Bayly began their operations immediately.

"During the course of this day a great number of families came from different parts of the coast, and took up their residence close to us, so that there was not a spot in the cove where a hut could be put up that was not occupied by them, except the place where we had fixed our little encampment.

"It is curious to observe with what facility they build their huts. I have seen about twenty of them erected on a spot of ground, that, not an hour before, was covered with shrubs and plants. They generally bring some part of the materials with them, the rest they find upon the premises. I was present when a number of people landed and built one of these villages.

"Besides the natives who took up their abode close to us, we were occasionally visited by others whose residence was not afar off; and by some who lived more remote. Their articles of commerce were, curiosities, fish, and women. The two first always came to a good market, which the latter did not. The seamen had taken a kind of dislike to these people, and were either unwilling, or afraid to associate with them; which produced this good effect, that I knew no instance of a man's quitting his station to go to their habitations.

"Amongst our occasional visitors was a chief named Kahoora, who, as I was informed, headed the party that cut off Captain Furneaux's people, and himself killed Mr. Rowe, the officer who commanded. To judge of the character of Kahoora, by what I had heard from many of his countrymen, he seemed to be more feared than beloved amongst them. Not satisfied with telling me that he was a very bad man, some of them even importuned me to kill him: and I believe they were not a little surprised that I did not listen to them; for according to their ideas of equity, this ought to have been done. But if I had followed the advice of all our pretended friends, I might have extirpated the whole race; for the people of each hamlet or village, by turns, applied to me to destroy the other.

"On the 16th, at daybreak, I set out with a party of men, in five boats, to collect food for our cattle. Captain Clerke, and several of the officers, Omai, and two of the natives accompanied me. We proceeded about three leagues up the sound, and then landed on the east side at a place where I had formerly been. Here we cut as much grass as loaded the two launches.

"As we returned down the sound, we visited Grass Cove, the memorable scene of the massacre of Captain Furneaux's people. Whilst we were at this place, our curiosity prompted us to inquire into the circumstances attending the melancholy fate of our countrymen, and Omai was made use of as our interpreter for this purpose. The natives present answered all the questions that were put to them on the subject without reserve, and like men who are under no dread of punishment for a crime of which they are not guilty. For we already knew that none of them had been concerned in the unhappy transaction. They told us, that while our people were sitting at dinner, surrounded by several of the natives, some of the latter stole, or snatched from them, some bread and fish, for which they were beat. This being resented, a quarrel ensued, and two New Zealanders were shot dead by the only two muskets that were fired. For before our people had time to discharge a third, or to load again those that had been fired, the natives rushed in upon them, overpowered them with their numbers, and put them all to death.

"We stayed here till the evening, when, having filled the rest of the boats with grass, celery, and scurvy-grass, we embarked to return to the ships, where some of the boats did not arrive till one o'clock the next morning; and it was fortunate that they got on board then, for it afterwards blew a perfect storm. In the evening the gale ceased, and the wind having veered to the east, brought with it fair weather.

"By this time more than two-thirds of the inhabitants of the Sound had settled themselves about us. Great numbers of them daily frequented the ships, while our people were there melting some seal blubber. No Greenlander was ever fonder of train-oil than our friends here seemed to be. They relished the very skimmings of the kettle; but a little of the pure stinking oil was a delicious feast.

"Having got on board as much hay and grass as we judged sufficient to serve the cattle till our arrival at Otaheite, and having completed the wood and water of both ships, on the 24th we weighed anchor and stood out of the cove.

"While we were unmooring and getting under sail, many of the natives came to take their leave of us, or rather to obtain, if they could, some additional presents from us before we left them. Accordingly, I gave to two of their chiefs two pigs, a boar, and a sow. They made me a promise not to kill them, though I must own I put no great faith in this. The animals which Captain Furneaux sent on shore here, and which soon after fell into the hands of the natives, I was now told were all dead; but I was afterwards informed that Tiratou, a chief, had a great many cocks and hens in his possession, and one of the sows. . . ."

Some curious analogies in explorers' preconceptions of Virginia

GARY DUNBAR

3

Myth exists as a prime generating factor in the decision to migrate. Though the mythical goal is seldom realized, the processes of mobility and discovery are just as real as if the myth had been realized. Gary Dunbar in this short article points out the role of the myth of a west-flowing navigable waterway to the Pacific Ocean ("East India Sea") as a spur to settlement. He also notes the erroneous use of analogies in preconceptions of climate, topography, and mineral resources of Virginia and the American Northeast. (He points out that the assumption was that latitudes in North America would geographically resemble similar latitudes in South America and Eurasia.) This use of primary sources to better comprehend initial attitudes towards, and decisions about a landscape is a historical facet of cultural geography. As such it draws upon a massive body of travel literature, journals, and manuscripts in all languages and from all periods.

Early observers made ample errors in interpreting Virginia's natural landscapes after they had viewed them, but even more curious were the views they held concerning this land before they arrived. The English, who had learned precious little about the New World after almost a century of Spanish voyaging, had to rely upon rumors, fanciful *mappaemundi,* and analogies from known lands for their information about temperate America. Lacking real knowledge, the English confidently presumed that the climate, topography, and mineral resources of North America would be the same as those of the same latitudes in Eurasia and in Spanish South America.

Still untested by adequate observation, the classical notion of rigid latitudinal zonation of climates was regarded as immutable by Europeans. Even before Raleigh's first expedition to Roanoke Island returned to England, Richard Hakluyt, the famous English arm-chair "geog-

Gary S. Dunbar, "Some Curious Analogies in Explorers' Preconceptions of Virginia," *The Virginia Journal of Science,* IX (New Series), No. 3 (1958), pp. 323–326.

rapher" (really just a compiler of travel narratives), prepared his "Discourse of western planting" which stated that Mediterranean crop plants could easily grow in the same latitudes in North America (Taylor, 1935). Thomas Hariot, the accurate scientific observer, spent the winter of 1585–1586 in what is now northeastern North Carolina and southeastern Virginia, but he reported only that the climate was "answerable to . . . the South part of Greece, Italy, and Spaine." (Quinn, 1955). Thus the original belief that Virginia's climate should be the same as that of the Mediterranean lands because of the sameness of latitude was reinforced by a veracious traveler who had wintered there. John Smith was among the first to modify the view that lands in the same latitude necessarily have the same climate when he said concerning Virginia: "The sommer is hot as in *Spaine;* the winter colde as in *Fraunce* or *England*" (Smith, 1910). However, Virginia has humid, not dry Mediterranean, summers, and even though the average January (coldest month) temperatures at Jamestown and London are about the same, nevertheless the former has a greater range and experiences more frequent change. When the more northerly colonies of New England and the Middle Atlantic region were settled, their cold winters could not be compared at all with England's, and yet the homeland lay in higher latitudes than all the American colonies. The colonists could simply not understand the climatic differences between east coast and west coast locations.

The Jamestown explorers set out with some odd notions about the size and shape of the North American continent. Hope apparently still persisted in finding the "Sea of Verrazano" not far from the Atlantic seaboard (Cumming, 1938). The 1607 colony was instructed by the London Company to commence exploration immediately to reach this sea not far to the westward. The explicit instructions read as follows:

> You shall do your best endeavour to find out a safe port in the entrance of some navigable river . . .
> You must observe if you can, whether the river on which you plant doth spring out of mountains or out of lakes. If it be out of any lake, the passage to the other sea will be more easy, and (it) is like[ly] enough, that out of

the same lake you shall find some spring which run (s) the contrary way towards the East *India* Sea; for the great famous rivers of *Volga, Tan* (a) *is* [Don], and *Dwina* have three heads near joyn (e) d; and yet the one falleth into the *Caspian* Sea, the other into the *Euxine* [Black] Sea, and the third into the *Paelonian* [White] Sea (Smith, 1910).

These instructions show that the English believed in the close proximity of the "East India Sea" to the Atlantic in the latitude of Chesapeake Bay and that they further hoped that the river systems of North America were similar to those of Russia where rivers whose sources are close together flow in different directions and provide easy transport from sea to sea. They apparently believed that the continents were so much alike in their natural features that such a prediction about North America was justified. The men of the 17th century were naturally unaware that the Russian situation was largely the result of heavy continental glaciation, a configuration without parallels in Virginia (Taylor, 1934).

William Berkeley, governor of Virginia from 1642 to 1652 and from 1660 to 1677, was from the beginning of his term interested in the fur trade and also in the possibility of finding a water route to Asia. In 1669 he wrote the following to Lord Arlington:

> I did this last spring resolve to make an Essay to doe his Majestie a memorable service which was in the Company of Two hundred Gent who had engaged to goe along with me to find out the East India sea, and we had hopes that in our Journy we should have found some Mines of silver; for certaine it is that the spaniard in the same degrees of latitude has found many. But my Lord unusual and continued Raynes hindred my intentions (Alvord and Bidgood, 1912).

Here Berkeley is not only stating his belief in the nearness of the East India Sea but also shows that he subscribed to the time-honored notion that lands in the same latitudes possessed identical mineral resources. Earlier, in 1616, John Smith had also voiced this view when he said, concerning New England: "Southward, in the same height [latitude], is the richest of gold Mynes, *Chily* and *Baldiuia,* and the mouth of the great Riuer of *Plate,* &c. (Smith, 1910).

Another analogy with South America was drawn by John Lederer, the mysterious German physician whom Berkeley allowed to make three trips westward from the Virginia settlements in 1669 and 1670 with the intention of finding the East India Sea but who never went beyond the Blue Ridge. Lederer embellished his account with tales of pearls and peacocks, and, although he never even penetrated the Great Valley, concluded that the "Indian ocean" was to be found just on the other side of the Appalachians. He stated:

> I am brought over to their opinion who think that the Indian ocean does stretch an arm or bay from California into the continent as far as the Apalataean mountains, answerable to the Gulfs of Florida and Mexico on this side. Yet I am from believing with some, that such great and navigable rivers are to be found on the other side the Apalataeans falling into the Indian ocean, as those which run from them to the eastward. My first reason is derived from the knowledge and experience we already have of South-America, whose Andes send the greatest rivers in the world (as the Amazones and Rio de la Plata, etc.) into the Atlantick, but none at all into the Pacifique sea. (Alvord and Bidgood, 1912).

Lederer did not realize that the Andes, even though they lie close to the sea, do "send" some rivers down to the Pacific and also that the Appalachians are in no way comparable to the great western cordillera of South America.

These examples demonstrate the inherent pitfalls in the early explorers' attempts to predict what the natural landscapes of unknown lands would be like by analogy with known lands of the same latitude. As the colonists gained in experience they realized that latitude alone is not an indicator of climate—and certainly not of shapes of continents, the nature of river systems, and of the location of mineral bodies.

Literature cited

Alvord, C. W. and L. Bidgood. 1912. The First Explorations of the Trans-Allegheny Region by the Virginians, 1650–1674. *The Arthur H. Clark Company, Cleveland.*

Cumming, W. P. 1938. Geographical Misconceptions of the Southeast in the Cartography of the Seventeenth and Eighteenth Centuries. Journal of Southern History, *4: 476–492.*

Quinn, D. B. 1955. The Roanoke Voyages, 1584–1590. *2 vols. Hakluyt Society, 2nd series, CIV–CV. London.*

Smith, John. 1910. Travels and Works of Captain John Smith. *2 vols. Edited by E. Arber and A. G. Bradley. John Grant, Edinburgh.*

Taylor, E. G. R. 1934. Late Tudor and Early Stuart Geography, 1583–1650. *Methuen & Co., Ltd., London.*

————1935. The Original Writings and Correspondence of the Two Richard Hakluyts. *2 vols. Hakluyt Society, 2nd series, LXXVI–LXXVII. London.*

Civilizing the Kanaka

MARK TWAIN

4

The migrations attendant upon the slave trade of the seventeenth through nineteenth centuries have caused the most serious demographic

Mark Twain, *Following the Equator* (Hartford: The American Publishing Company, 1898), pp. 83–90.

anomalies that exist today, because of the tragic fact that the migrating groups by and large had no interest in making these moves. When migration does not have the prime quality of man himself opting to relocate, then the resultant patterns—both social and demographic—fail to harmonize with the goal area. Clearly, all migra-

tions introduce anomalies in the goal area, but migrations which move people against their will intensify these anomalies, and the subsequent assimilation of the immigrants into the host society is significantly retarded.

Mark Twain, in Following the Equator, *discusses a short-range slave trade and migration between islands of the New Hebrides in the South Pacific and Queensland in northeast Australia. His use of arguments between those profiting from the trade and those dedicated to its cessation gives the reader a fine perspective on each group's justification for its activities. Of particular interest are Twain's own comments on the veneer of "civilization" with which the Kanaka (Melanesian for man or native) returned home after their three-year tenure in the sugar plantations of Queensland.*

Captain Wawn is crystal-clear on one point: He does not approve of missionaries. They obstruct his business. They make "Recruiting," as he calls it ("Slave-Catching," as *they* call it in their frank way) a trouble when it ought to be just a picnic and a pleasure excursion. The missionaries have their opinion about the manner in which the Labor Traffic is conducted, and about the recruiter's evasions of the law of the Traffic, and about the traffic itself: and it is distinctly uncomplimentary to the Traffic and to everything connected with it, including the law for its regulation. Captain Wawn's book is of very recent date; I have by me a pamphlet of still later date—hot from the press, in fact—by Rev. Wm. Gray, a missionary; and the book and the pamphlet taken together make exceedingly interesting reading, to my mind.

Interesting, and easy to understand—except in one detail, which I will mention presently. It is easy to understand why the Queensland sugar planter should want the Kanaka recruit: he is cheap. Very cheap, in fact. These are the figures paid by the planter: £20 to the recruiter for getting the Kanaka—or "catching" him, as the missionary phrase goes; £3 to the Queensland government for "superintending" the importation; £5 deposited with the Government for the Kanaka's passage home when his three years are up, in case he shall live that long; about £25 to the Kanaka himself for three years' wages and clothing; total payment for the use of a man three years, £53; or, including diet, £60. Altogether, a hundred dollars a year. One

can understand why the recruiter is fond of the business; the recruit costs him a few cheap presents (given to the recruit's relatives, not to the recruit himself), and the recruit is worth £20 to the recruiter when delivered in Queensland. All this is clear enough; but the thing that is not clear is, what there is about it all to persuade the recruit. He is young and brisk; life at home in his beautiful island is one lazy, long holiday to him; or if he wants to work he can turn out a couple of bags of copra per week and sell it for four or five shillings a bag. In Queensland he must get up at dawn and work from eight to twelve hours a day in the cane-fields—in a much hotter climate than he is used to—and get less than four shillings a week for it.

I cannot understand his willingness to go to Queensland. It is a deep puzzle to me. Here is the explanation, from the planter's point of view; at least I gather from the missionary's pamphlet that it is the planter's:

> When he comes from his home he is a savage, pure and simple. He feels no shame at his nakedness and want of adornment. When he returns home he does so well dressed, sporting a Waterbury watch, collars, cuffs, boots, and jewelry. He takes with him one or more boxes well filled with clothing, a musical instrument or two, and perfumery and other articles of luxury he has learned to appreciate.

For just one moment we have a seeming flash of comprehension of the Kanaka's reason for exiling himself: he goes away to acquire *civilization*. Yes, he was naked and not ashamed, now he is clothed and knows how to be ashamed; he was unenlightened, now he has a Waterbury watch; he was unrefined, now he has jewelry, and something to make him smell good; he was a nobody, a provincial, now he has been to far countries and can show off.

It all looks plausible—for a moment. Then the missionary takes hold of this explanation and pulls it to pieces, and dances on it, and damages it beyond recognition.

> Admitting that the foregoing description is the average one, the average sequel is this: The cuffs and collars, if used at all, are carried off by youngsters, who fasten them round the leg, just below the knee, as ornaments. The Waterbury, broken and dirty, finds its

way to the trader, who gives a trifle for it; or the inside is taken out, the wheels strung on a thread and hung round the neck. Knives, axes, calico, and handkerchiefs are divided among friends, and there is hardly one of these apiece. The boxes, the keys often lost on the road home, can be bought for 2s. 6d. They are to be seen rotting outside in almost any shore village on Tanna. (I speak of what I have seen.) A returned Kanaka has been furiously angry with me because I would not buy his trousers, which he declared were just my fit. He sold them afterwards to one of my Aniwan teachers for 9d. worth of tobacco—a pair of trousers that probably cost him 8s. or 10s. in Queensland. A coat or shirt is handy for cold weather. The white handkerchiefs, the 'senet' (perfumery), the umbrella, and perhaps the hat, are kept. The boots have to take their chance, if they do not happen to fit the copra trader. 'Senet' on the hair, streaks of paint on the face, a dirty white handkerchief round the neck, strips of turtle shell in the ears, a belt, a sheath and knife, and an umbrella constitute the rig of returned Kanaka at home the day after landing.

A hat, an umbrella, a belt, a neckerchief. Otherwise stark naked. All in a day the hard-earned "civilization" has melted away to this. And even these perishable things must presently go. Indeed, there is but a single detail of his civilization that can be depended on to stay by him: according to the missionary, he has learned to swear. This is art, and art is long, as the poet says.

In all countries the laws throw light upon the past. The Queensland law for the regulation of the Labor Traffic is a confession. It is a confession that the evils charged by the missionaries upon the traffic had existed in the past, and that they still existed when the law was made. The missionaries make a further charge: that the law is evaded by the recruiters, and that the Government Agent sometimes helps them to do it. Regulation 31 reveals two things: that sometimes a young fool of a recruit gets his senses back, after being persuaded to sign away his liberty for three years, and dearly wants to get out of the engagement and stay at home with his own people; and that threats, intimidation, and force are used to keep him on board the recruiting-ship, and to hold him to his contract. Regulation 31 forbids these coercions. The law requires that he shall be allowed to go free; and

another clause of it requires the recruiter to set him ashore—per boat, because of the prevalence of sharks. Testimony from Rev. Mr. Gray:

There are "wrinkles" for taking the penitent Kanaka. My first experience of the Traffic was a case of this kind in 1884. A vessel anchored just out of sight of our station, word was brought to me that some boys were stolen, and the relatives wished me to go and get them back. The facts were, as I found, that six boys had recruited, had *rushed* into the boat, the Government Agent informed me. They had all "signed"; and, said the Government Agent, "on board they shall remain." I was assured that the six boys were of age and willing to go. Yet on getting ready to leave the ship I found four of the lads ready to come ashore in the boat! This I forbade. One of them jumped into the water and persisted in coming ashore in my boat. When appealed to, the Government Agent suggested that we go and leave him to be picked up by the ship's boat, a quarter mile distant at the time!

The law and the missionaries feel for the repentant recruit—and properly, one may be permitted to think, for he is only a youth and ignorant and persuadable to his hurt—but sympathy for him is not kept in stock by the recruiter. Rev. Mr. Gray says:

A captain many years in the traffic explained to me how a penitent could be taken. 'When a boy jumps overboard we just take a boat and pull ahead of him, then lie between him and the shore. If he has not tired himself swimming, and passes the boat, keep on heading him in this way. The dodge rarely fails. The boy generally tires of swimming, gets into the boat of his own accord, and goes quietly on board.

Yes, exhaustion is likely to make a boy quiet. If the distressed boy had been the speaker's son, and the captors savages, the speaker would have been surprised to see how differently the thing looked from the new point of view; however, it is not our custom to put ourselves in the other person's place. Somehow there is something pathetic about that disappointed young savage's resignation. I must explain, here, that in the traffic dialect, "boy" does not always mean boy;

it means a youth above sixteen years of age. That is by Queensland law the age of consent, though it is held that recruiters allow themselves some latitude in guessing at ages.

Captain Wawn of the free spirit chafes under the annoyance of "cast-iron regulations." They and the missionaries have poisoned his life. He grieves for the good old days, vanished to come no more. See him weep; hear him cuss between the lines!

> For a long time we were allowed to apprehend and detain all deserters who had signed the agreement on board ship, but the 'cast-iron' regulations of the Act of 1884 put a stop to that, allowing the Kanaka to sign the agreement for three years' service, travel about in the ship in receipt of the regular rations, cadge all he could, and leave when he thought fit, so long as he did not extend his pleasure trip to Queensland.

Rev. Mr. Gray calls this same restrictive cast-iron law a "farce." "There is as much cruelty and injustice done to natives by acts that are legal as by deeds unlawful. The regulations that exist are unjust and inadequate—unjust and inadequate they must ever be." He furnishes his reasons for his position, but they are too long for reproduction here.

However, if the most a Kanaka advantages himself by a three-years course in civilization in Queensland, is a necklace and an umbrella and a showy imperfection in the art of swearing, it must be that *all* the profit of the traffic goes to the white man. This could be twisted into a plausible argument that the traffic ought to be squarely abolished.

However, there is reason for hope that that can be left alone to achieve itself. It is claimed that the traffic will depopulate its sources of supply within the next twenty or thirty years. Queensland is a very healthy place for white people—death-rate 12 in 1,000 of the population—but the Kanaka death-rate is away above that. The vital statistics for 1893 place it at 52; for 1894 (Mackay district), 68. The first six months of the Kanaka's exile are peculiarly perilous for him because of the rigors of the new climate. The death-rate among the new men has reached as high as 180 in the 1,000. In the Kanaka's native home his death-rate is 12 in time of peace, and 15 in time of war. Thus exile to Queensland—with the opportunity to acquire civilization, an umbrella, and a pretty poor quality of profanity—is twelve times as deadly for him as war. Common Christian charity, common humanity, does seem to require, not only that these people be returned to their homes, but that war, pestilence, and famine be introduced among them for their preservation.

Concerning these Pacific isles and their peoples an eloquent prophet spoke long years ago—five and fifty years ago. In fact, he spoke a little too early. Prophecy is a good line of business, but it is full of risks. This prophet was the Right Rev. M. Russell, LL.D., D.C.L., of Edinburgh:

> Is the tide of civilization to roll only to the foot of the Rocky Mountains, and is the sun of knowledge to set at last in the waves of the Pacific? No; the mighty day of four thousand years is drawing to its close; the sun of humanity has performed its destined course; but long ere its setting rays are extinguished in the west, its ascending beams have glittered on the isles of the eastern seas. . . . And now we see the race of Japhet setting forth to people the isles, and the seeds of another Europe and a second England sown in the regions of the sun. But mark the words of the prophecy: "He shall dwell in the tents of Shem, and Canaan shall be his servant." It is not said Canaan shall be his *slave*. To the Anglo-Saxon race is given the scepter of the globe, but there is not given either the lash of the slave-driver or the rack of the executioner. The East will not be stained with the same atrocities as the West; the frightful gangrene of an enthralled race is not to mar the destinies of the family of Japhet in the Oriental world; humanizing, not destroying, as they advance; uniting with, not enslaving, the inhabitants with whom they dwell, the British race may, etc., etc.

And he closes his vision with an invocation from Thomson:

> Come, bright Improvement! on the car of Time,
> And rule the spacious world from clime to clime.

Very well, Bright Improvement has arrived, you see, with her civilization, and her Waterbury, and her umbrella, and her third-quality profanity, and her humanizing-not-destroying machinery, and her hundred-and-eighty-death-rate, and everything is going along just as handsome!

But the prophet that speaks last has an advantage over the pioneer in the business. Rev. Mr. Gray says:

What I am concerned about is that we as a Christian nation should wipe out these races to enrich ourselves.

And he closes his pamphlet with a grim Indictment which is as eloquent in its flowerless straightforward English as is the hand-painted rhapsody of the early prophet:

My indictment of the Queensland-Kanaka Labor Traffic is this:

1. It generally demoralizes and always impoverishes the Kanaka, deprives him of his citizenship, and depopulates the islands fitted to his home.

2. It is felt to lower the dignity of the white agricultural laborer in Queensland, and beyond a doubt it lowers his wages there.

3. The whole system is fraught with danger to Australia and the islands on the score of health.

4. On social and political grounds the continuance of the Queensland Kanaka Labor Traffic must be a barrier to the true federation of the Australian colonies.

5. The Regulations under which the Traffic exists in Queensland are inadequate to prevent abuses, and in the nature of things they must remain so.

6. The whole system is contrary to the spirit and doctrine of the Gospel of Jesus Christ. The Gospel requires us to help the weak, but the Kanaka is fleeced and trodden down.

7. The bed-rock of this Traffic is that the life and liberty of a black man are of less value than those of a white man. And a Traffic that has grown out of 'slave hunting' will certainly remain to the end not unlike its origin.

Of migrants and migration

JOHN STEINBECK   5

Few authors have so powerfully captured migration and its rigors as John Steinbeck. In The Grapes of Wrath, *the inter-chapters afford comments on the forces shaping the life of the Joad family as well as the thousands of other Americans who uprooted themselves from midwestern farmlands and moved west seeking land and work in the 1930s. In this short essay Steinbeck illustrates the social cohesion experienced by migrating groups and points out the changes*

wrought upon people by the process of migration. The impact of ostracism and the keen awareness of environment necessary to find adequate camp sites are made real by the novelist. Though other long-range group migrations would have different particular characteristics the general impact of such movement is accurately described in this selection.

The cars of the migrant people crawled out of the side roads onto the great cross-country highway, and they took the migrant way to the West. In the daylight they scuttled like bugs to the westward; and as the dark caught them, they clustered like bugs near to shelter and to water. And because they were lonely and perplexed, because they had all come from a place of sadness and worry and defeat, and because they were all going to a new mysterious place, they huddled together; they talked together; they shared their lives, their food, and the things they hoped for in the new country. Thus it might be that one family camped near a spring, and another camped for the spring and for company, and a third because two families had pioneered the place and found it good. And when the sun went down, perhaps twenty families and twenty cars were there.

In the evening a strange thing happened: the twenty families became one family, the children were the children of all. The loss of home became one loss, and the golden time in the West was one dream. And it might be that a sick child threw despair into the hearts of twenty families, of a hundred people; that a birth there in a tent kept a hundred people quiet and awestruck through the night and filled a hundred people with the birth-joy in the morning. A family which the night before had been lost and fearful might search its goods to find a present for a new baby. In the evening, sitting about the fires, the twenty were one. They grew to be units of the camps, units of the evenings and the nights. A guitar unwrapped from a blanket and tuned—and the songs, which were all of the people, were sung in the nights. Men sang the words, and women hummed the tunes.

Every night a world created, complete with furniture—friends made and enemies established; a world complete with braggarts and with cowards, with quiet men, with humble men, with kindly men. Every night relationships that make a world, established; and every morning the world torn down like a circus.

At first the families were timid in the building and tumbling worlds, but gradually the technique of building worlds became their technique. Then leaders emerged, then laws were made, then codes came into being. And as the worlds moved westward, they were more complete and better furnished, for their builders were more experienced in building them.

The families learned what rights must be observed—the right of privacy in the tent; the right to keep the past black hidden in the heart; the right to talk and to listen; the right to refuse help or to accept, to offer help or to decline it; the right of son to court and daughter to be courted; the right of the hungry to be fed; the rights of the pregnant and the sick to transcend all other rights.

And the families learned, although no one told them, what rights are monstrous and must be destroyed: the right to intrude upon privacy, the right to be noisy while the camp slept, the right of seduction or rape, the right of adultery and theft and murder. These rights were crushed, because the little worlds could not exist for even a night with such rights alive.

And as the worlds moved westward, rules became laws, although no one told the families. It is unlawful to foul near the camp; it is unlawful in any way to foul the drinking water; it is unlawful to eat good rich food near one who is hungry, unless he is asked to share.

And with the laws, the punishments—and there were only two—a quick and murderous fight or ostracism; and ostracism was the worst. For if one broke the laws his name and face went with him, and he had no place in any world, no matter where created.

In the worlds, social conduct became fixed and rigid, so that a man must say "Good morning" when asked for it, so that a man might have a willing girl if he stayed with her, if he fathered her children and protected them. But a man might not have one girl one night and another the next, for this would endanger the worlds.

The families moved westward, and the technique of building the worlds improved so that the people could be safe in their worlds; and the form was so fixed that a family acting in the rules knew it was safe in the rules.

There grew up government in the worlds, with leaders, with elders. A man who was wise found that his wisdom was needed in every camp; a man who was a fool could not change his folly with his world. And a kind of insurance developed in these nights. A man with food fed a hungry man, and thus insured himself against hunger. And when a baby died a pile of silver coins grew at the door flap, for a baby must be well buried, since it has had nothing else of life. An old man may be left in a potter's field, but not a baby.

A certain physical pattern is needed for the building of a world—water, a river bank, a stream, a spring, or even a faucet unguarded. And there is needed enough flat land to pitch the tents, a little brush or wood to build the fires. If there is a garbage dump not too far off, all the better; for there can be found equipment—stove tops, a curved fender to shelter the fire, and cans to cook in and to eat from.

And the worlds were built in the evening. The people, moving in from the highways, made them with their tents and their hearts and their brains.

In the morning the tents came down, the canvas was folded, the tent poles tied along the running board, the beds put in place on the cars, the pots in their places. And as the families moved westward, the technique of building up a home in the evening and tearing it down with the morning light became fixed; so that the folded tent was packed in one place, the cooking pots counted in their box. And as the cars moved westward, each member of the family grew into his proper place, grew into his duties; so that each member, old and young, had his place in the car; so that in the weary, hot evenings, when the cars pulled into the camping places, each member had his duty and went to it without instruction: children to gather wood, to carry water; men to pitch the tents and bring down the beds; women to cook the supper and to watch while the family fed. And this was done without command. The families, which had been units of which the boundaries were a house at night, a farm by day, changed their boundaries. In the long hot light, they were silent in the cars moving slowly westward; but at night they integrated with any group they found.

Thus they changed their social life—changed as in the whole universe only man can change. They were not farm men any more, but migrant men. And the thought, the planning, the long staring silence that had gone out to the fields, went now to the roads, to the distance, to the West. That man whose mind had been bound with acres lived with narrow concrete miles. And his thought and his worry were not any more with rainfall, with wind and dust, with the thrust of the crops. Eyes watched the tires, ears listened to the clattering motors, and minds struggled with oil, with gasoline, with the thinning rubber between air and road. Then a broken gear was tragedy. Then water in the evening was the yearning, and food over the

fire. Then health to go on was the need and strength to go on, and spirit to go on. The wills thrust westward ahead of them, and fears that had once apprehended drought or flood now lingered with anything that might stop the westward crawling.

The camps became fixed—each a short day's journey from the last.

And on the road the panic overcame some of the families, so that they drove night and day, stopped to sleep in the cars, and drove on to the West, flying from the road, flying from movement. And these lusted so greatly to be settled that they set their faces into the West and drove toward it, forcing the clashing engines over the roads.

But most of the families changed and grew quickly into the new life. And when the sun went down—

Time to look out for a place to stop.

And—there's some tents ahead.

The car pulled off the road and stopped, and because others were there first, certain courtesies were necessary. And the man, the leader of the family, leaned from the car.

Can we pull up here an' sleep?

Why, sure, be proud to have you. What State you from?

Come all the way from Arkansas.

They's Arkansas people down that fourth tent.

That so?

And the great question, How's the water?

Well, she don't taste so good, but they's plenty.

Well, thank ya.

No thanks to me.

But the courtesies had to be. The car lumbered over the ground to the end tent, and stopped. Then down from the car the weary people climbed, and stretched stiff bodies. Then the new tent sprang up; the children went for water and the older boys cut brush or wood. The fires started and supper was put on to boil or to fry. Early comers moved over, and States were exchanged, and friends and sometimes relatives discovered.

Oklahoma, huh? What county?

Cherokee.

Why, I got folks there. Know the Allens? They's Allens all over Cherokee. Know the Willises?

Why, sure.

And a new unit was formed. The dusk came, but before the dark was down the new family was of the camp. A word had been passed with every family. They were known people—good people.

I knowed the Allens all my life. Simon Allen, ol' Simon, had trouble with his first wife. She was part Cherokee. Purty as—as a black colt.

Sure, an' young Simon, he married a Rudolph, didn' he? That's what I thought. They went to live in Enid an' done well—real well.

Only Allen that ever done well. Got a garage.

When the water was carried and the wood cut, the children walked shyly, cautiously among the tents. And they made elaborate acquaintanceship gestures. A boy stopped near another boy and studied a stone, picked it up, examined it closely, spat on it, and rubbed it clean and inspected it until he forced the other to demand, What you got there?

And casually, Nothin'. Jus' a rock.

Well, what you lookin' at it like that for?

Thought I seen gold in it.

How'd you know? Gold ain't gold, it's black in a rock.

Sure, ever'body knows that.

I bet it's fool's gold, an' you figgered it was gold.

That ain't so, 'cause Pa, he's foun' lots a gold an' he tol' me how to look.

How'd you like to pick up a big ol' piece a gold?

Sa-a-ay! I'd git the bigges' old son-a-bitchin' piece a candy you ever seen.

I ain't let to swear, but I do, anyways.

Me too. Le's go to the spring.

And young girls found each other and boasted shyly of their popularity and their prospects. The women worked over the fire, hurrying to get food to the stomachs of the family—pork if there was money in plenty, pork and potatoes and onions. Dutch-oven biscuits or cornbread, and plenty of gravy to go over it. Side-meat or chops and a can of boiled tea, black and bitter. Fried dough in drippings if money was slim, dough fried crisp and brown and the drippings poured over it.

Those families which were very rich or very foolish with their money ate canned beans and canned peaches and packaged bread and bakery cake; but they ate secretly, in their tents, for it would not have been good to eat such fine

things openly. Even so, children eating their fried dough smelled the warming beans and were unhappy about it.

When supper was over and the dishes dipped and wiped, the dark had come, and then the men squatted down to talk.

And they talked of the land behind them. I don' know what it's coming to, they said. The country's spoilt.

It'll come back though, on'y we won't be there.

Maybe, they thought, maybe we sinned some way we didn't know about.

Fella says to me, gov'ment fella, an' he says, she's gullied up on ya. Gov'ment fella. He says, if ya plowed 'cross the contour, she won't gully. Never did have no chance to try her. An' the new super' ain't plowin' 'cross the contour. Runnin' a furrow four miles long that ain't stoppin' or goin' aroun' Jesus Christ Hisself.

And they spoke softly of their homes: They was a little cool-house under the win'mill. Use'-ta keep milk in there ta cream up, an' watermelons. Go in there midday when she was hotter'n a heifer, an' she'd be jus' as cool, as cool as you'd want. Cut open a melon in there an' she'd hurt your mouth, she was so cool. Water drippin' down from the tank.

They spoke of their tragedies: Had a brother Charley, hair as yella as corn, an' him a growed man. Played the 'cordeen nice too. He was harrowin' one day an' he went up to clear his lines. Well, a rattlesnake buzzed an' them horses bolted an' the harrow went over Charley, an' the points dug into his guts an' his stomach, an' they pulled his face off an'—God Almighty!

They spoke of the future: Wonder what it's like out there?

Well, the pitchers sure do look nice. I seen one where it's hot an' fine, an' walnut trees an' berries; an' right behind, close as a mule's ass to his withers, they's a tall up mountain covered with snow. That was a pretty thing to see.

If we can get work it'll be fine. Won't have no cold in the winter. Kids won't freeze on the way to school. I'm gonna take care my kids don't miss no more school. I can read good, but it ain't no pleasure to me like with a fella that's used to it.

And perhaps a man brought out his guitar to the front of his tent. And he sat on a box to play, and everyone in the camp moved slowly in toward him, drawn in toward him. Many men can chord a guitar, but perhaps this man was a picker. There you have something—the deep chords beating, beating, while the melody runs on the strings like little footsteps. Heavy hard fingers marching on the frets. The man played and the people moved slowly in on him until the circle was closed and tight, and then he sang "Ten-Cent Cotton and Forty-Cent Meat." and the circle sang softly with him. And he sang "Why Do You Cut Your Hair, Girls?" And the circle sang. He wailed the song, "I'm Leaving Old Texas," that eerie song that was sung before the Spaniards came, only the words were Indian then.

And now the group was welded to one thing, one unit, so that in the dark the eyes of the people were inward, and their minds played in other times, and their sadness was like rest, like sleep. He sang the "McAlester Blues" and then, to make up for it to the older people, he sang "Jesus Calls Me to His Side." The children drowsed with the music and went into the tents to sleep, and the singing came into their dreams.

And after a while the man with the guitar stood up and yawned. Good night, folks, he said.

And they murmured, Good night to you.

And each wished he could pick a guitar, because it is a gracious thing. Then the people went to their beds, and the camp was quiet. And the owls coasted overhead, and the coyotes gabbled in the distance, and into the camp skunks walked, looking for bits of food—waddling, arrogant skunks, afraid of nothing.

The night passed, and with the first streak of dawn the women came out of the tents, built up the fires, and put the coffee to boil. And the men came out and talked softly in the dawn.

When you cross the Colorado river, there's the desert, they say. Look out for the desert. See you don't get hung up. Take plenty water, case you get hung up.

I'm gonna take her at night.

Me too. She'll cut the living Jesus outa you.

The families ate quickly, and the dishes were dipped and wiped. The tents came down. There was a rush to go. And when the sun arose, the camping place was vacant, only a little litter left by the people. And the camping place was ready for a new world in a new night.

But along the highway the cars of the migrant people crawled out like bugs, and the narrow concrete miles stretched ahead.

Migration and settlement in the Peruvian Montana: the Apurimac Valley

NORMAN R. STEWART   6

The most common catalyst for migration, whether by individuals or groups, is the belief that movement to a goal area will result in improved economic opportunities. A significant migration pattern—not in terms of numbers of people moved but in terms of potential for

Norman R. Stewart, "Migration and Settlement in the Peruvian Montana: The Apurimac Valley," *The Geographical Review*, LV, No. 2 (1965), pp. 143–148, 152–157.

future economic development—is the flow of farmers from crowded rural areas to thinly peopled frontiers. Such migrations most frequently occur with minimal governmental assistance.

Norman Stewart has clearly shown the variety of handicaps these isolated migrants face. The significance of the migration of the serranos into the Apurimac Valley is that the selva can be considered as a possible frontier area for other peoples, from vastly dissimilar regions of Peru. Such a potential adds a new dimension to Peruvian economic development.

For some time growth of the population in highland Peru has been outdistancing the resources available for its support. Natural increase among the largely Indian population of the sierra has not been matched by expanding agricultural production. On the contrary, archaic latifundia continue to monopolize the best lands, and primitive methods of cultivation become progressively less rewarding. The traditional safety valve for the surplus population of the highlands has been the irrigated oases of the desert coast. In the last few decades, however, migration from the sierra has far exceeded the absorptive capacity of the coastal plantations, and the stream of highland émigrés has been directed increasingly toward the coastal cities, particularly Lima. The appalling slums (*barriadas*) that ring the capital city are conclusive evidence that the urban habitat is equally incapable of accommodating the surplus.

Inevitably, attention has turned to Peru's part of the Amazon selva, the *montaña,* as a source of relief for the acute population pressure of the coast and the sierra. Professional opinion is sharply divided on the settlement value of the montaña, and Peruvian geographers and planners tend to emphasize problems rather than prospects. Yet even the most pessimistic authorities agree that on the margins of the Amazon Basin, at intermediate altitudes, there still remains a large reservoir of potentially productive land, and it is with respect to this region that interest in pioneer settlement is currently the most active.

Colonization on the fringes of the Peruvian montaña is not new.[1] However, the most serious and carefully planned thrusts toward the selva have been undertaken only recently. In preliminary surveys for one such project, investigators discovered that in Ayacucho Department a spontaneous migration of highland Quechua to the valley of the Rio Apurimac (Fig. 1) has been going on for at least a generation.[2] To what extent, and for how long, *serranos* have been filtering into the selva cannot yet be determined accurately, but such voluntary migrations and their consequences provide some interesting problems for planners, and valuable insights into processes of tropical pioneer settlement.

The Apurimac Valley

In 1961–1962 the writer was privileged to accompany several official expeditions into the Apurimac region. The parties, consisting largely of Peruvian agricultural engineers, were prepared to take a census of the local population, to conduct surveys of land use and capability, and, on the basis of these data, to organize the resettlement of serrano migrants, most of whom were squatting on land owned by others. Field parties were well equipped (including a helicopter and outboard motors), but considering the nature of the terrain the surveys were necessarily superficial.

In its northward flow toward a junction with the Mantaro (and eventually the Ucayali) the Apurimac winds between two mountain ranges that rise to more than ten thousand feet. Relatively level land is confined to discontinuous terraces about fifteen feet above the main level of the river. These flats range in area from a few acres to several hundred; some are large enough to accommodate landing strips for twin-engined aircraft. Adjacent slopes are steep, and in many places precipitous. The river itself is turbulent, and its level fluctuates considerably; during the rainy period (November to May) the current is swift and the river turgid, and at low water bedrock sills produce extensive rapids. Navigation is limited to native balsa rafts and dugouts, and journeys are often hazardous. Owing to physical limitations, and to the fact that the river passes through long stretches without fixed settlement, the Apurimac is of little real or potential utility in communication or commerce.

---

1 For substantial contributions on historical and other facets of the problem see W. V. Drewes: The Economic Development of the Western Montaña of Peru As Related to Transportation, *Andean Air Mail and Peruvian Times,* Supplement, Lima, 1958; and Robert C. Eidt: Pioneer Settlement in Eastern Peru, *Annals Assn. of Amer. Geogrs.,* Vol. 52, 1962, pp. 255–278.

2 "A Program for the Industrial and Regional Development of Peru" (Arthur D. Little, Inc., Cambridge, Mass., 1960).

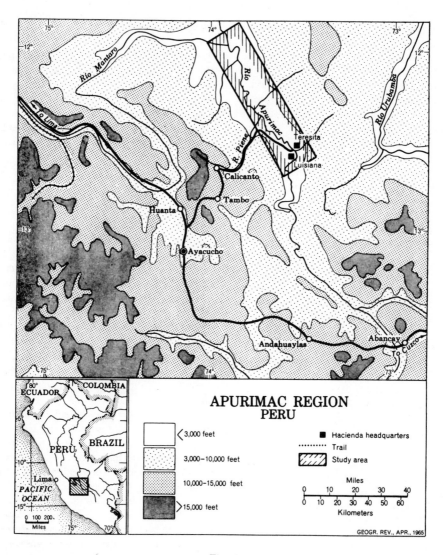

Fig. 1

Climatic and edaphic characteristics of the Apurimac Valley are imperfectly known, but the experience of its inhabitants indicates no serious limitations to tropical agriculture. The region, most of which is above two thousand feet, is without frost, and in spite of distinct seasonality precipitation is sufficient to support luxuriant selva and tropical perennials such as cacao and bananas. Soils are strongly acidic but appear to be less severely leached than latosols in the Amazon lowlands immediately to the east.[3]

[3] "A Program for the . . . Development of Peru" [see footnote 2 above], p. 83.

The settlement process

The movement of serranos into the Apurimac Valley is difficult to document, either chronologically or quantitatively. Our census data suggest continuous migration during the last quarter of a century, and perhaps longer. However, the pace has apparently been accelerating in the last decade; more than half of the highlanders interviewed had come to the selva within the past six years. Estimates based on our admittedly small population sample place the number of serranos living along the Apurimac between Luisiana and the Mantaro (Fig. 2) at about five thousand, mostly adult males.

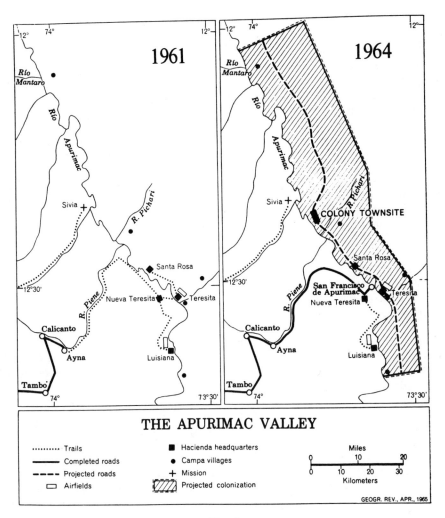

Fig. 2

The data clearly indicate that the only significant source area for migrants is the Cordillera adjoining, and most accessible to, the lower Apurimac; all serranos interviewed came from communities in northern Ayacucho Department, with Huanta and its immediate environs supplying the largest number (Fig. 1). The several trails over which migrants have entered the selva were apparently known and well traveled before the turn of the present century, and are undoubtedly much older.

Not unexpectedly, most of the serranos interviewed regarded their sojourn in the selva as temporary. Many had migrated simply to explore opportunities or for "a couple of years" to overcome some pressing financial problem.

Even among those who have settled in the area the resolve to return was commonly expressed. However, it is clear that once time and energy have been invested in clearing, planting, and building, the attachment to the highlands weakens. Contacts between serranos and their home communities are infrequent and casual; many migrants have not left the selva for five years or more.

In attempting to fashion a new life in the selva, highland Indians face a number of obstacles. Not the least of these is the fact that most of the land in the vicinity of the Apurimac is already occupied by two distinct groups. Native Indian subsistence agriculture and tropical latifundia represent functioning ecological systems that place different, and often conflicting, demands on the land. To the serrano, these competing forms of occupance constitute the basic framework within which his own patterns must be rationalized.

The tropical-forest tribe of the region, the Campa, although only recently considered "pacified," offers little hindrance to the intensification of settlement. The Campa are few in number and appear to be decreasing rapidly. Our helicopter survey revealed five small Campa villages near the right bank of the river. These villages, consisting of three to seven structures, are on hacienda land, and most of their inhabitants have been enticed or coerced into the plantation labor supply. The Campa are shifting cultivators but tend to value land primarily for its hunting potential. Thus plans for future development of the region purposely ignore the natives on the assumption that as population increases and wildlife becomes less abundant the Campa will voluntarily retreat farther into the forest. The logic of the premise is debatable, but it would appear that, in this area at least, the Campa are neither numerically nor technologically capable of seriously contesting the advance of settlement.

Tropical latifundia along the Apurimac present more complex problems. Almost all land on both sides of the river is owned in large blocks by Peruvians of European descent, most of whom live elsewhere. Only three properties have agricultural enterprises of any consequence, and two of these, Hacienda Teresita and Hacienda Luisiana, dominate the socioeconomic complex of the area. The best croplands in the valley are monopolized by their commercial cultivation of coca and barbasco (*cube*), cacao, coffee, and bananas. In addition, these two enterprises control the most appropriate airfield sites, and both have landing strips, which provide their owners with an extraordinary commercial advantage.

In the haciendas,[4] which currently exploit the most productive lands and hold title to most of the remainder, highland Indians have

encountered many of the problems they sought to avoid through migration. Out of necessity, serranos are drawn to haciendas to seek employment, only to become enmeshed in the web of debt peonage and similar mechanisms used to stabilize the labor supply.

Notwithstanding these competing forms of occupance, serranos have managed to establish themselves as agricultural pioneers in the hinterland of the left bank of the Apurimac. The processes by which they have accomplished this differ somewhat, but for most highlanders the haciendas are an indispensable link in the transition from migrant to independent agricultural settler. New migrants commonly drift to haciendas, work for several years, then move as squatters to some remote corner of the property. They earn little on the haciendas, but they gain valuable experience in tropical agriculture. Although the knowledge thus acquired is rudimentary, it serves to accelerate the process of familiarization with the new habitat.

The hacienda owners regard serrano settlement with a degree of ambivalence. Instinctively, they are reluctant to surrender land under any pretext; on the other hand, they are inclined to view any development of the area as advantageous, so long as their predominant role in regional economics remains unchallenged. In addition, the *hacendados* claim their traditional prerogatives, including the right to demand labor in exchange for the use of their land. The relationships between squatters and owners remain ill defined and require further study. Our investigation suggests that some form of traditional highland symbiosis may persist. Clearly, however, among serrano migrants the sense of obligation to owners of land is declining.

The settlement pattern

The spontaneous character and poor organization of highland migrations are reflected in the random pattern of the resulting settlement. Aerial photographs flown in 1961–1962 indicate that serranos prefer the more accessible west bank. In 1962 several families had opened clearings on the opposite bank, but the lack of a bridge across the Apurimac has restricted the flow of settlement. Clearings are scattered along the hill slopes within a few miles of the river; the immediate banks, which have been largely preempted by haciendas, are avoided.

---

[4] The nomenclature of tropical latifundia still lacks precision. Apurimac properties lie along the continuum of subtypes between the traditional "hacienda" and the exclusively commercial "plantation." However, "hacienda" conforms to local usage and is employed here.

Concentrations of pioneer settlements are difficult to detect. Trails connecting hacienda headquarters or leading to highland population centers are favored sites, but relationships between settlement patterns and communication do not appear to be precise. The tendency toward group settlement is marked, though isolated clearings occur. Our census data suggest that recent migrants preferred to pioneer in company with one or more friends or relatives. Two small *aynas*,[5] one consisting of five family heads, decided to move together to the selva.

Regardless of the size of such groups, or of the nature of the relationships between members, initial forest clearing is usually accomplished by common effort. The cleared area is then subdivided among individual families, who construct dwellings on their own plots. Both the area of the clearings and the size of the individual parcels vary considerably.[6] Many informants claimed to "have" as much as one hundred acres but admitted that they would aspire to much less if forced to pay for the land. In eleven clearings personally visited, the area actually cleared or cultivated averaged twenty acres to a family.

In serrano land use, subsistence crops of manioc, maize, beans, cotton, and bananas and various other tropical fruits are of considerable importance. It is obvious, however, that subsistence is not the primary objective of migration. All serranos grow crops for which they expect some return; on the farms visited these were among the first crops planted and occupied most of the cultivated land. Coca and barbasco, the mainstays of the local hacienda economy, are likewise the most important commercial crops of the serranos. Smaller amounts of bananas, coffee, and cacao are also produced.[7]

Agricultural methods strongly reflect tropical pioneering circumstances and experience acquired on the haciendas. Forests are felled, and the debris burned, during the relatively dry months (June to November). The simplicity of specific cultivation practices is reflected in the tools. The digging stick, the hoe, and the ax are basic. A short-handled, curved-bladed brush hook (*curvo*) is also general and is widely preferred to the machete. Plots are cultivated down slopes rather than across them, and there is no visible evidence that crop rotation, terracing, fertilization, or any other form of conservation is practiced. Extensive second growth observed on some slopes suggests that land rotation is developing as the typical response to soil erosion and depletion.

Cooperative labor pervades the entire settlement pattern. A few older, more successful pioneers hire their neighbors or Campa for agricultural labor. However, typical Quechua forms of mutual assistance have been brought to the selva, and these predominate in nonagricultural contexts as well as in the preparation and cultivation of land. Cooperation is closely linked with group settlement, and neighborly interdependence is strong. By combining their energies, the serranos have been able to engage almost immediately in commercial production. Equally important, bonds of obligation have tended to inhibit surrender to discouragement, since abandonment of land implies abandonment of responsibilities to others.

In marketing their agricultural products the serranos face enormous obstacles. Until 1959 coca and barbasco were transported by mule or human carrier to the terminus of the truck road at Calicanto—an arduous journey requiring two to four days, depending on the weather and the load. Produce was then sold to "middlemen," who, according to informants, set prices so low that profits were negligible. In 1958 hacendados induced serranos to provide labor for two airfields, and a year later the Peruvian military transport service (SATCO) inaugurated weekly

---

5 *Ayna* (*aine, ayni*) refers to an institutionalized form of mutual assistance in which group members exchange labor on a man-for-man, day-for-day basis. For a complete description of the ayna, which apparently was an ancient Quechua practice, see Bernard Mishkin: The Contemporary Quechua, *in* Handbook of South American Indians (edited by Julian H. Steward), *Bur. of Amer. Ethnology Bull. 143*, Vol. 2, 1946, pp. 411–470, reference on pp. 419–420; and John Howland Rowe: Inca Culture at the Time of the Spanish Conquest, *ibid.*, pp. 183–330, reference on p. 255.

6 It may be noted that variation in farm size is inconsistent with forms of mutual assistance such as the ayna, the smooth functioning of which depends on approximately equal labor requirements among members.

7 Much of the cacao is apparently a local wild variety known as *cacao chuncho*. Young plants encountered in the forest are often transferred to farm plots, but gathering from wild plants is also practiced.

flights from Lima to the Apurimac (weather permitting). However, this improvement in communications has not necessarily worked to the advantage of the serrano pioneers. As "agents" for SATCO, the hacendados fix freight rates to their own advantage and actively encourage the sale of produce to haciendas. In such transactions the serranos fare no better than in the marketplace of Calicanto, and many still prefer to take their chances in the highlands.

Problems and prospects

By their migrations to the Apurimac the highland Quechua have refuted the generally accepted notion that they are repelled by, or cannot function within, the tropical forest. The serranos have voluntarily accepted the challenges of an entirely different habitat and have experienced remarkably little difficulty in reorienting their cultural patterns to fit their new circumstances. The processes by which they have made these adjustments invite systematic analysis by cultural geographers, but traditional conservatism does not appear to function as a barrier to successful montaña settlement.[8]

At present, however, serrano colonization lacks many elements essential to stable and productive frontier settlement. Fundamental to all other problems is the absence of firm, legal attachment to the land. The casual and exploitive character of pioneer cultivation reflects a tenuous and temporary hold on the basic resource. The impact of future legal tenure on serrano occupance is difficult to predict, but without the security inherent in title ownership the development of rational and permanent qualities in the land-use system is unlikely.

Economic factors also conspire against stability. Isolation and hacienda monopoly have already been identified as sources of difficulty. In addition, the principal products of the region are subject to the vagaries of world market prices. Income from coca remains fairly stable, but supplies of barbasco now exceed the demand, and the outlook for the other traditional crops is not bright. In these contexts the serrano is in a poor competitive position and is less prepared than the hacendado to search for profitable alternatives.

Social dislocation is both symptomatic of general instability and a source of additional pressure on the serranos. Our population sample indicates that migration of stable family units is not characteristic of the Apurimac frontier; married pioneers commonly leave their families in the highlands. This behavior is rationalized by the lack of educational and medical facilities but may well reflect an underlying feeling of impermanence. Informants expressed concern for the welfare of their families in the sierra, but return visits are infrequent; at least three pioneers have established second "families" in the montaña.

The character of Apurimac settlement and its implications for the development of the montaña have recently attracted official attention. In the last three years the Peruvian government has approached the problem in several ways. Of direct concern is the decision by the Institute of Agrarian Reform and Colonization to attempt the systematic reorganization of serrano settlement in the Apurimac Valley. On the basis of surveys conducted in 1961–1962, most of the gently sloping land on the right bank of the river was selected as the site of a planned agricultural colony (Fig. 3). Expropriation procedures are under way, and farms and a townsite have been surveyed. Serranos in the area will be provided with credit for the purchase of eighty-acre parcels; an experimental farm and social, educational, and medical amenities are planned. The project is frankly experimental: the reservoir of planning experience is not great, and the serranos themselves are skeptical and suspicious of government intentions. However, early in 1964 a new road from the sierra reached the river, and a new town, San Francisco de Apurimac, was founded at its terminus.[9] Engineers expect to bridge the Apurimac and connect with roads in the new colony by 1966.

Selection of the Apurimac for experimental

---

[8] Superficial evidence suggests that the native Campa as well as the haciendas contribute to Quechua cultural change. Some house types and agricultural methods point to Campa origins, and the preparation of chicha from manioc is identical to Campa practice.

[9] *Andean Air Mail and Peruvian Times*, Jan. 31, 1964, p. 18. The town was reported to have sixty resident families on the day of its official inauguration (Jan. 26, 1964).

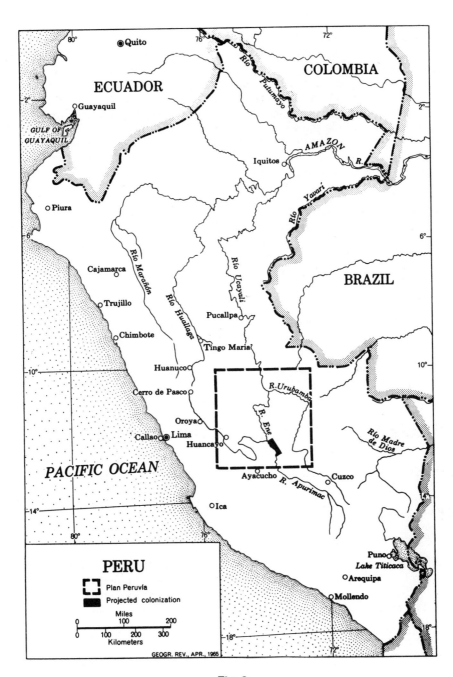

Fig. 3

colonization was motivated by the fact that the valley lies within the area of *Plan Peruvía,* a broad-scale regional development plan adopted by the Peruvian government in 1960.[10] Peruvía focuses on exploitation of the hydroelectric potential of the Mantaro (an Apurimac tributary) and the concomitant development of resources in the adjacent montaña. Implementation of the plan has been uneven, but topographical and geological surveys are complete,

[10] Eidt, *op. cit.* [see footnote 1 above], pp. 272–273.

and construction of access roads is under way. Work on the first power unit, rated at 330,000 kilowatts, was scheduled to begin late in 1964.[11] Lima and various urban-industrial centers in the highlands will undoubtedly absorb most of the initial energy output, but the facility is expected to provide the stimulus for the growth of settlement in the central Peruvian montaña.

The Apurimac Valley is included in another recent proposal, which, though still in the discussion stage, may profoundly alter the relationships between the Pacific republics and their Amazon territories. In 1963 President Belaunde of Peru suggested an international "marginal highway" to link the montañas of Colombia, Ecuador, Peru, and Bolivia. The project has been accepted in principle, and funds for feasibility surveys have been made

available.[12] New roads planned for the Apurinac colony are to be incorporated into the Peruvian segment of this "Bolívar Highway."

The colonization of the Apurimac, and the larger development schemes of which it is a part, represent important steps toward solution of the interrelated problems of population maldistribution and expansion of the effective national territory to Peru's international boundaries. Settlement of the montaña cannot be viewed as a substitute for land reform or intensification of agriculture in the sierra. Selva migration, even when organized and facilitated, is at best gradual. However, along the Apurimac the serrano has demonstrated a capacity for successful tropical-forest pioneering. If such settlement can be encouraged and stabilized, Peru may yet win the struggle to accommodate its burgeoning population at an acceptable standard of living.

[11] *Andean Air Mail and Peruvian Times*, Nov. 22, 1963, p. 1.

[12] *Andean Air Mail and Peruvian Times*, Nov. 15, 1963, p. 1.

The Middle Ages collide with the 20th century

STANLEY MEISLER

7

In the nations suffering from the contemporary ill of "underdevelopment," the most critical pattern of mobility is the inflow of underemployed rural population to urban areas. The pattern of under- or un-employment is generally continued, and the supposed food surplus created in the countryside by rural depopulation is consumed by relatives left on the farmstead, while the migrant makes new food demands upon the urban economy. The problems related to this particular rural-urban migration are given sharp focus in this newspaper article by Stanley Meisler. Though Meisler's article is concise to the point of being simplistic, it does an excellent job of highlighting a virtually universal crisis in mobility. This migration is of further interest to the cultural geographer because of the patterns of diffusion, settlement, and development generated by such a flow.

The Los Angeles Times, November 17, 1968, sec. B, pp. 1–3.

Nairobi—Hundreds of thousands of Africans turn their backs on the land every year and push into Africa's choking cities, searching for what they call the high life—schools, bicycles, doctors, jazz, shoes, cash.

But the cities cannot satisfy their dreams.

The result is a searing, persistent social problem that mocks economic planners and frightens politicians. The towns bulge with thousands of unemployed Africans who are barely housed, barely clothed, and barely fed. They often turn resentful at governments that promise much but can do little.

But so far, the resentments, cooled by hope for a better life in the future, have not flamed into street violence.

Unhealthy growth rate

Africa, which hardly had any towns and cities in the 19th century, now has a few hundred, all growing at unhealthy rates. Nairobi, which now has a population of 460,000, swells by 7% every year, more than twice as fast as the growth of Los Angeles between 1950 and 1960. Nairobi may have 1.2 million people by 1985 and 3.5 million by the end of the century. Other African cities grow even faster. Accra increases 7.8% a year, Abidjan 9.7%, Lusaka 13.7%, and Lagos 14%.

Most of the new people are migrants from the rural lands. Less than 10% of the population of Nairobi, for example, was born in the city. The rest came to seek a new kind of fortune.

This rush to the towns differs in significant ways from the urbanization experienced since the industrial revolution.

Largely agricultural

Industrialization, in fact, seems to have very little to do with pulling Africans to the towns. African countries are largely agricultural. Most of their tribesmen till the soil in traditional ways and produce only enough to feed the family and earn a bit of money to pay for taxes and school fees.

The cities are 20th-century islands implanted in this traditional African world by the old colonial governments. Government and commerce are the main activities. They have large bureaucracies and busy markets, but few factories.

Industrialization is far too meager to justify the number of Africans who rush into the cities.

In short, the African is drawn to the cities by more than economics. The city has become the only symbol of the modern world to the African brought up in his peasant world. In a sense, he can move from the middle ages to the 20th century by going to the city.

If an African has had a few years of schooling, if his imagination has been excited by newspapers and the radio, if he feels a need to break from his traditional ways, if he wants to be modern, there is only one place he can go—the city. And he will go there even when it does not make economic sense to do so.

In "People of the City," a novel about life in Lagos, Biafran Cyprian Ekwensi catches the essence of the yearning of the city when he describes the young girl who would be content to wear out her shoes walking in the air-conditioned atmosphere of department stores, to linger all day in the foyer of hotels with not a penny in her handbag, rather than live in the country and marry papa's choice.

But, when Africans show up in the city, they do not become a part of it. Instead, the newcomers camp on the fringes.

Two cities

As a result almost every African city is really two cities. The first is the modern, active city where people work and trade and produce. The second, which may sometimes have as many people, is the dirty, crowded, abject city where people wait for a change to move in the mainstream. Social scientists call it the transitional city.

Nairobi, capital of Kenya, is a modern city of pleasant office buildings and jacaranda-lined boulevards. Its economy is dominated by whites, Asians and highly educated Africans who employ thousands of poor Africans.

But Nairobi is also a transitional city with thousands of even poorer Africans living in squalor.

No vacancies

Since 1960, almost all the shops and offices of Nairobi have displayed signs that say "hakuna kazi"—Swahili for "no vacancies."

Dr. Munyua Waiyaki, a member of Parliament for a district of 100,000 people said: "The majority of people in my district do not work."

As a singer in a popular Swahili jazz tune puts it, "now I'm in Nairobi and I haven't got work yet. Now what do I do?"

Statistics are stark. Every year, more than 100,000 primary school graduates in Kenya fail to gain admission to secondary schools. And whatever education they receive makes the Africans dissatisfied with work on family farms. They join the Kenya labor supply instead, a large number drifting to Nairobi.

But the city has few jobs available. In 1966, total African employment in Nairobi increased by only 14,000. The situation is so bad that every time an employer offers a job he probably creates additional unemployment. News of the opening entices even more Africans into the city.

Unemployment forces those in the city to develop a primitive economy of their own, one that does not show in government statistics.

In Mathare Valley, a Nairobi quarter of 20,000 squatters, landlords build mud houses and rent out tiny rooms. Traders sell cartons of milk and bits of bony meat. Boys peddle tin cans of water and bags of charcoal. Women distill an illegal gin called Kangarikia—a Swahili word that means "kill me quick." Other women sell their bodies to the police and airmen barracked on the nearby hill.

The statistically unemployed are kept from destitution by this embryonic economic and by family ties. African societies expect a man with an income to take care of all his relatives, no matter how distant. A salaried government worker in Nairobi, for example, is likely to have from five to 10 unemployed uncles, cousins, and nephews living with him.

As in any poor and overcrowded city, housing in Nairobi is unhealthy and inadequate. For a city of Nairobi's size and growth, city planners estimate that 4,000 new houses must be built a year. In the first five years of Kenyan independence, fewer than 1,000 houses were built each year. In the next five years, the city council plans to build 2,000 a year.

A typical Nairobi house for low-income workers has walls of dried mud or of cement block and a roof of corrugated iron. The door opens to a dank, dark corridor that has tiny, padlocked rooms on either side. There may be seven or eight of these rooms, and each houses a family.

Primitive quarters

A room eight feet square will rent for $6 to $7 a month. There may be three or four beds, a few chairs, a dresser, a table and a jiko, the little pot and charcoal stand used for cooking. Shirts and stockings usually litter the room. Spider webs lace the ceiling. There is no electricity. A narrow window, covered with wire but no glass, usually lights the room. Outside, the city provides water and a stinking lavatory.

The city also has various housing projects that rent two-room apartments with bathroom and kitchen for up to $17 a month plus $4 for utilities. But there is a waiting list of 25,000.

The lack of jobs and housing tends to make family life abnormal. The city is crowded with thousands of men who have left their wives and children on the farm while they look for work.

Broken families

Families break up. Tribal authority weakens. Children wander the streets. As a result, petty thievery, prostitution, and major crime grow.

Dissatisfaction, frustration, and resentment are growing in the city. The people turn sullen when they see, on the one hand, a new class of rich African government officials and business executives and, on the other, their own class of impoverished jobless, homeless people. They believe little is being done for them.

"There is a kind of disappointment about us (the politicians in power)," said Dr. Walyaki. "Is it a good sign for the future? I don't think it is."

Despite the disappointment, there have been no riots or other civil disturbances in Nairobi since Kenya became independent five years ago. The same is true of most of the other big cities of Africa.

There are several reasons for this. First, the built-in welfare system of African family life eases some of the frustrations. A jobless man can stave off hunger by sponging off his cousin.

Second, Africans seem to be prepared to put up with far more than the urban poor of Europe and America. Though their dreams may be high, their expectations are probably low. An African is not content with unemployment and squatter housing, but he may be prepared to accept it, at least for awhile.

Third, Africans are so new to the city that they may still look on their frustrations as temporary. The problems have not festered long enough to cause violence.

Finally, many Africans have faith that their leaders, who brought them out of colonialism, will someday bring them out of poverty. There may be a good deal of resentment against politicians in Nairobi, but there still is a great deal of reverence of the father of the country, President Jomo Kenyatta.

Government officials know they have explosive problems on their hands and are trying to deal with them. But they are handicapped by limited funds.

Most government officials feel that the rush to the city can be slowed only if the government will transform and modernize the rural areas. Rural transformation has become the slogan of Kenya planners and their foreign advisers. The theory is simple: If the government invests enough money, the rural areas will become prosperous and hold on to their population.

President Kenyatta is continually urging people to leave the cities and return to the land.

But little is known about the techniques of modernizing the traditional ways of rural Africa. The cost, in fact may be more than African government can afford. And, even if governments succeed in transforming their rural areas, there is no guarantee that this will stop the rush to the city.

The origin of leeboards

EDWIN DORAN, JR.

8

To find diffusion patterns for any given invention or trait, the cultural geographer turns to historical evidence for the initial occurrence of the phenomenon in question. A documented chronology of the expansion of an invention entails research into travel accounts, local histories and gazetteers, and period histories compiled through collections of whatever written sources were available. Such a quest is bound to be both time-consuming and, in the end, somewhat disturbing because of the gaps which remain after even the most thorough of searches.

This article by Edwin Doran is an articulate example of the pursuit of just such a chronology. The range of historical sources encountered and integrated in the pursuit of the invention and diffusion of the leeboard, as well as use of personal communication with people likely to have materials relevant to leeboards, combine to make this a touchstone article for the cultural geographer.

Introduction

The association of leeboards with Dutch sailing craft is so intimate that mention of one tends to evoke an image of the other. The connexion between the large, boardlike object which can be lowered into the water to inhibit leeway and confer considerable weatherliness and a typical broad-beamed, shallow-draft Dutch hull appears so logical that it comes as something of a surprise to learn that this close relationship begins abruptly about the year 1600.

Curiosity about the origin of leeboards was expressed in a query in this journal more than forty years ago,[1] but no response has ever appeared. Several suggestions on their origin, most of them assuming diffusion of the idea from other locations rather than invention by the Dutch, have been made elsewhere through the decades of the twentieth century. In one of his delightful essays on sailing, Belloc (1951, p.

Edwin Doran, Jr., "The Origin of Leeboards," *The Mariner's Mirror*, LIII, No. 1 (1967), pp. 39–53.

[1] C.T.R., 1924, p. 102. For full details of works quoted, see pp. 48–49.

128) speculated on a Dutch invention. Clark (1904, p. 126) suggested that the idea of lee-boards had been derived from Spanish observation of their use on Peruvian sailing rafts in the early sixteenth century; this notion is repeated as late as 1962 by Phillips-Birt (p. 91). Derivation of leeboards from China is suggested by Chatterton (1912, p. 73), Brindley (1923, p. 318) and Smyth (1929, p. 456). A recent hypothesis by Bowen (1959, p. 301) would have their source in the balance-board canoes of Palk Strait between India and Ceylon.

The reason for this confusion is apparent. The similarity of the Northwest European device to others encountered around the world during the Century of Discovery and its appearance well after other types of leeway boards became known lends credence to the idea of diffusion rather than independent invention. On the other hand, despite considerable search in the sixteenth-century literature, there is at this time no known direct evidence of transmission of the leeboard idea to Europe. No one heretofore has made an attempt to assemble all shreds of evidence, of any type that might be useful toward a solution, for a definitive study of the problem. The comments which follow are an effort in that direction. The weight of evidence clearly points toward China as the place of origin of leeboards and to diffusion of the idea to the Netherlands in the late sixteenth century.

Technical comment

Since even James Hornell, the great authority on primitive craft, is ambiguous occasionally in his use of terms, it seems appropriate to note that the words 'leeboard', 'centreboard', and 'daggerboard' are used hereafter in conformance with their dictionary definitions (Kerchove, 1961, pp. 135, 196, 444). A leeboard lies against and outside the lee side of a craft and pivots in a fore and aft direction, a centreboard is located along the fore-and-aft centreline in a well and pivots on a thwartships axis, and a daggerboard slides up and down, usually in a well amidships, without pivoting. The non-committal term 'leeway board' will be used generically for all such devices. The function of such boards and of keels and rudders in inhibiting leeway is described in numerous introduc-

tions to the art of sailing. Here also will be found adequate descriptions of the greater utility of such boards, in comparison with keels, on shallow-draft vessels operating in shoal waters.

Centreboard distribution and history

Since the centreboard appears in the West nearly two hundred years after the critical part of this study and plays no significant role it may be disposed of with brevity. In 1774 Lieut. Schank of the Royal Navy invented a 'drop keel', a daggerboard, which soon achieved some popularity. The device was used on a revenue cutter built in 1790, on the 60-ton brig *Lady Nelson* in 1798, and on some 43 gun vessels of the Royal Navy in 1799. A 'leeboard through the bottom', a pivoting centreboard, was patented in 1811, after which many vessels were equipped, including an 80 ft schooner in 1828 and even a 265 ft vessel. After 1850 centreboards were widely used in the United States and somewhat less so on the Continent.[2]

Daggerboard distribution and history

Small sailing yachts of the present are commonly equipped with either centreboards or daggerboards and are found all over the world in places where Western ideas have penetrated. There are at least three areas, however, in which economic use is still made of craft with daggerboards. All three areas are out of the main stream of Western culture, are relatively primitive, and make use of sailing rafts.[3]

---

[2] Comments taken from Chapelle (1951, pp. 38, 40), Clark (1904; pp. 138, 148, 204) and Phillips-Birt (1962, p. 95). A word of caution may be interjected here before abandoning the subject of centreboards. This device is widely used on Oriental craft from Northern Annam into South China and on the basis of this fact alone would appear to be of considerable antiquity. Whether it precedes European centreboards is unknown and indeed whether Lieut. Schank's idea was completely original or based on knowledge of Oriental boards is also unknown. Descriptions of Oriental centreboards are to be found in Paris (1955), Smyth (1929, p. 456), Worcester (1947, p. 21) and Worcester (1959, p. 136).

[3] For an excellent overview on the subject of rafts see Nelson (1961).

Brazil. On the east coast, particularly in the vicinity of Recife, is found the *jangada,* a sailing raft constructed from logs (Lane-Poole, 1940, pp. 333-8). Seaworthy enough for fishing many miles offshore and to have accomplished a voyage from Recife to Rio de Janeiro and return, the jangada is an interesting and relatively little-known craft. The long and narrow daggerboard is thrust down a slot cut through the centre log and adjusted in height dependent on the point of sailing. Although a long and narrow steering paddle is now used, there is some evidence that in the past the oar may have been raised and lowered vertically in order to steer by changing the location of the centre of lateral resistance in relation to that of the centre of effort of the sail (Edwards, 1965, pp. 96, 97). Authorities differ as to the length of time jangadas have been used along this coast, and the issue remains unresolved.

Peru. The sailing rafts of the coast of Peru have been much publicized by the Heyerdahl *Kontiki* voyage. The present use of small sailing rafts in fishing communities along the northern coast of Peru is much less widely known (Edwards, 1960). These small craft are sailed by means of three long and narrow daggerboards, forward, about the centre, and at the stern, which are raised and lowered to change the relative locations of centres of effort and of lateral resistance. This procedure is also documented for earliest Spanish contact in the sixteenth century and represents a tenacious retention of an ancient technique.

Annam-Formosa. Relatively sophisticated sailing rafts of bamboo are found along the coast of Annam and in southern Formosa; proximity and similarity in form allow them to be considered as one type despite a considerable area between in which more advanced junk types have supplanted the rafts. Both the Annamese and Formosan rafts have multiple daggerboards, but their shapes and locations are somewhat different. Formosan rafts have two or three daggerboards, often two abreast near the forward end of the raft and one amidships aft, which are nearly as wide as they are long.[4] The

rafts in Annam have several long and narrow dagger boards which are spaced from fore to aft more or less along the centreline.[5]

Details are wanting but there seems to be some evidence that these rafts also may have been steered by raising and lowering the daggerboards in the same way that the Peruvian balsas were steered; alteration of centre of lateral resistance by shifting the boards' locations is clearly documented (see Edwards, 1965, p. 99). Although these rafts are thought to be of great antiquity no adequate evidence supports this conclusion. It is a reasonable inference, but only that, to suppose that bamboo rafts are a primitive boat type which probably preceded the use of junks along the South China coast.

Leeboard distribution

In the twentieth century leeboards are part of the sailing equipment of certain canoes and small prams and other types of yachts used only for recreational purposes. Around the turn of the century they were also in use on a variety of commercial craft, mainly of the scow type, in the coastal waters of the United States (see Chapelle, 1951). Both of these occurrences may be neglected since they clearly postdate the period of about 1600 with which we have most concern; only three areas of leeboard use remain to be considered. (Please refer to Fig. 1 for locations of the craft which follow.)

Coromandel. Along the Coromandel coast of India, including the northern and western coasts of Ceylon, are found both canoes and rafts which employ leeway boards (Fig. 2a). Balance-board canoes, particularly in the vicinity of Palk Strait, are fitted with two long and narrow quarter-rudders and as well with a leeboard of the same shape (see Hornell, 1946,

---

4 Worcester (1956, p. 304); also illustrated in Hornell (1946, plate xiiiA) and in Casson (1964, p. 14).

5 Paris (1955, plates 45–52). It may be noted here that at least one Annamese raft, that of Dông-hói, at about latitude 19° N., employs leeboards rather than daggerboards. Its location is shown on the map which accompanies the next section below. Despite the intervening gap it would appear to be related to the large area of Chinese leeboards farther north —and very possibly the antecedent form. For details and an excellent large-scale map see Paris (1955, p. 64 and carte no. 1).

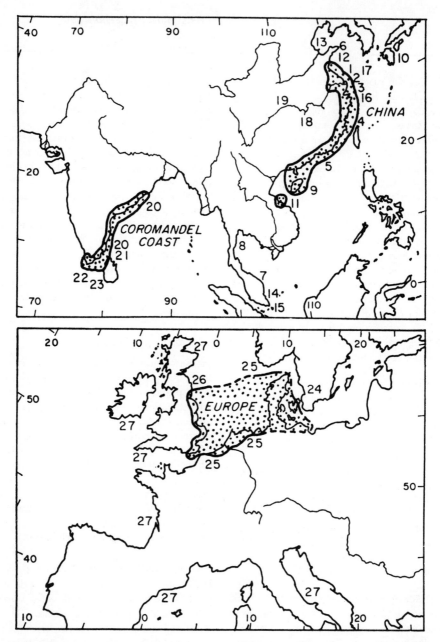

Fig. 1. Worldwide distribution of lee-boards. Numbers refer to sources which are acknowledged at end of this article. References for distributions in the various areas are as follows: China, 1–19; Coromandel Coast, 20–23; and Europe, 24–27. 1, Audemard (1957–63, p. 2–56); 2, Audemard (1957–63, p. 5–67); 3, Donnelly (1924, p. 5); 4, Donnelly (1923, p. 226); 5, Lovegrove (1932, p. 243); 6, Sigaut (1954, pp. 161–74); 7, Smyth (1929, p. 390); 8, Smyth (1929, p. 436); 9, Smyth (1929, pp. 456, 459); 10, Smyth (1929, pp. 485–498); 11, Paris (1955, p. 64); 12, Waters (1938, pp. 49–67); 13, Waters (1939, pp. 62–88); 14, Waters (1940, pp. 79–95); 15, Waters (1946, pp. 155–167); 16, Waters (1947, p. 28); 17, Worcester (1947, plates 41, 42, 48, 53, 68, 70); 18, Worcester (1961, pp. 187–95); 18, Worcester (1940); 20, Nelson (1961, plate 15; Hornell, 1946, p. 61); 21, Hornell (1946, p. 260); 22, Hornell (1943, p. 42); 23, Sopher (1966); 24, Smyth (1929, p. 25); 25, Smyth (1929, pp. 70–95); 26, Smyth (1929, pp. 132–98); 27, Smyth (1929, negative evidence from many pages).

pp. 261, 262). The *oruwa* outrigger canoe of the north-western Ceylon also uses a long and narrow leeboard forward, in conjunction with a steering paddle aft, to resist making leeway

(Hornell, 1943, p. 42; Sopher, 1966, personal communication and photographs). Several types of raft are in use, among them a large seven-log raft employed primarily in seeking

Fig. 2a. Palk Strait balance-board canoe. (From Howell, 1946)

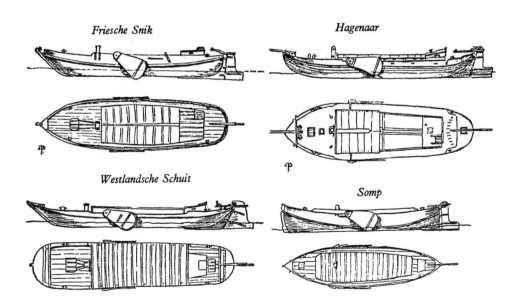

Fig. 2b. Four modern leeboard types (From *M.M.*, viii, p. 156.)

flying fish. These craft sail many miles offshore and inhibit leeway by the use of a steering paddle and 'two powerful leeboards' (Hornell, 1946, p. 66). Whether these are truly leeboards or whether they are daggerboards is unclear from the text and indeterminable from the illustrations. Hornell (1946, p. 66) states that 'the craft is employing three leeboards, a curious and significant fact seeing that the great sailing rafts of Formosa employ the same number'.[6] Since the Formosa rafts certainly use daggerboards perhaps that is what he means; but the closely adjacent canoes utilize leeboards and the most logical assumption would be similarity in their respective boards' shape and use.[7]

China. Since the literature in English and French on Chinese junks is not extensive, the data on distribution of junks with leeboards are

_____

[6] Paris (1955, p. 64) refers to a Hornell paper of 1923 which describes these leeboards more fully.

[7] Although Sopher (1966, personal communication) did not actually see leeboards in use on these Coromandel rafts he concludes they are much more likely to have been used than daggerboards because the precisely shaped and tapered logs fit so closely that it would be difficult to thrust a board between them.

limited (see Fig. 7). 'Hainan to north Shanghai' expresses the distribution succinctly.

The characteristics of Chinese leeboards are known in some detail. The boards are sizeable, up to 10 ft or more in length, are two or three times as long as wide, and made of several planks secured with cross-braces (Fig. 3). A short and stout wooden axle on which to pivot rests on the gunwale between two vertical members which prevent fore-and-aft movement; a chain from the end of the axle to a thwart-ships beam prevents outward movement of the upper part of the leeboard but allows the lower part to move outward, broken-wing fashion, if upon tacking the board inadvertently remains down on the windward side. Boards are rigged in pairs, one on each side of the vessel, and are alternately raised and lowered as each side becomes the lee on successive tacks to windward; in some cases two boards are rigged on each side to provide double pairs of leeboards. When combined with a large and powerful rudder, which also can be lowered in deep water, leeboards add considerable weatherliness to the typical shallow-draft junk hull.[8]

_____

[8] This description is summarized from a variety of sources on junks. In addition to the works of Audemard, Waters, and Worcester, which are cited

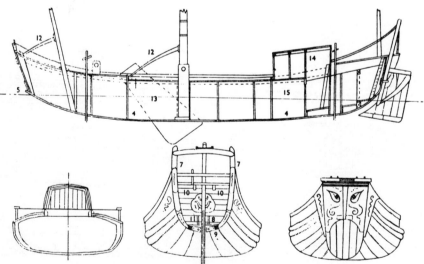

Fig. 3. The Hangchow trader, a modern Chinese leeboard type. (From Worcester, 1947).

Dutch. The concentration of North-west-European leeboards in Dutch waters is too well known to require further comment. The British distribution from Brighton around to Yorkshire and the use of leeboards in eastern Denmark are also reasonably well known (Smyth, 1929, pp. 25, 70–95, 132–98). Leeboards are notably absent in all other European waters.[9]

A description of Dutch leeboards would essentially duplicate the description of Chinese boards above (excluding the description of rudders; see Fig. 2*b*). It may be noted that the shapes of Dutch boards vary from ovate to fairly long, but the ratio of length to width ranges only between 1.7 to a little over 3.0. An analogous chain fitting to allow the board to rise rather than breaking off when caught down on the windward side is noted on an American leeboard scow by Chapelle (1951, p. 71).[10]

Leeboard history

Coromandel. No good evidence exists on the antiquity of the leeboard canoes and rafts of the Coromandel coast of India. Hornell has assumed considerable age for these craft on the basis of conservatism of primitives and seafarers in general, and it is known that this part of the sub-continent has a number of relict character-istics indicating great age. Analogy with the well-documented history of Peruvian sailing rafts, known to have existed continuously from the 1530's down to the present, would also tend to indicate great age for these leeboard types. It is a reasonable assumption that European navigators of the early sixteenth century en-countered these craft and noted their charac-teristics; it is conceivable that the idea of leeboards was taken back to Europe from observations of these craft.

China. Utilization of leeboards by the Chinese before 1500 is an almost certainly established fact. A document of 1637 clearly describes lee-boards on the 'sea boat' and comments that this craft was in use as far back as the Yüan Dynasty (1206–1368).[11] Stronger substantiation of the existence of leeboards in China long be-fore 1500 will be provided in the near future.[12]

Netherlands. The continued use of leeboards by the Dutch and by people of neighbouring areas from the early seventeenth century to the present is so well known as to need no comment.[13] A number of authors also have commented on the sudden appearance of lee-boards about 1600. A painting attributed to Saenredam and of about 1600 shows several leeboarders in Amsterdam and is among the earliest paintings which illustrate them (Chat-terton, 1912, fig. 10). Crone, who probably speaks on the subject with more authority than anyone else, states (1943, p. 149) that leeboards were introduced into the Netherlands in the second half of the sixteenth century and soon came into general use. He illustrates the Pieter Bast map of Amsterdam of 1597 which shows

---

as sources for data in Fig. 2, it may be useful here to cite the principal sources in English: Donnelly (1920, 1925 *a*, *b*, 1926, 1936), Hornell (1934), Moll (1923), Spencer (1938), Waters (1955), Wiens (1955), Worcester (1948, 1954, 1959 *a*, *b*).

[9] The use of a type of leeway board to prevent lee-ward set by Portuguese drift fishermen may be of some significance since these were the first Europeans to visit the China coast.

[10] According to Hartog (letter of 24 May 66) Dutch vessels do not have such chain fittings.

[11] Ting (1925) translates this document and Don-nelly has appended descriptive notes. Wheatley, in letters of 16 August 1965 and 22 January 1966, com-ments on it: 'In the first place a more accurate translation of the title of the work with which V. K. Ting is dealing would be *The Exploitation of the Works of Nature* (. . .), and it was written by Sung Ying-hsing . . . in 1637, not 1639 as Ting and Donnelly (*Mariner's Mirror*, xi, no. 4, October 1925) say. The book is a sort of general overview of technology. In reply to your query, I think it is a reasonable inference that the leeboard was in use before A.D. 1500, particularly as the Sea Boat is men-tioned in connexion with the Yüan Dynasty. . . .'

[12] Professor Joseph M. Needham, letter of 14 March 1966, mentions evidence on this point which will appear in vol. 4, part 3 of *Science and Civilization in China* (Cambridge University Press). A Chinese document of A.D. 759 describes 'floating boards' attached to the sides of ships which prevent them from being driven sideways or from overturning. Although possibly these could be construed as out-riggers the most likely deduction from the entire description and from the complete absence of outriggers in all modern Chinese types is that they are leeboards.

[13] Excellent histories of nautical development, each of which comments on Dutch leeboards in the last several centuries, are those by Chatterton (1912), Phillips-Birt (1962) and Casson (1964).

many leeboarders; but on the Anthonizoon map of 1544 not a single one appears. Additional small bits of negative evidence are the lack of leeboards on boats on a copy of a late fifteenth century Flemish MS. and in the realistic paintings of Bruegel of the period *c.* 1560 (Nance, 1920, p. 344; Denis, 1961, various plates).

On the basis of extant information, and recognizing the danger inherent in the use of negative evidence, it appears reasonable to agree with Crone and accept the notion of first appearance of leeboards in Europe in the latter sixteenth century.

Early European contacts with board-users

It has been noted that early contacts of Europeans with users of leeboards on the Coromandel coast may be reasonably inferred but are not proved. In the same way the chronology is such that Europeans could well have seen the bamboo rafts of Annam-Formosa or the jangada of Brazil early in the sixteenth century. But no documentation of such eyewitness has been found, nor is there other than inferential evidence of the existence of these craft at the time of early contacts. The case for Peru is quite different and a good summary of Spanish descriptions of balsa rafts in the sixteenth century is provided by Edwards (1965, pp. 66–71). The leeboard idea could have come from any of these sources and reached the Low Countries by the latter part of the century.

Europeans also encountered Chinese vessels early in the sixteenth century and from that time onward. Although leeboards were in use in China there appears to be no written evidence of their observation by Europeans. By 1517 Tomé Pires had written of his experiences in Malacca, mentioning the junk trade with China, and had arrived in Canton on the first Portuguese mission to the Chinese (Cortesão, 1944). Among the many Portuguese in the fleet there could have been someone who later mentioned in Europe the strange device noted on certain Chinese junks.

The first accounts of China published in Europe and based on personal acquaintance with the area also have only negative evidence (Boxer, 1953). Galeote Pereira reports in some detail, based on his imprisonment in China about 1548, but does not mention leeboards.

Gasper da Cruz, as of 1556, and Martín de Rada, as of 1575, mention the tremendous number of ships at Canton and describe the great *yulohs* or sweeps used to propel vessels but again do not mention leeboards. However, the Portuguese trade along the South-east China coast, illicit for years and more or less legal after the establishment of Macao in 1557, must without question have made hundreds of Portuguese aware of leeboards. Perhaps during this period and certainly after about 1580 there also were Dutch observers on the China coast who must have seen many examples of leeboards. Although Linschoten's account of China is second-hand he mentions, in a letter of 1584 to his parents, encountering Dirck Gerritz, a Dutch gunner who had made a previous trip to China and was going again.[14]

As Dutch contacts with the Far East increased there must have been many opportunities for the leeboard idea to be introduced into the Netherlands. The persons most likely to have done so would have been seamen, not noted for literacy and not likely to have been recorded in print, who observed the efficiency with which shallow-draft Chinese junks sailed to windward. The utility of such a device would have had far greater appeal to the Dutch, with the constant necessity of sailng in shoal waters, than for the Portuguese. And the ease with which Chinese leeboards could be added to Dutch craft, with no requirement for reconstruction of a major order, must have been appealing.

It is quite clear, then, that Europeans could have obtained the idea of leeboards from any of the five sources which have been described. The chronology is correct for all possibilities, and there is no direct evidence extant which identifies the source from which the idea was taken.

The argument

Since direct evidence, to the best of our knowledge, is denied us we must proceed on circumstantial evidence alone. If enough data

---

14 Burnell Tiele (1885, p. xxvi). Further attempts to ascertain any early European statements about leeboards had negative results in perusal of each of the following accounts of voyages: Foster (1934), Frampton (1745), Groeneveldt (1898), Langhenez (1745), Staunton (1853).

of the latter type can be presented, we may with reasonable probability assume that a solution has been found.

Chronology tells us with considerable certainty that Dutch leeboards appeared later than the other five possible sources of leeway boards, but gives no hint on a probable source.

Since the major function of all types of boards is to inhibit leeway, we can derive no help from this aspect. But two other functions differentiate among the various board locations. In all cases the daggerboards on sailing rafts are shifted about to change sailing balance, a function not found in the three leeboard locations. And the use of daggerboards in steering by changing lateral resistance, known certainly for Peruvian balsas, seems likely for the Brazil and Annam–Formosa rafts.

Several aspects of the form of the various boards may have utility for the problem. Vertically sliding daggerboards are used in the Annam–Formosa, Peru and Brazil raft locations, whereas pivoting leeboards are used in the Coromandel, China and Dutch locations. The same differentiation holds true for the type of

hull used: displacement hulls for the latter three (with the Coromandel and Annamese rafts as exceptions) and rafts in the former three. The physical manufacture of the leeway boards represents an interesting difference: several planks side by side form the boards in Formosa rafts, Chinese leeboards and Dutch leeboards; all others are formed of single planks. The ratio of board length to width also is instructive: Chinese and Dutch boards vary somewhat but always lie in the 1.7 to 3.0 range; Formosan boards are shorter and all others much longer. Whereas the several rafts (again excluding Coromandel and the Annamese Dông-hói, raft) maintain boards in place by friction the leeboards locations maintain boards in place by fittings; a difference exists here between the Coromandel leeboards which are lashed and the Chinese and Dutch boards which have wooden pivots and are at times secured by metal fittings.

Certain differences in the physical environment of the several locations may be noted. Deltaic areas with much shoal water characterize China, the Netherlands and Palk Strait;

Table 1

	Netherlands	China	Annam–Formosa	Coromandel	Peru	Brazil
Relative chronology correct . . .	+	+	+	+	+	+
Function						
Inhibit leeway	+	+	+	+	+	+
Sail balance	.	.	+	.	+	+
Steering	.	.	+?	.	+	+?
Form						
Type						
Daggerboard	.	.	+	.	+	+
Leeboard	+	+	+	+	.	.
Multiple planks in 1 board	+	+	+?	.	.	.
Hull						
Boat	+	+	.	+	.	.
Raft	.	.	+	+	+	+
Shape						
Boards 2–3 × length	+	+	.	.	.	.
Boards 1 × or 6–8 × length	.	.	+	+	+	+
Attachment						
Friction	.	.	+	.	+	+
Gunwale pivot	+	+	+?	+?	.	.
Use of metal	+	+	.	.	.	.
Environment (physical)						
Shoals, deltaic	+	+	.	+	.	.
Psychology						
Advanced culture	+	+	.	.	.	.
Could imitate with little structural modification	+	+	+	+	.	.

this is partially true of Annam and not at all
true of raft locations in Formosa, Peru and
Brazil. To the degree that man adapts himself
to local conditions and thus modifies his cultural inheritance this may have significance.

Two final suggestions of a psychological nature may be suggested. The ease with which a
task may be accomplished has some influence on
whether it is attempted or not. Clearly the adaption of Palk Strait or Chinese leeboards to
Dutch craft could have been made easily and
with minor structural modifications. Use of
daggerboards would involve cutting a slot in the
bottom of a perfectly good and watertight boat
plus the invention of some sort of well to exclude the water; neither of these would seem
attractive to a Dutch sailor.

Finally, all areas using leeway boards must to
Europeans have seemed most primitive, with
the exception of the Chinese. To copy a primitive device might not have been appealing, but
to utilize a sophisticated device developed by a
people technically in advance of the Dutch at
the time might well have seemed more attractive.

A tabular summary of these arguments is
presented in Table 1 for easy comparison.

Conclusion

As noted in the tabulation above, only Chinese
and Dutch leeboards are paired through the
entire list of culture traits. It would appear
highly unlikely that this pairing could have
occurred by chance and that there is a high
degree of probability that Dutch leeboards were
copied from Chinese leeboards in the latter sixteenth century and successfully superimposed
on the Dutch craft of that day. In conclusion,
Needham's statement with regard to magnetism, also known in China long before Europe,
may be quoted as pertinent to leeboards: 'Although we do not know the way-stations
through which it came, its priority of time is
such as to place the burden of proof on those
who would wish to believe in an independent
discovery' (Crombie, 1963, p. 144). Considering
the similarities of function, form, environment,
and psychology which have been cited the
burden of proof also would seem to rest now on
those who would derive Dutch leeboards from
any source other than the Chinese.

Bibliography

Audemard, L. (1957–63). Les Jonques chinoises.
Rotterdam: Maritiem Museum 'Prins Hendrik.'
Belloc, Hilaire (1951). On Sailing the Sea. *London:
Rupert Hart-Davis.*
Bowen, Richard Lebaron Jr. (1959). *The origins of
fore-and-aft rigs.* American Neptune, *xix, pp. 155–
99, 274–306.*
Boxer, C. R. ed. (1953). South China in the Six-
teenth Century. Being the Narratives of Galcote
Pereira, Fr. Gaspar da Cruz, O.P., Fr. Martin de
Rada, O.E.S.A. (1550–1575. *London: Hakluyt Soc.
Publ., series II, no. 106.*
(Brindley), H. H. B. (1923). Chinese Junks. *By
Ivon Donnelly. A Lecture Delivered at Tientsin,
M.M., ix, pp. 318–20.*
Burnell, A. C. & Tiele, P. A. eds. (1885), The
Voyage of John Huyghen van Linschoten to the
East Indies. From the Old English Translation of
1598 . . . , *pp. 70–71. London: Hakluyt Soc. Publ.,
series I.*
Casson, Lionel (1964). Illustrated History of Ships
and Boats. *Garden City, New York: Doubleday.*
Chapelle, Howard I. (1951). American Small Sail-
ing Craft. *New York: W. W. Norton.*
Chatterton, E. Keble (1912). Fore and Aft. *London:
Seeley, Service. Second Edition:* Fore and Aft
Craft and Their Story, *1957.*
Clark, Arthur H. (1904). The History of Yachting,
1600–1815. *New York: Putnam's.*
Cortesão, A., ed. (1944). The Suma Oriental of
Tomé Pires. . . . *London: Hakluyt Soc. Publ.,
series II, no. 89.*
Crombie, A. C., ed. (1963). Scientific Change:. . . .
*Symposium of the History of Science, University
of Oxford, 9–15 July 1961. New York: Basic Books.*
Crone, G. C. E. (1943). Onze Schepen in de Gouden
Eeuw. *Amsterdam: P. N. Kampen and Zoon.*
C. T. R. (1924). Leeboard and centreboard. *M.M.,
x, p. 102.*
Denis, Valentin, ed. (1961). All the Paintings of
Pieter Bruegel. *New York: Hawthorn.*
Donnelly, Ivon A. (1920). Chinese Junks. A Book of
Drawings in Black and White. *Shanghai: Kelley
and Walsh.*
Donnelly, Ivon A. (1923). *Foochow pole junks.*
M.M., *ix, pp. 226–31.*
Donnelly, Ivon A. (1924). *River Craft of the Yang-
tzekiang.* M.M., *x, pp. 4–16.*
(Donnelly) I.A.D. (1925a). *The distribution of the
oculus in Chinese vessels.* M.M., *xi, pp. 203–4.*
Donnelly, Ivon A. (1925b). *Early Chinese ships and
trade.* M.M., *xi, pp. 344–54.*
Donnelly, I. A. (1926). *The 'Oculus' in Chinese
craft.* M.M., *xii, p. 339.*
Donnelly, Ivon A. (1936). *Strange craft of China's
inland waters.* M.M., *xxii, pp. 410–21.*
Edwards, Clinton R. (1960). *Sailing rafts of Sechura:
history and problems of origin.* Southwestern
Journal of Anthropology, *xvi, pp. 368–91.*
Edwards, Clinton R. (1965). *Aboriginal Watercraft
on the Pacific Coast of South America. Ibero-
Americana: 47. Berkeley: University of California
Press.*

Foster, Sir William, ed. (1934). The Voyage of Thomas Best to the East Indies, 1612–14. *London: Hakluyt Soc. Publ., series II, vol. lxxv.*

Frampton, John (1745). *An account of the empire of China.* (Transl. of discourse by Barnadine of Escalanta.). *In* A Collection of Voyages and Travels . . . from the . . . Library of the Late Earl of Oxford, *vol. II. London: Thomas Osborne.*

Groeneveldt, W. P. (1898). *De Nederlanders in China.* De Eerste Bemoeiingen om den Handel in China en de Vestiging in de Pescadores, 1601–1624. *The Hague: M. Nijhoff.*

Hornell, J. (1934). *The origin of the junk and sampan.* M.M., xx, pp. 331–7.

Hornell, James (1943). *The fishing and coastal craft of Ceylon.* M.M., xxix, pp. 40–53.

Hornell, James (1946). Water Transport: Origins and Early Evolution. *Cambridge University Press.*

Kerchove, Rene de (1961). International Maritime Dictionary, 2nd ed. *New York: Van Nostrand.*

Lane-Poole, R. H. (1940). *Primitive craft and medieval rigs in South America.* M.M., xxvi, pp. 333–8.

Langhenez, Bernardt (1745). *The description of a voyage made by certain ships of Holland into the East Indies . . . in 1595–7 . . . In* A Collection of Voyages and Travels . . . from the Library of the Late Earl of Oxford, *vol. II. London: Thomas Osborne.*

Lovegrove, H. (1932). *Junks of the Canton and West River system.* M.M., xviii, pp. 241–53.

Moll, G. (1923). *The navy of the province of Fukien.* M.M., ix, pp. 364–76.

(Nance) R. M. N. (1920). *Smack-sails, XVth century.* M.M., vi, pp. 343–4

Nelson, J. G. (1961). *The geography of the balsa.* American Neptune, xxi, pp. 157–95.

Paris, Pierre (1955). Esquisse d'une ethnographie navale des peuples annamites, 2nd ed. *Rotterdam: Maritiem Museum 'Prins Hendrik.'*

Pazolt, A. J. (1922). *Dutch types.* M.M., viii, pp. 155–6.

Phillips-Birt, Douglas (1962). Fore and Aft Sailing Craft. *London: Seeley, Service.*

Sigaut, Etienne (1960). *A northern type of Chinese junk.* M.M., xlvi, pp. 161–74.

Smyth, Herbert W. (1929). Mast and Sail in Europe and Asia. *London: Blackwood.*

Sopher, David, E. (1966). *Personal communication.*

Spencer, J. E. (1938). *The junks of the Yangtze.* Asia, xxxviii, pp. 466–70.

Staunton, Sir George T., ed. (1853). The History of the Great and Mighty Kingdom of China and the Situation Thereof . . . *by Juan Gonzalez de Mendoza. London: Hakluyt Soc. Publ., series I, nos. 14–15.*

Ting, T. V., transl. (1925) 'Things produced by the works of nature,' published 1639. M.M., xi, pp. 234–45. Notes by I. A. Donnelly, pp. 245–50.

Waters, D. W. (1938). *Chinese junks: the Antung trader.* M.M., xxiv, pp. 49–67.

Waters, D. W. (1939). *Chinese junks: the Pechili trader.* M.M., xxv, pp. 62–88.

Waters, D. W. (1940). *Chinese junks, an exception: The Tonkung.* M.M., xxvi, pp. 79–95.

Waters, D. W. (1946). *Chinese junks—The Twaqo.* M.M., xxxii, pp. 155–67.

Waters, D. W. (1947). *Chinese junks—The Hangchow trader and fisher.* M.M., xxxiii, pp. 28–38.

Waters, D. W. (1955). *The straight, and other, Chinese Yulohs.* M.M., xli, pp. 60–1.

Wheatley, Paul (1965). *Letter of 16 August.* Continued on 22 January 1966.

Wiens, Herold J. (1955). *Riverine and coastal junks in China's commerce.* Economic Geography, XXXI, pp. 248–64.

Worcester, G. R. G. (1940). Junks and Sampans of the Upper Yangtze. *China: The Maritime Customs, III—Misc. Series, no. 51. Shanghai: Statistical Department of Inspectorate General of Customs.*

Worcester, G. R. G. (1947). The Junks and Sampans of the Yangtze. A Study in Chinese Nautical Research, *vol. I, Introduction; and Craft of the Estuary and Shanghai Area. Shanghai: Statistical Department of the Inspectorate General of Customs.*

Worcester, G. R. G. (1948). *The Chinese war junk.* M.M., XXXIV, pp. 16–25.

Worcester, G. R. G. (1954). *The Amoy fishing boat.* M.M., XL, pp. 304–8.

Worcester, G. R. G. (1956). *Four small craft of T'aiwan.* M.M., XLII, pp. 302–12.

Worcester, G. R. G. (1959a). *Six small craft of Kwangtung.* M.M., XLV, pp. 130–44.

Worcester, G. R. G. (1959b). *The Junkman Smiles. London: Chatto and Windus.*

Worcester, G. R. G. (1961). *Four junks of Kiangsi.* M.M., XLVII, pp. 187–35.

The origin of infield-outfield agriculture in Scotland

IAN M. MATLEY

9

Ian M. Matley relies almost entirely on linguistic evidence in this short article to trace the diffusion of the infield-outfield agricultural system. The custom of farming more intensively those lands near villages and farmsteads while using the lands further distant in a less intensive manner is not unique to Western Europe. It was, however, developed to a highly regularized pattern of land husbandry by the seventeenth century in Europe. It is because of the areal extent of its practice that the diffusion of this pattern from an uncertain hearth arouses the interest of cultural geographers. Matley suggests that inadequate use has been made of the linguistic evidence for origin and diffusion of the trait. Turning to relevant languages for etymologies, he posits tentatively that this agricultural system is probably Scottish in origin. In conclusion he notes that there is need to wed linguistic evidence with other field evidence in order to gain some certainty about this land pattern in the British Isles. His final statement is that the "question of whether it is an ancient system, gradually diffused throughout the Atlantic fringe of Europe . . . still remains to be answered." Each investigation into the paths of diffusion of culture traits thus anticipates subsequent research avenues.

In recent years geographers and economic historians have carried out significant work on the distribution and origin of infield-outfield agriculture. In particular such scholars as E. E. Evans, P. Flatrès, A. Geddes, S. Jaatinen, J. H.

Johnston, D. McCourt, H. Uhlig and others have shown the widespread occurrence of this type of agriculture in western Europe and examined its origins. Uhlig in particular has summarized the available evidence on the distribution of infield-outfield agriculture to demonstrate that this type of agriculture, apart from its occurrence on the European continent, existed at one time in such scattered areas of England as Warwickshire, East Yorkshire, Kent, Sherwood Forest, Hampshire and East Anglia, and that it was not confined exclusively to the highland and Celtic areas of Great Britain.[1] The theory of a Celtic origin of the infield-outfield system in a highland environment was accepted for many years, due mainly to the work of H. Gray.[2] The fact that the system still exists in a limited form in such areas of Celtic culture as the Western Isles of Scotland, western Ireland and Brittany, while few traces exist in other parts of the British Isles, has tended to strengthen this theory.

The fact that we know for certain that the infield-outfield system at one time was the predominant form of agriculture over the whole of Scotland and not only in the Highlands and islands is of obvious importance in the study of the origin of the system. However, little evidence has been produced which would indicate whether infield-outfield agriculture originated

---

Ian M. Matley, "The Origin of Infield-Outfield Agriculture in Scotland: The Linguistic Evidence," *The Professional Geographer*, XVIII, No. 5 (1966), pp. 275–279. Reproduced by permission of the Association of American Geographers.

[1] a) Uhlig, H.; "Old Hamlets with Infield and Outfield Systems in Western and Central Europe", *Geografiska Annaler*, Vol. 43, nos. 1–2, 1961, p. 288.
b) See, for example, the account of infield-outfield farming at Carburton, Nottinghamshire, in 1615 in M. W. Beresford and J. K. S. St. Joseph, *Medieval England, an Aerial Survey*, Cambridge, 1958, pp. 46–49.

[2] Gray, H., *English Field Systems*, Cambridge, Mass., 1915.

with the Celtic-speaking inhabitants of early Scotland and spread to the areas settled by an English-speaking population or the other way around. Written records of Scottish agriculture before the end of the eighteenth century are scarce, and little evidence can be extracted from them on the probable area of origin of the system. The proven existence of infield-outfield agriculture in England, and especially northern England, is perhaps the strongest evidence we have to date for the origin of the system outside highland Scotland.

Few attempts have been made to examine the linguistic evidence. This is all the more remarkable since a specialized vocabulary appertaining to infield-outfield agriculture exists in both Scottish Gaelic and the Lowland Scottish dialect of English. As far as Gaelic is concerned this vocabulary is not extensive. In fact no single word for "infield" exists with any widespread usage. Perhaps the nearest to a common Gaelic term is *dubh-thalamh* "black land," used in the Outer Hebrides.[3] Uhlig reports the use of the word *geadhail* on Jura, referring to the infield of a local croft.[4] This word, meaning "plowed land" is not very common and its widespread use as a term for the infield is not proven. Likewise no general Gaelic term exists for "outfield", but the practice (possibly employed even before the introduction of the potato to the Western Isles in the middle of the eighteenth century), of planting potatoes on the outfield in "lazy-beds" or *feannagan* (singular: *feannag*) led to the use of this term for the cultivated ridges of the outfield.[5] The infield was also divided into strips or ridges, known in Gaelic as *iomairean* (singular: *iomaire*). The ownership of the strips of land was generally rotated, lots being drawn every one to three years to ensure that each family had an equal chance to work the more fertile parts of the infield area. This system was known in Lowland Scots as *runrig, runridge,* or, as is also found in Ireland, *rundale* or *rendal*. In Scottish

Gaelic the name *roinn-ruith* was applied to this system, being generally translated as "division-run."[6] Certainly *roinn* means a share or division, while *ruith* means to run or flow, but it seems very likely that this is an example of folk etymology, the Gaelic term being derived from the Lowland Scots *runrig*. The Lowland Scots term seems to come from the practice of dividing the field into ridges or *rigs* running parallel to one another, although some authorities support the interpretation of *run* as referring to the sharing of the ridges in sequence.[7] Although both of these versions agree with the literal translation of *roinn-ruith*, the latter is not a common term. Carmichael, writing in the 1880's, said that it was a word used only by old people, the more common Gaelic term being *mor earann,* meaning "great division" or *mor fhearann,* meaning "great land."[8] The reason for Carmichael's indecision on the exact form of the term is due to the identical pronunciation of both forms and the probable inability of his informants to spell the words for him.

There has been some debate on the origin of the Lowland Scots *runrig*. Grant suggests that it is of Anglian origin,[9] being introduced from northern England by the Anglian-speaking population which moved into southern Scotland in the seventh century. Others support the Celtic origin of the term. Maxwell agrees that *rig* is the Lowland Scots form of "ridge," being derived from Old English *hrycg*, through Middle English *rigge*. He argues, however, that if the term was originally Lowland Scots in origin it would take the form *rinrig* instead of *runrig*. He thus supports the Gaelic origin of the term.[10] His argument is weakened, however, by the existence of the forms *rynryg* in a document of 1437 and *rinrig* in documents of 1583 and

---

[3] Collier, A., *The Crofting Problem*, Cambridge, 1953, p. 53.

[4] Uhlig, H., "Typen Kleinbäuerlicher Siedlungen auf den Hebriden", *Erdkunde*, Vol. 13, no. 2, May, 1959, pp. 102–103.

[5] Evans thinks that the "lazy-bed" technique as practiced in Ireland is older than the introduction of the potato. See E. E. Evans, *Irish Folk Ways*, New York, 1957, p. 143.

[6] Carmichael, A., "Grazing and Agrestic Customs of the Outer Hebrides", (A Report to the Crofter Royal Commission in 1883–1884), *Celtic Review*, Vol. 10, December, 1914–June 1916, p. 42.

[7] Symon, J. A., *Scottish Farming Past and Present*, Edinburgh and London, 1959, p. 17.

[8] Carmichael, A., *op. cit.*, p. 42.

[9] Grant, I. F., *The Social and Economic Development of Scotland before 1603*, Edinburgh, 1930, p. 107.

[10] Maxwell, H., "Runrig", *Scottish Historical Review*, Vol. 13, no. 50, January, 1916, p. 207.

1585, all referring to areas in the Scottish Lowlands.[11]

The non-Celtic origin of the term *runrig* is further suggested by the more obvious Germanic origin of *rundale* or *rendal,* which appear in Scots manuscripts of 1545 and 1593 as *ryndale* and *rindaill.*[12] In spite of Johnston's suggestion that the word comes from the Gaelic *rinndeal* "a piece of land of fixed extent, a boundary,"[13] it is of Middle English origin, *dale* being a portion of land.[14] *Dale* is linked to Dutch and Frisian *deel* and Scandinavian *del,* a division or share. The occurrence of the term *rundale* and *rendal* in the Orkneys and Shetlands, often in the form *rigg* and *rendal,*[15] raises the question of a possible Scandinavian origin. The term might well have been introduced into Ireland by the Norse settlers there. However, the occurrence of the term *rundale* in documents referring to the Scottish Lowlands does not suggest a Scandinavian origin as the region was never settled by Norsemen. No record of a Scandinavian word similar to *rundale* exists, the system being known in parts of Norway as *aarkast,* literally "year cast or throw" referring to the casting of lots annually for strips of land.[16] It is in fact possible that *rundale* was introduced into the Irish vocabulary by Scots settlers in Ulster in the early seventeenth century, if Flatrès' theory of the introduction of the concept of an infield and outfield into Ireland by this route is accepted.[17] Finally, the existence of the terms *changedale,* reported by Arthur Young on his tour of Ireland in the 1770's, and *morrowingdale,* reported by McCourt from Londonderry,[18] as synonyms for *rundale,* indicate the variety of words of obviously non-Celtic origin which applied to this system of land tenure.

An extensive vocabulary existed in Lowland Scots applying to infield-outfield agriculture, most of its elements being clearly of Germanic origin. Because of the extensive nature of this vocabulary and the variations found in different regions of Scotland only the most frequently-used terms will be discussed. The infield was generally known as the *intoon, i.e.,* that nearest the *toon* or farmstead (Old English *tun,* a farmstead or village), the *croftland* (Old English *croft,* a small enclosed field) or the *feyland* (the verb *fey* is used throughout northern England with the meaning of spreading manure on the fields). The infield was divided into divisions or *kavels* (a word found also in northern England, perhaps from Old Norse *kafli,* a piece or bit. Compare Dutch and Frisian *kavel,* a lot or parcel, generally of land), and these in turn were plowed into high ridges or *rigs* (see above). The *rigs* were often separated from one another by unplowed strips, known as *balks* (Old English *balca,* a ridge) or *mearings* (Old English *gemaere,* a boundary), the latter term being found in Ireland and parts of England. At either end of the field ran the *rig-head* or *fleed,* a strip of land on which the plow was turned. The word *fleed* is of uncertain origin but may be the Aberdeenshire pronunciation of *flood,* referring to the frequent flooding of these strips of land by water running off the *rigs,* which in Scotland always ran down and not across the slopes. The infield was divided in some areas into separate divisions, each carrying a different crop in *shift* or rotation.[19] These divisions were known as *shots* (a word for a division of land found also all over England) or *breaks* (Old English *braec,* a strip of land). The preliminary furrows made to mark the line of *rigs* and other divisions were known as *feerings* (Old English *fryian,* to cut a furrow).

The infield was manured before carrying a series of crops, in many cases with dung mixed with turf, a preparation known as *midden-feil.* Although this practice can be traced all over Scotland, from the Lothians to the Shetlands, the word *feil* is of Celtic origin, being from the

11 "Runrig", *Oxford English Dictionary,* Vol. 8 (Poy-Ry), Oxford, 1933, pp. 916–917.

12 "Rundale", *ibid.,* p. 909.

13 Johnston, A. W., "Runrig", *Scottish Historical Review,* Vol. 13, no. 51, April, 1916, p. 318.

14 "Rundale", *Oxford English Dictionary,* p. 909.

15 *The Statistical Account of Scotland,* Edinburgh, 1793, Vol. 7, p. 398.

16 Evans, E. E., "Ecology of Peasant Life in Western Europe" in Thomas, W. C. (ed.) *Man's Role in Changing the Face of the Earth,* Chicago, 1956, p. 229.

17 Flatrès, P. *Géographie Rurale de Quatre Contrées Celtiques,* Rennes, 1957, pp. 130–131.

18 McCourt, D., "Infield and Outfield in Ireland," *Economic History Review* (2nd series), Vol. 7, no. 3, 1955, p. 373.

19 Handley, J. E., *Scottish Farming in the Eighteenth Century,* London, 1953, p. 39.

Gaelic *fal,* a turf or sod. Another term, however, existed in the Gaelic-speaking areas of Scotland, a mixture of dung, turf, and seaweed known as *flagais*.[20] That dung and turf manuring is an ancient Europe practice has been demonstrated by G. Niemeier, who traces *Plaggen*-manuring in northern Germany back to about the third to first centuries B.C. by means of C14 dating.[21] Another method of manuring, found not only in the Highlands and Islands but also in Banff and Aberdeenshire, was the use of *foud* or the smoke-blackened thatch of cottages, which was spread on the fields. This word is also of Celtic origin, being derived from the Gaelic *fod,* a turf. The derivation of these two terms probably reflects the antiquity of the practices to which they refer. Another manuring technique of probable antiquity is the use of sea-wrack or *ware* (Old English *war.* seaweed), a practice once found in most of the coastal districts of Scotland and still followed in the Outer Hebrides and Western Ireland. Because of its continued existence in these areas it has often been regarded as a typically Celtic practice, but it may in fact date back to pre-Celtic times. In coastal areas or around the mouths of rivers *sletch,* or marine and river silt, was used as manure. This is a northern English term, allied to Dutch and Frisian *slyk.*

A highly specialized series of Lowland Scots terms existed to describe the crops grown on the infield, all being of demonstratively Germanic origin. The first crop of oats after a crop of *bere* (a species of barley) was known as the *aith* or *aitliffcrap,* probably from *aift,* after or *aits,* oats. After this second crop of oats was grown, known as the *awald* or *yavel,* a term also applied to the second crop of oats on the outfield after grass. The origin of this term is obscure but may come from Middle English *walten,* to turn. These crop terms, along with others, often with local variations, were found almost exclusively in the Lowland areas with only a limited number of Gaelic equivalents in the Highlands. There is no doubt that the infield-outfield system reached its level of maximum efficiency as a farming system in the Lowland areas, and primitive as the techniques

were, they were superior to those of the Highland farmers. The existence of a more specialized agricultural vocabulary appertaining to the cultivation of the infield in particular suggests this.

The outfield or *out-toon* was utilized in different ways, depending on the part of the country. The practice of making *lazybeds* for the growing of potatoes was found not only in the Highlands and Islands but also in the Lowlands and northern England, but in general the outfield seems to have been utilized in the Lowlands for the growing of grain. In Aberdeenshire in the eighteenth century the outfield was divided into *faulds* (Old English *fald,* fold, cattle pen) and *faughs* (Old English *feah,* fallow land). The former consisted of parts of the outfield which were surrounded by sod walls within which the cattle were penned at nights and also at intervals during the day in order to add manure to the top soil. The land would then be cropped for a number of years and then abandoned to grass. The *faughs* were those parts of the outfield that were not manured but were prepared for a crop by slight fallowing.[22] The practice of folding cattle and sheep on the outfield for a period was known as *toathing* or *tathing,* a northern English expression, probably from Norse *taδ,* manure.

On most Scottish farms the arable land was divided from the pasture by a *loaning-dyke.* The term *loan* (Old English *lone,* a path or lane) was used both for the opening between grain fields along which the cattle were driven to the pastures, and for the milking green near the farm. The *dyke* was generally a wall built of stones removed from the fields. (Old English *dic,* a ditch and by extension, a wall built with material removed from a ditch.) Another wall, the *head-dyke,* separated the green pasture from the heather-covered moor. Livestock was sometimes grazed on the *lizzure* or *leissure,* a pasture between the grain fields. This word, found in Scotland, Ireland, and England, sometimes in the form *leasow,* comes from Old English *laes,* a pasture. Otherwise they were driven to the common pastures beyond the farm-land, known as the *out-ca', ca'* being the Lowland Scots form of *call,* used with the old meaning of to drive or herd livestock.

Transhumance was not confined to the High-

20 McDonald, A., *Gaelic Words and Expressions from South Uist and Eriskay,* Dublin, 1958, p. 127.

21 Uhlig, H., *Geografiska Annaler,* Vol. 43, nos. 1–2, 1961, p. 289.

22 Handley, J. E., *op. cit.,* pp. 42–45.

land regions of Scotland. The existence of the element *shiel* in Lowland placenames, as well as other evidence, shows that this was not a practice of Celtic-speaking areas only.[23] The term *shiel*, a summer pasture or a temporary hut at such a pasture, is better known in northern England. The word comes from northern Middle English *shale, schele*, of obscure origin, perhaps from Old Norse *skali*, a temporary *hut*.[24] The association of the term *shieling* with the Highlands and Islands is due to the survival of transhumance in those areas until recently, the native Gaelic term being *airidh*. The practice of restricting the number of livestock kept on the common pastures by any individual in proportion to the rent of his farm, as still carried on in parts of the Highlands today, is known as *souming* or *sooming*. This term is simply the Lowland Scots form of the English *summing*, and the practice was once found in many areas of southern Scotland. The Gaelic term *sumachadh* is a verbal noun derived from the Lowland Scots *soom* and is therefore not of pure Celtic origin.

This review of terms used in Scotland in connection with the practice of infield-outfield agriculture by no means exhausts the known list. However, it is hoped that enough examples have been given to demonstrate the following points. First, practically all the terms are of Old or Middle English origin, with a few possibly stemming from Old Norse. Only two terms have a probable Celtic origin. One would have expected a much greater number of terms to have shown traces of Celtic origin if the infield-outfield system in Scotland had originated with the Celtic-speaking population. Second, many of the terms found in Lowland Scots are also found in northern England and in some cases even further south. That infield-outfield agriculture was also practiced in these areas suggests that the diffusion of the system in Scotland may have been from south to north rather than from the highland to the lowland regions. Third, the existence of a few terms of possible Norse origin strengthens the case for seeking the origin of some of the elements of Scottish infield-outfield agriculture in northern England, as much of that region was settled by the Norsemen and the Danes.

It is not suggested, however, that the linguistic material discussed here can do more than strengthen the evidence obtained from other sources, and even this evidence is far from conclusive. Although in the case of Scotland there does seem to be some indication that infield-outfield agriculture originated with or was introduced by a population speaking a northern dialect of English, we are still in the dark about the origins of the system when viewed on a European scale. The question of whether it is an ancient system, gradually diffused throughout the Atlantic fringe of Europe, or whether it is an adaptation by man at different times and different places to a specific combination of environmental conditions and population density, still remains to be answered.

---

[23] Symon, J. A., *op. cit.*, p. 20.

[24] "Shiel", *Oxford English Dictionary*, Vol. 9, (S-Soldo) Oxford, 1933, p. 689.

Analysis of a contemporary settlement frontier

CHRISTOPHER L. SALTER

10

Deciding to migrate is a highly complex process. While there are attractions present in the goal area, there are continuing attractions present in the hearth area. The decision to move is obviously a recognition that the goal area attractions seem to be superior to the qualities of the hearth area. The determination, however, of these attractions and forces of repulsion is difficult because each individual migrates for a different reason. In this article, I suggest that in one case the decision to move is predicated upon deteriorating economic circumstances in the hearth area. Such a phenomenon is in no way rare, but in this case the goal area being considered is such that the usual inertia to be overcome in a decision to move is compounded by the uncertainty of gain in the goal area.

The peculiar nature of a marginal region and the necessary inputs to the decision to move to such a region are the concerns of my paper. The model of this particular migration pattern at the conclusion of the paper is an attempt to point out the regularities in migration between two very distinct regions.

"Frontier" has long been a magical word to social scientists. Made popular by Frederick Jackson Turner and his school of American historians at the turn of the century, the frontier has become an appealing concept to most of us who are interested in social change

and settlement patterns.[1] The frontier setting evokes a wealth of ideas. Individuality, economic opportunity, large land holdings, innovation, independence—all are hallmarks of this myth of new beginnings in new lands.[2]

To Orientalists, the term frontier conjures up new goal areas for the so-called surplus population now concentrated in alluvial plains and coastal and river margins all through Asia. Such places as Hokkaido, Sumatra, the Chinese Northwest, and Mindoro begin to assume mystical, El Dorado-like qualities. But these dreams in no way truly reflect the settlement potentials in these contemporary frontiers. These areas, and others akin to them, must be seen as belonging to a special class of frontiers which might be more aptly called "marginal regions." The single word "frontier" does not adequately reflect the harshness of the undersettled regions of Asia.

This paper, therefore, will attempt to delimit marginal region within the context of cultural geography and to cite one example in Asia, defining its marginality and noting the activities which may lead to its subsequent transformation.

"Marginal land" denotes land whose crops

Christopher L. Salter, "Analysis of a Contemporary Settlement Frontier," paper given at the 1969 Meetings of the Association for Asian Studies, Western Branch, Tucson, Arizona, October 18–19, 1969.

1 Turner, Frederick J., "The Significance of the Frontier in American History," *Annual Report of the American Historical Association for the Year 1893*, pp. 190–227. Also see Gene M. Gressley, "The Turner Thesis—a Problem in Historiography," *Agricultural History*, Vol. 32, No. 4 (October, 1958), pp. 227–249.

2 An elaboration on the nature of this word frontier is developed by Fulmer Mood in "Notes on the History of the World Frontier," *Agricultural History*, Vol. 22, No. 2 (April, 1948), pp. 78–83.

are just adequate to pay for their planting, harvesting, and marketing.[3] The concept of economic marginality implies that the investor will invariably gain a better return on his capital if he ignores lands which are characterized by either high planting cost, low relative yields, or both. Capital would be better invested in lands already showing a margin of surplus. Marginal lands could easily occur, then, as pockets of poor soils surrounded by relatively productive lands. Modification of such soils could turn these regions into economically productive areas.[4]

Within the context of cultural geography, however, the term "marginal land" assumes broader and culturally significant conditions. This marginality is better described by an inventory of cultural and geographic characteristics which, when compounded, delimit a subregion quite unlike the normative region to which it stands as relatively marginal.

If one were to attempt to create a model of a contemporary frontier, the geography of marginality might be indicated in the following manner.

Assume Region X and Region Y where:

a. *Region X is a marginal region with population density less than one-fifth that of Region Y.*[5]

b. *Region Y is a normative region possessing rural and urban sectors and defined here as any cohesive region with average population densities at least three times the national population density. These population differentials are suggestive rather than absolute. Though the demographic catalyst is the prime one for the interaction of the two regions X and Y, it is impossible to state at exactly what relative density a migration stream will begin active flow from Y to X.*

c. *Region X is accessible generally with some difficulty from Region Y. The border or borderland between the two regions may be defined by an element of topography such as a mountain massif or body of water; or any element of physical geography such as an agriculturally restrictive isohyet; or an administrative line of national or (rarely) international status. It is invariably more rigorous to travel between Region X and Region Y than within Region Y alone.*[6]

d. *Region X and Region Y have highly disparate demographic and settlement patterns, notwithstanding the fact that the length of the settlement histories of the two regions is frequently the same.*

e. *Region X and Region Y have dissimilar physical environments with Region X being characterized by calamity conditions such as drought, flood, earthquakes, or other natural hazards considered as detrimental to settlement. An important corollary of this characteristic, however, is that the reputation which Region X has for these calamity conditions usually exceeds their reality. These conditions also serve to differentiate the marginal region from the frontier region of a given nation. A frontier is a relatively unsettled region adjacent to a settled region, and the distance from markets and lack of services produce a low migration gradient toward the frontier. Though every marginal area possesses qualities of a frontier, not all frontiers possess the particular qualities of a marginal area.*

f. *Region X is characterized by a subsistence and peasant economy with the village being the primary container of population, while Region Y has a well-developed urban sector in addition to an agrarian population which is surplus-oriented and commercialized.*

g. *A migration stream flows between Region X and Region Y working a relatively negative effect on Region X. This is due to the fact that the emigrants from Region Y (the normative region) to Region X are generally people who have failed to be successful within the context of a devel-*

[3] Sloan, Harold Stephenson, and Arnold John Zurcher, *A Dictionary of Economics* (New York: Barnes and Noble, Inc., 1958).

[4] Bauer, P. T., and B. S. Yamey, *The Economics of Under-Developed Countries* (Cambridge: Cambridge University Press, 1960), pp. 52–57; Paddock, William, and Paul Paddock, *Hungry Nations* (Boston: Little, Brown and Co., 1964), see especially pp. 16–40. Myint, H., *The Economics of the Developing Countries* (London: Hutchinson and Co., 1965), see especially pp. 23–52. Additional comments on the relative value of investment in the peasant sector vs. investment in the industrial sector of a developing economy occur in most general texts on the process of economic development. Though the distinction of marginal–nonmarginal land is not always explicit, there generally is an allusion to the comparative value of investing in already productive activities as opposed to investing in something lacking its own economic momentum.

[5] As will be more clearly seen below, demographic disparities between Region X and Region Y are of great moment, but the quantitative relationship between them is extremely difficult to generalize. The suggestion of a relationship on the order of 1:5 is utilized here to show the necessary presence of the relatively low population density levels obtaining in Region X.

[6] This is a near tautology because of the invariable thinness of the transport network within a marginal area. The important point is that access does exist to Region X from Region Y. It frequently coincides with very early travel routes which were laid out in initial premature settlement of the marginal region. These paths of access were never fully developed because of the immature nature of the migration stream from Region Y to Region X.

oped and thriving region. The emigrants from Region X, however, are most frequently the best educated and most ambitious, and as a result they move into the flow pattern from Rural Region X to Urban Region Y.

h. *With the exception of interregion transport and externally produced commodities, the average cost of living is lower in Region X than Region Y.*[7]

i. *The major source of migrants to both regions is Rural Region Y. Despite the relatively greater economic opportunities available through migration from Rural Region Y to anywhere in Region X, the migration stream of greatest magnitude is from Rural Region Y to Urban Region Y. That is to say, considerations of economy are not adequate to overcome the psychological inertia minimizing migration to the marginal region. Clearly the interaction between Region X and Region Y is not simply predicated upon economic realities.*

These conditions of relationship between the two regions, therefore, define a marginal region within the context of cultural geography. The lines of interrelationship embrace economics, migration gradients, diverse physical geography, and perception of both hearth area and distant environments. In sum, the marginal land concept concerns more than return on agricultural capital and labor.

How can Region X come to resemble Region Y vis à vis population support and economic growth? This question is asked by government planners and researching academicians, but it is much more personally relevant for the people, who are deciding whether or not to migrate. These people may be resident in both Regions X and Y. Concerns for change are also felt by the resident entrepreneurs of both regions.

The major catalyst of developmental activity in Region X is technology.[8] However, it is diffi-

cult to support this thesis because it presupposes one or both of the following: that the migrants who generate the new growth can take significant advantage of costly new technology; or, that the government which holds sway over Region X and Region Y invests enough capital in Region X to overcome several of the negative conditions enumerated above. Neither of these phenomena occurs with regularity. The people who are responsible for the increased growth and settlement activity are most frequently peasant farmers employing a technology that has changed but little within the last century, except perhaps for the use of some chemical fertilizer.

The suggested course of change in Region X is as follows. Population pressures in Region Y build up to a general level adequate to initiate considerations of migration among those who are economically marginal to society in Region Y,[9] including unlanded tenant farmers, and small plot holders unable to meet local tax burdens and loan repayment schedules. There would also be a small number of speculators and small merchants who anticipate significant changes in the demography of Region X. This band, then, mostly made up of family heads who have left family behind to locate land before sending for the women and children, set out independently for the marginal area. It is the feedback from these people, coupled with increasing pressures on the land and family economy of the marginal people in Region Y, which stimulates the subsequent migration stream toward Region X. When a critical mass

---

[7] This condition is primarily a function of a lower cost for the tertiary sector in Region X as well as the nonexistence of a multitude of cash-demanding activities which range from recreation and entertainment to consumption of consumer goods which are precluded from market in Region X usually because of the failure of the population to meet threshold demands for a given class of goods.

[8] Baldwin, Robert E., "Patterns of Development in Newly Settled Regions," in *Agriculture in Economic Development,* ed. Eicher, Carl, and Lawrence Witt, (New York: McGraw-Hill, 1968), pp. 238–259. Note especially sections IV and V. Also see Schultz, Theodore W., *Transforming Traditional Agriculture* (New Haven: Yale University Press, 1964), esp. pp. 130–174.

[9] Robert Park made an interesting comment on the nature of this man in "Human Migration and the Marginal Man," *American Journal of Sociology,* Vol. XXXIII (May, 1928), pp. 881–893, in which he suggested some aspects of the decision-making process involved in this migration. The economic facet of the decision, however, can be summarized by the process of a small landholder borrowing on his land (or a tenant borrowing on future harvests) for some capital need in the farm or family. Because of poor management or as a result of conditions beyond his control, the man is forced to forfeit his collateral, and this begins his marginal role in the normative region. Obviously, such a category would be made up of not only nearly destitute farmers who have lost all but also heads of households who have seen the writing on the wall and choose to get out of this demanding environment before they are forced to give up all of their land or credit.

of peasant farmers locates near some transport line or water source, minor market center activities begin, and sections of Region X slowly become attractive enough to entice merchants of Region Y to emigrate.

This growth occurs in spite of the calamity conditions mentioned above. Floods, droughts, earthquakes, and other settlement hazards are not adequate to stop the immigration into Region X, because the single most important catalyst in this immigration is a population density/pressure which is unbearable to marginal peoples in Region Y.[10] Calamity conditions may continue to deter more normal forms of economic investment in the marginal region, but the peasant stock and virtually uncapitalized farmers or laborers see these conditions as no more dangerous to them than the competition for land or employment in Region Y. And the potential gain, should they be able to avoid damage from any of these calamities, is greater than potential gains in Region Y.

The next significant transformation of Region X comes when the government and well-capitalized entrepreneurs note the persistence of migration to this region. Since growth and development in Region Y has been the *sine qua non* for the vitality of the migration stream toward Region X, there has also emerged in both regions a class of investors who have gained from the appreciation in land values as well as increased crop yields through more sophisticated farming techniques. These opportunists may well begin to look anew at potentials for development in Region X, for as stated in the assumptions above, all production inputs excepting transport and externally produced commodities are less expensive in Region

X than Region Y. Once the capital flow from Region Y to Region X begins, marginality has started to decline.

Let us apply this model and its transformation to the island of Taiwan.

Region X is defined as the rift valley lying between the eastern flank of the Central Mountain Range and the western scarps of the Coast Range in east Taiwan. This valley is spoken of in various places as the Taitung Rift Valley, eastern Taiwan Rift Valley, or, simply as Eastern Taiwan. In Chinese the most common term for this region is *Tungtai*.[11] This includes both the rift valley and the thin littoral with its settlements on the eastern flank of the Coast Range bordering the Pacific Ocean. Region Y is defined as the western coastal plains of the island and is delimited by the Formosa Strait on the west and the slopes of the Central Mountain range above 1000' above sea level on all other sides. This montane barrier between the two regions has played a significant role in the marginality of Tungtai for two reasons. Obviously, the massif is an impediment to transport and migration, but nearly as significant is that fact that the mountains have been home to a number of aboriginal groups, which has made travel from the western coastal plans to the east coast unnaturally perilous. Though there are many trails lacing across the mountains between the two sides of the island, an adequate motor road was not constructed until the late 1950's.

The relationship in population densities between Tungtai and the western coastal plains has been as follows:

Table 1. Population growth on Taiwan, 1900–1965

	Tungtai		Western Coastal Plains		Taiwan	
	Population	Density (km.²)	Population	Density	Population	Density
1900	40,000	7	2,980,000	348	3,123,302	70
1950	285,687	33	6,850,000	720	7,555,588	148
1955	359,784	44	8,300,000	1240	9,080,474	252
1965	550,432	66	10,951,000	1510	11,883,525	351

10 Cf. note 5.

11 Chen, Cheng-siang, *A Geography of Taiwan* (Taipei: Fu-Min Geographical Institute of Economic Development, 1959–1961). 3 volumes (in Chinese). For detailed discussion of Tungtai, see Vol III, pp. 1200–1234.

It can be seen from these figures that the island of Taiwan has experienced a most profound demographic change in the last half-century. It is during this period that the marginal nature of Tungtai began to be modified by a flow of immigrants, giving Eastern Taiwan a 1400% increase for the same period which witnessed less than a 400% increase for the entire island. The migration of land-seeking peasants to Tungtai since 1949, particularly within the last decade, not only has occasioned settlement and economic growth which is unprecedented for Tungtai but has been the most rapid on the entire island during that period.

The environmental conditions differentiating Tungtai from the western coastal plains are several. Owing to the genesis of the rift valley as a graben between the upthrust Central Range and the Coast Range, seismic activity is a regular feature of the Tungtai region. There is an average of 160 earth tremors recorded annually in Taiwan and, due to the nature of the Tungtai geologic structure, a majority of these are felt in eastern Taiwan.[12] The Tungtai region has more seismic activity, but the really devastating quakes more frequently occur in the crowded, densely built-up west. This seismic activity is one of the "calamity conditions" that gives the marginal area its character.

Because the Central Mountain Range is so high, the Pacific typhoons which frequent the Taiwan latitudes from May to November are inclined to blow themselves out on the windward side of the island. This storm activity results in torrential downpours which funnel quickly into the rift valley, overflowing seasonal stream beds and dykes. The result is that nearly one-third of the valley floor is made up of gravels contained in impermanent alluvial fans. The flooding and potential inundation of river-margin paddy land with gravel and sand further contribute to the "calamity conditions." The gravity of this potential destructiveness is shown by the fact that major streams draining the east side of the Central Range may fluctuate in flow patterns and rates of discharge from a minimum of ten to 20 cusecs to as high as 600 cusecs.[13] Such a condition not only threatens the adjacent farmsteads, but it also increases governmental costs in the construction of a transport network.

It is these two elements of physical geography (the seismic activity and the typhoon hazard) which characterize Tungtai for the majority of the population of the western coastal plains. The unpredictable nature of these conditions, however, allows a potential migrant to think of them as no more formidable obstacles to security than the inexorable advance of cash demands on his family economy. For this reason, the initial migrants to the marginal Tungtai region were peasant farmers at the subsistence level, who could commit all and commit nothing to an attempt to settle the mountain flanks or the valley floor. In 1949, when the western coastal plains experienced an abnormal population increase due to the immigration of nearly 2 million people from the Chinese mainland, a migration stream from the west to the east was established which has flowed steadily for more than 20 years.

This stream has paralleled an important transformation in the economic and cultural patterns of the Tungtai region. The commercial growth of Tungtai has been such that urban areas in the western coastal plains are now also supplying migrants. These migrants come with minor capital resources and locate themselves either within the several urban centers of Hualien, Taitung, Yuli, or Chengkung, or they bring new or expanded services and goods to the villages which are growing due to the expansion and intensification of the land use in Tungtai. In either case, the alternatives now open for the migrant to eastern Taiwan include subsistence farming with shifting fields on government-owned land to administrative roles in Hualien and Taitung. Such a diversity of potential goal areas stimulates a like diversity in the type of people drawn from the hearth area of the western coastal plains.[14]

---

12 Hsieh, Chiao-min, *Taiwan—Ilha Formosa* (London: Butterfields, 1964), pp. 20, 27.

13 Chen, *op. cit.*, p. 1203.

14 Lee, Everett S., "A Theory of Migration," *Demography*, Vol. 3, No. 1 (1966), pp. 47–57. Lee finds the same difficulty in citing the exact combination of influences in the hearth area and the goal area which precipitate migration. Though an inventory of factors affecting the decision to migrate can be made, the actual decision to move is invariably a personal and individual one which falls without the generalized framework of a model. The importance of this fact is frequently hidden by model builders through the inclusion of the stated assumption that "all other things considered equal, a move will occur

Notwithstanding the significant changes which have taken place in the goal area (Tungtai) since 1950, the region continues to be classified as a marginal area as defined above. Relatively high transport costs and consequent market isolation prevent the establishment of a normal interregional capital flow in the fields of light and heavy industry. Investment capital moves toward labor-intensive rather than capital-intensive activities, not because of a paucity of capital on the island but rather because of the marginal nature of the Tungtai region. The only facets of recent development which anticipate the inflow of external capital are the food processing industries and the fresh fruit exporting firms. These have been generated not by normal market activity but by considerable government investment and speculation. The fact that pineapple and Valencia sweet orange industries have been successful suggests that the marginality of Tungtai may be truly breaking down with continued interest in Tungtai on the part of entrepreneurs and firms in the western coastal plains.[15] This will in turn give the selection process in migration different parameters and result in a continued upgrading (economically) in the migrants from the western coastal plains to Tungtai.[16]

Following this, government investment in the transportation network and private investment in the directly productive activities of the growing urban base in the marginal region will reduce the importance of the subsistence sector, minimize transportation cost differentials between the western coastal plains and Tungtai, and facilitate the construction of more flood control systems and earthquake-proof structures, which will diminish the destructiveness of the "calamity conditions." Ultimately, the marginal people of Tungtai will begin to view other regions in Taiwan as potential goal areas for agricultural colonization.

Thus the transformation of Tungtai from a marginal area to a productive microcosm of the western coastal plains is begun. Though differences in crops and urban complexity will exist, the basic distinctions between marginal and normative regions will no longer obtain.

Conclusions

A marginal region within the context of cultural geography is considered to be an under-settled area characterized by an allegedly harsh physical geography and relative isolation. It is a place where only a marginal man from a normative area would migrate. It is similar to a frontier in its unsettledness, but the very low relative population densities as well as the characteristic "calamity conditions" give the marginal region a distinctive settlement history and growth pattern. The relationship between frontier and the marginal area is that all marginal areas are frontiers, but only particularly harsh frontiers can be classified as marginal areas.[17] In the context of Taiwan, as in all cases excepting where development is inaugurated by a government migration-stimulation

---

at this time. . . ." In migration—if research is concerned with the moment when the decision to move is enacted—it is not reasonable to discount "all other things." This is partly because migration streams are not made up exclusively of beings who are motivated either rationally or economically. And denied the certainty of those two factors, the abstractor must deal with each migrant at a personal level.

[15] Salter, Christopher L., "Non-Utilized Potential in Economic Development," *Industry of Free China* (November, 1962), pp. 1–24.

[16] With the establishment of a more normal capital flow between the normative and the incipiently normative region, the selection process in migration to the marginal area becomes more akin to a normal frontier migration situation. Baldwin, *op. cit.*, p. 241 characterizes this population as migrants "from middle and higher income groups of the developed region and either possessing the necessary funds for migration or . . . able to borrow them in the capital market." This quality seldom characterizes the initial migrating group to a marginal area, though an unsettled frontier without restrictive climatic or edaphic characteristics might draw early from such a relatively prosperous segment of the hearth area population.

[17] Obviously, such a distinction is necessarily vague at the level of abstraction. If one is to consider the Southern Hemisphere, the distinction between frontier and marginal area is more difficult to evaluate because of the still inadequate build-up of rural demographic pressures vis à vis the unsettled areas. In the Northern Hemisphere, and particularly the eastern half, the lines are more clearly drawn between the frontiers still remaining which have relatively minor intervening obstacles and the more patently underpopulated marginal areas. In Japan, mainland China and Taiwan, and the island of Java migration streams are beginning to gain efficiency as marginal regions long unsettled in these countries develop now with unprecedented growth.

scheme, technology alone is inadequate to generate the development of a marginal area. There must be sufficient population pressure and economic activity in some region of the country to create a marginal rural population which is actively considering migration to a new hearth. The marginal area then begins to receive a steady flow of subsistence and peasant farmers who open new land despite the negative qualities of the marginal region's physical environment. See Fig. 1.

Within the context of Taiwan, the rift valley and its mountain flanks called Tungtai is an excellent example of a marginal region. Virtually unaffected by the spectacular demographic changes in Taiwan until the early 1920's, Tungtai is now involved in a growth and change sequence which, if continued at the present pace, will transform the east side from a marginal area into a normal frontier area and subsequently into a fully productive sector of the Taiwan economy.

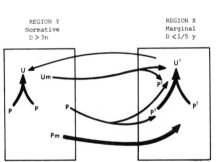

STAGE 1

Population density and pace of economic development of Region Y have not yet reached the critical level to create a sizable segment of Pm who find migration to Region X more desirable than inter-Region Y migration or the continued status quo. Migration flow patterns are generally characterized by orthodox rural to urban flow with the attendant psychological burdens being the most significant intervening obstacle to such a migration.

REGION Y
Normative
D < 3n

REGION X
Marginal
D < 1/5 y

LEGEND

U = urban center

P = peasant hearth

Pm = marginal peasant population

Um = marginal urban population

D = density of population

n = national average population density

x = average population density for Region X

y = average population density for Region Y

X = a marginal region

Y = a normative region

↑ = direction and relative magnitude of migration stream

STAGE 2

Population density and the pace of economic development of Region Y reach levels adequate to generate a class of Pm who are not able to meet the cash demands of the economy of Region Y, nor are they inclined to accept urban marginality for rural marginality. The Pm class therefore moves in new quantity into the migration stream from Pm to P' in Region X. The intervening obstacles are fundamentally physical in such a migration.

REGION Y
Normative
D > 3n

REGION X
Marginal
D < 1/5 y

STAGE 3

In this stage the pattern of Region X approximates Region Y at STAGE 1. At the same time, a new marginal region begins to serve as the goal area for some of the migrants leaving Region X.

Note: Relative population densities vary considerably from example to example and cannot be viewed as adequate catalyst alone for the transition from Stage 1 to Stage 2.

Figure 1. The transportation of a marginal region.

Husbandry of the earth

2

The axial concern of cultural geography is the pattern of man's husbandry of the earth. Venerable men like Cato, Varro, Pliny the Elder, Columella, and even Mencius have written of the vital bond which of necessity exists between the farmer, the landscape, and society. In more recent times, men such as George Perkins Marsh, Eduard Hahn, Paul Vidal de la Blache, Carl Sauer, and many of the authors included within this anthology have attempted to comprehend the imprint man has made on the landscape in his quest for sustenance. Nowhere does man's modification of the earth attain the magnitude that it does within the realm of animal and plant husbandry, with the associated fires, plant and animal extinctions, hybrids, and domestication. It is through this modification that man has made the earth his, and it is by this same dominion that he has slowly begun to realize the potential destructiveness he possesses.

The diversity of man's husbandry

Recent ecologic-ethnographic studies of preliterate and subsistence populations have corroborated a fact which cultural geographers have sensed for a long time. Primitive peoples, sometimes functioning in modes which have seen only minor modification since they were codified by ritual at their inception, are really quite sophisticated in their demands upon the environment. Their awareness of the myriad uses to which plants such as bamboo of the Asian world and agave of the American world can be put is one example of ingenious husbandry. Both plants are used for food, fibre, and fencing. Agave also produces spines which function as needles, and it provides the fermented beverage pulque. Bamboo is also important in construction. These two examples could be matched by numerous others demonstrating the resourcefulness of peasants. Their ingenuity is further borne out in agricultural systems on a larger scale.

Clifford Geertz, in the selection from his monograph Agricultural Involution, describes how Indonesians of the Outer Islands use unirrigated land. The substratum is used for root crops, the surface for melons and squashes, the first meter above ground for grains and grasses, the second meter for maize and coffee bushes, and upper heights for tree crops and shade

*trees. Nonetheless, nineteenth century Euro-
pean observers called these people poor and
lazy farmers. Instead of the North European
pattern of well-plowed fields, cultivated and
given to only one crop at a time, the Europeans
saw the hillsides covered with casually cultivated, multi-cropped fields which seemed to
bespeak a general agricultural chaos. This very
"chaos," however, provided these swidden (shifting cultivation) populations with sufficient
return on land and labor to afford some village
stability and seasonal surplus to support highly
elaborate ritual activities. Such is the diversity
of husbandry: though the means of gaining the
products differ in aspects of technology and
goal, both systems produced the necessary quantities for distinctly structured socio-economic
systems.*

*James Parsons, in his observations on the
netting, marketing, and eating of 3- to 4-ounce
starlings, points out the very definite regional
lines which enclose both the netters and the
eaters of this bird. The bird is not unique to
this part of southern Spain, nor is there any
exceptional protein deficiency there because of
some other faunal lack. The catching and consuming of starlings is simply an example of
regional diversity in diet preference manifested
in a unique way. The particular use of the
canebreaks discussed in Parsons' article is also a
good example of the use of vegetation as a tool
in the harvest of the earth's resources.*

*The significant generalization to draw from
these vignettes of diversity—and they run
through the entire anthology, not just this
section—is that primitive systems of land and
animal husbandry are basically attuned to their
native habitats. The aspects of destruction,
nonsurplus, and disorder which academics have
inventoried can frequently be traced to intro-
ductions from the West which made unprecedented demands for surplus. It is not argued
that the systems are compatible with contemporary economic and monetary goals; but these
patterns of husbandry have maintained stable
societies for millennia and have given rise many
times to great civilizations.*

The overt product of man's husbandry: a tailored landscape

*One of the classic landscapes created by man is
the terraced rice field, which graces slopelands,*

*basin bottoms, and coastal plains through
South, Southeast, and East Asia. The selection
from* Agricultural Involution *contains a detailed comment on the ecology of such a field
system. From this base, Geertz points out the
demographic and socioeconomic consequences
of this particular choice for landscape modification and rice growing.*

*Less dramatic, but still very visible upon the
landscape are the long, straight, evenly spaced
rows of the bean farmer Henry David Thoreau.
Even as a neophyte, Thoreau sees the farming
world breaking the forest pattern. In Thoreau's
words, he has "made the earth say beans."
Simple enough, but once man demands to have
the earth say such, forests are felled, land is
ploughed, straight rows mark the field, and man
has become an agent of landscape change.
Clarence Glacken pursues this same forest
modification theme in the excerpt from* Traces
on the Rhodian Shore. *The forest had myriad
resources for agrarian man, ranging from swine
forage to fuel supply. Gathering and hunting
also provided a food resource, but the most
desirable use of the European forest was the
clearing of it. Access to the rich midlatitude
forest soils was the dominant goal of agrarian
man. This same pattern has characterized the
dominion of man through temperate and tropical forests since he learned to make fire and to
plant.*

*The Mexicans, to whom maize is "tyrant" in
Lesley Byrd Simpson's* Many Mexicos, *offer still
another field pattern—another example of cultural choices visible upon the land. The steep
hills with the rows of mixed maizes running
perpendicular to the contour change from year
to year as the heavy summer rains pound upon
the exposed slopes. Rills come, then rivulets,
then gullies, and finally the slopes are so badly
eroded that they become virtually useless to
agricultural man. Given adequate time for re-
growth of secondary forest on these slopes they
could produce again for man, but owing to
increased population pressures they must be
returned to milpa too soon. As a result, man's
landscape sculpting in this instance becomes
increasingly ill-suited to his needs.*

*The ruination of upland slopes and the po-
tential elimination of the starling are two examples of overt, easily visible products of man's
husbandry. J. E. Spencer's paper on charcoal
and forest clearance in search of fuel and Rus-*

sell Lord's selection from The Care of the Earth, which takes note of the vine, grazing, and tree crops, focus on additional manifestations of the search for sustenance. In the case of charcoal, the forest is initially thinned out (not cleared), so that man sees the significance of the gathering trait only after decades or centuries. Lord suggests that part of the blame for the decline of the Roman Empire can be put upon the society which no longer saw the farmer as a first-class citizen. As farming fell into comparative disrepute, yields decreased, and landscapes less overtly bore the mark of man with the relaxation of patterns of cultivation. As fields were taken out of production, the slow encroachment of stout grasses or secondary forest erased all marks of man's earlier and more productive control. Such a pattern, in addition to others of a very different genesis, anticipates the next theme.

The subtle product of man's husbandry: modified flora and fauna

The view that man has a major influence in the modification of landscape was advanced in 1864 by George Perkins Marsh, in Man and Nature. Though this was certainly not the first time that man had begun to see himself as having attained a real dominion over nature, Marsh's volume holds a unique position because of the particular attention cultural geographers have been giving it during the last two decades. Marsh's point in writing the book, which was subtitled Physical Geography as Modified by Human Action, was not only to note man's role in the past, but also to warn him that he was unwittingly destroying the productivity of his habitat. Animal and plant extinctions were cited as two examples of how man's cultural choices had greater ramifications than he realized. As man opted to favor one species over another, the whole pattern of survival was changed. This selective and destructive process continued with the creation of crossbreeds and hybrids. The end result is the subtle product of man's husbandry. The terraced, paddy rice landscape, for example, leaves no doubt in the viewer's mind of the presence of man.

Gerardo Budowski's paper on tropical savannas is an excellent example of man's pursuit of husbandry. Budowski's thesis is that the extensive savanna areas of the New World are the product not of climatic and edaphic conditions but rather the consequence of man's continued use of fire for agricultural and hunting purposes. His bibliography at the conclusion shows the range of sources he has pursued to support his argument that this particular vegetation form is a product of man.

Carl Sauer's article suggests his own concern with the genesis of the savanna. Sauer, in fact, did much to arouse curiosity about the relationship between forest clearance and savanna development through his early writing on the origins of the American Great Plains. In "Man in the Ecology of Tropical America" he further develops the concept of man, armed with fire, clearing away virgin tropical forest as he plants his recent domesticates and then stands by helpless as grasses move in to replace the casually cultivated food and fibre crops.

The subtle product, then, is the landscape which man has fashioned—not so much by premeditation, but by the accumulation of minor acts which now stand as major landscape modifications.

Dissimilar ecologic adaptation to similar habitat

Cultural geography owes much of its vitality to the negative reaction to environmental determinism, a school of geography which had a large following for the first three decades of this century in the United States. The concept of physical environment "determining" cultural configuration has always been an anathema to anyone who sees man as an ecologic dominant; as a creature of either individual or collective strength. Mencius said this in the fourth century B.C. when he advised that: "When Heaven sends down calamities, it is still possible to escape them. When we occasion the calamities ourselves, it is not possible any longer to live." And much the same idea is implicit in this excerpt from Voltaire's essay on climate: "Climate has some influence, government a hundred times more; religion and government combined more still."

It has been the burden of cultural geography to call attention to examples of man's cultural choice transcending the determinants of the physical landscape. One of the most decisive examples of this is the swidden/sawah dichotomy, with its distinct demographic and cul-

tural patterns. Geertz notes well the mechanics of the two systems. If you add the observation that swidden did not originate on slope lands but on coastal plains and level lands, and from that draw the obvious conclusion that both lowland and upland environments permit either swidden or sawah, then one may well ponder man's decision to have one or the other of the systems. Inasmuch as the cultural patterns—demographic, land tenure, economic—related to this decision are so distinct, this particular example well illustrates the influence of dissimilar ecologic adaptation to similar habitat.

A good example of the ascendancy of technology in the creation of a contemporary landscape is the occupance of the tidal lands by the Chinese described in Ju Chih-chuan's article. Though social change is lauded more vigorously than agrarian technology, reality favors the latter as the reason for the new productivity of this land between two seas. New and massive inputs of labor and technology are bringing about very significant modifications in the cultural landscape of Communist China—particularly in areas which have been on the margins of productivity in the past. Though the most notable changes in the Chinese nation are most frequently discussed in political and social terms, man's ambitious husbandry of the land must also be included in the inventory of changes wrought since the Second World War.

J. Desmond Clark, in "Culture and Ecology in Prehistoric Africa," deals with the other end of the technological spectrum in showing that man's mark may be left on the landscape with only a modicum of technology at his disposal. Clark's article might be compared with the article on general landform shaping by Berl Golomb and Herbert M. Eder. The latter article is an inventory of the diverse ways in which man's husbandry of the earth has left its unique mark on the landscape. Though technologies vary, the common result is evidence of man's activity in creating a humanized landscape.

The cultural geographer is increasingly able to chart and evaluate the genesis and growth of these patterns of husbandry through time. Such competence yields exciting studies on cultural development predicated upon field systems, modes of land tenure, implement invention and diffusion, and plant and animal domestication. These phenomena give meaning to the cultural landscape.

The bean-field

HENRY DAVID THOREAU

11

In virtually all of the scholarly literature on land and animal husbandry, the farmer is seen only as a member of a vast land-tied population. Henry David Thoreau, in this selection from his classic Walden, *gives a thoroughly personal view of the farmer as the husband of the earth. Thoreau's bean field and its cultivation are sketched here in terms both agrarian and philosophical; his commentary does not stop with the mechanics of bean growing but includes also the question of the agrarian artisan in human tradition.*

Though obviously not a milestone in the literature of cultural geography per se, *this selection from Thoreau nicely points up the need to maintain a human perspective on these acts, which both nurture mankind and pattern the face of the earth.*

Meanwhile my beans, the length of whose rows, added together, was seven miles already planted, were impatient to be hoed, for the earliest had grown considerably before the latest were in the ground; indeed they were not easily to be put off. What was the meaning of this so steady and self-respecting, this small Herculean labor, I knew not. I came to love my rows, my beans, though so many more than I wanted. They attached me to the earth, and so I got strength like Antæus. But why should I raise them? Only Heaven knows. This was my curious labor all summer,—to make this portion of the earth's surface, which had yielded only cinquefoil, blackberries, johnswort, and the like, before, sweet wild fruits and pleasant flowers, produce instead this pulse. What shall I learn of beans or beans of me? I cherish them, I

Henry David Thoreau, *Walden* (Boston and New York: Houghton Mifflin and Company, 1906), 171–184.

hoe them, early and late I have an eye to them; and this is my day's work. It is a fine broad leaf to look on. My auxiliaries are the dews and rains which water this dry soil, and what fertility is in the soil itself, which for the most part is lean and effete. My enemies are worms, cool days, and most of all woodchucks. The last have nibbled for me a quarter of an acre clean. But what right had I to oust johnswort and the rest, and break up their ancient herb garden? Soon, however, the remaining beans will be too tough for them, and go forward to meet new foes.

When I was four years old, as I well remember, I was brought from Boston to this my native town, through these very woods and this field, to the pond. It is one of the oldest scenes stamped on my memory. And now to-night my flute has waked the echoes over that very water. The pines still stand here older than I; or, if some have fallen, I have cooked my supper with their stumps, and a new growth is rising all around, preparing another aspect for new infant eyes. Almost the same johnswort springs from the same perennial root in this pasture, and even I have at length helped to clothe that fabulous landscape of my infant dreams, and one of the results of my presence and influence is seen in these bean leaves, corn blades, and potato vines.

I planted about two acres and a half of upland; and as it was only about fifteen years since the land was cleared, and I myself had got out two or three cords of stumps, I did not give it any manure; but in the course of the summer it appeared by the arrowheads which I turned up in hoeing, that an extinct nation had anciently dwelt here and planted corn and beans ere white men came to clear the land, and so, to some extent, had exhausted the soil for this very crop.

Before yet any woodchuck or squirrel had

run across the road, or the sun had got above the shrub oaks, while all the dew was on, though the farmers warned me against it,—I would advise you to do all your work if possible while the dew is on,—I began to level the ranks of haughty weeds in my bean-field and throw dust upon their heads. Early in the morning I worked barefooted, dabbling like a plastic artist in the dewy and crumbling sand, but later in the day the sun blistered my feet. There the sun lighted me to hoe beans, pacing slowly backward and forward over that yellow gravelly upland, between the long green rows, fifteen rods, the one end terminating in a shrub oak copse where I could rest in the shade, the other in a blackberry field where the green berries deepened their tints by the time I had made another bout. Removing the weeds, putting fresh soil about the green stems, and encouraging this weed which I had sown, making the yellow soil express its summer thought in bean leaves and blossoms rather than in wormwood and piper and millet grass, making the earth say beans instead of grass,—this was my daily work. As I had little aid from horses or cattle, or hired men or boys, or improved implements of husbandry, I was much slower, and became much more intimate with my beans than usual. But labor of the hands, even when pursued to the verge of drudgery, is perhaps never the worst form of idleness. It has a constant and imperishable moral, and to the scholar it yields a classic result. A very *agricola laboriosus* was I to travellers bound westward through Lincoln and Wayland to nobody knows where; they sitting at their ease in gigs, with elbows on knees, and reins loosely hanging in festoons; I the home-staying, laborious native of the soil. But soon my homestead was out of their sight and thought. It was the only open and cultivated field for a great distance on either side of the road, so they made the most of it; and sometimes the man in the field heard more of travellers' gossip and comment than was meant for his ear: "Beans so late! peas so late!"—for I continued to plant when others had begun to hoe,—the ministerial husbandman had not suspected it. "Corn, my boy, for fodder; corn for fodder." "Does he *live* there?" asks the black bonnet of the gray coat; and the hard-featured farmer reins up his grateful dobbin to inquire what you are doing where he sees no manure in the furrow, and recommends a little chip dirt, or any little waste stuff, or it may be ashes or plaster. But here were two acres and a half of furrows, and only a hoe for cart and two hands to draw it,—there being an aversion to other carts and horses,—and chip dirt far away. Fellow-travellers as they rattled by compared it aloud with the fields which they had passed, so that I came to know how I stood in the agricultural world. This was one field not in Mr. Coleman's report. And, by the way, who estimates the value of the crop which nature yields in the still wilder fields unimproved by man? The crop of *English* hay is carefully weighed, the moisture calculated, the silicates and the potash; but in all dells and pond-holes in the woods and pastures and swamps grows a rich and various crop only unreaped by man. Mine was, as it were, the connecting link between wild and cultivated fields; as some states are civilized, and others half-civilized, and others savage or barbarous, so my field was, though not in a bad sense, a half-cultivated field. They were beans cheerfully returning to their wild and primitive state that I cultivated, and my hoe played the *Ranz des Vaches* for them.

Near at hand, upon the topmost spray of a birch, sings the brown thrasher—or red mavis, as some love to call him—all the morning, glad of your society, that would find out another farmer's field if yours were not here. While you are planting the seed, he cries,—"Drop it, drop it,—cover it up, cover it up,—pull it up, pull it up, pull it up." But this was not corn, and so it was safe from such enemies as he. You may wonder what his rigmarole, his amateur Paganini performances on one string or on twenty, have to do with your planting, and yet prefer it to leached ashes or plaster. It was a cheap sort of top dressing in which I had entire faith.

As I drew a still fresher soil about the rows with my hoe, I disturbed the ashes of unchronicled nations who in primeval years lived under these heavens, and their small implements of war and hunting were brought to the light of this modern day. They lay mingled with other natural stones, some of which bore the marks of having been burned by Indian fires, and some of the sun, and also bits of pottery and glass brought hither by the recent cultivators of the soil. When my hoe tinkled against the stones, that music echoed to the woods and the sky, and was an accompaniment to my labor which yielded an instant and immeasurable crop. It was no longer beans that I hoed, nor I that hoed beans; and I remembered with as much pity as pride, if I remembered at all, my acquaintances who had gone to the city to attend the oratorios. The nighthawk circled overhead in the sunny afternoons—for I sometimes made a day of it—like a mote in the eye, or in heaven's eye, falling from time to time with a swoop and a sound as if the heavens were rent, torn at last to very rags and tatters, and yet a seamless cope remained; small imps that fill the air and lay their eggs on the ground on bare sand or rocks on the tops of hills, where few have found them; graceful and slender like ripples caught up from the pond, as leaves are raised by the wind to float in the heavens; such kindredship is in nature. The hawk is aerial brother of the wave which he sails over and surveys, those his perfect air-inflated wings answering to the elemental unfledged pinions of the sea. Or sometimes I watched a pair of henhawks circling high in the sky, alternately soaring and descending, approaching and leaving one another, as if they were the embodiment of my own thoughts. Or I was attracted by the passage of wild pigeons from this wood to that, with a slight quivering winnowing sound and carrier haste; or from under a rotten stump my hoe turned up a sluggish portentous and outlandish spotted salamander, a trace of Egypt and the Nile, yet our contemporary. When I paused to lean on my hoe, these sounds and sights I heard and saw anywhere in the row, a part of the inexhaustible entertainment which the country offers.

On gala days the town fires its great guns, which echo like popguns to these woods, and some waifs of martial music occasionally penetrate thus far. To me, away there in my bean-field at the other end of the town, the big guns sounded as if a puffball had burst; and when there was a military turnout of which I was ignorant, I have sometimes had a vague sense all the day of some sort of itching and disease in the horizon, as if some eruption would break out there soon, either scarlatina or canker-rash, until at length some more favorable puff of wind, making haste over the fields and up the Wayland road, brought me information of the "trainers." It seemed by the distant hum as if somebody's bees had swarmed, and that the neighbors, according to Virgil's advice, by a faint *tintinnabulum* upon the most sonorous of their domestic utensils, were endeavoring to call them down into the hive again. And when the sound died quite away, and the hum had ceased, and the most favorable breezes told no tale, I knew that they had got the last drone of them all safely into the Middlesex hive, and that now their minds were bent on the honey with which it was smeared.

I felt proud to know that the liberties of Massachusetts and of our fatherland were in such safe keeping; and as I turned to my hoeing again I was filled with an inexpressible confidence, and pursued my labor cheerfully with a calm trust in the future.

When there were several bands of musicians, it sounded as if all the village was a vast bellows, and all the buildings expanded and collapsed alternately with a din. But sometimes it was a really noble and inspiring strain that reached these woods, and the trumpet that sings of fame, and I felt as if I could spit a Mexican with a good relish,—for why should we always stand for trifles?—and looked round for a woodchuck or a skunk to exercise my chivalry upon. These martial strains seemed as far away as Palestine, and reminded me of a march of crusaders in the horizon, with a slight tantivy and tremulous motion of the elm tree tops which overhang the village. This was one of the *great* days; though the sky had from my clearing only the same everlastingly great look that it wears daily, and I saw no difference in it.

It was a singular experience that long acquaintance which I cultivated with beans, what with planting, and hoeing, and harvesting, and threshing, and picking over and selling them,—the last was the hardest of all,—I might add eating, for I did taste. I was determined to know beans. When they were growing, I used to hoe from five o'clock in the morning till noon, and commonly spent the rest of the day about other affairs. Consider the intimate and curious acquaintance one makes with various kinds of weeds,—it will bear some iteration in the account, for there was no little iteration in the labor,—disturbing their delicate organizations so ruthlessly, and making such invidious distinctions with his hoe, levelling whole ranks of one species, and sedulously cultivating another. That's Roman wormwood,—that's pigweed,—that's sorrel,—that's piper-grass,—have at him, chop him up, turn his roots upward to the sun, don't let him have a fibre in the shade, if you do he'll turn himself t'other side up and be as green as a leek in two days. A long war, not with cranes, but with weeds, those Trojans who had sun and rain and dews on their side. Daily the beans saw me come to their rescue armed with a hoe, and thin the ranks of their enemies, filling up the trenches with weedy dead. Many a lusty crest-waving Hector, that towered a whole foot above his crowding comrades, fell before my weapon and rolled in the dust.

Those summer days which some of my contemporaries devoted to the fine arts in Boston or Rome, and others to contemplation in India, and others to trade in London or New York, I thus, with the other farmers of New England, devoted to husbandry. Not that I wanted beans to eat, for I am by nature a Pythagorean, so far as beans are concerned, whether they mean porridge or voting, and exchanged them for rice; but, perchance, as some must work in fields if only for the sake of tropes and expression, to serve a parable-maker one day. It was on the whole a rare amusement, which, continued too long, might have become a dissipation. Though I gave them no manure, and did not hoe them all once, I hoed them unusually well as far as I went, and was paid for it in the end, "there being in truth," as Evelyn says, "no compost or lætation whatsoever comparable to this continual motion, repastination, and turning of the mould with the spade." "The earth," he adds elsewhere, "especially if fresh, has a certain magnetism in it, by which it attracts the salt, power, or virtue (call it either) which gives it life, and is the logic of all the labor and stir we keep about it, to sustain us; all dungings and other sordid temperings being but the vicars succedaneous to this improvement." Moreover, this being one of those "worn-out and exhausted lay fields which enjoy their sabbath," had perchance, as Sir Kenelm Digby thinks likely, attracted "vital spirits" from the air. I harvested twelve bushels of beans.

But to be more particular, for it is complained that Mr. Coleman has reported chiefly the expensive experiments of gentlemen farmers, my outgoes were,—

For a hoe	$ 0 54	
Plowing, harrowing, and furrowing	7 50	*Too much.*
Beans for seed	3 12½	
Potatoes "	1 33	
Peas "	0 40	
Turnip seed	0 06	
White line for crow fence . .	0 02	
Horse cultivator and boy three hours	1 00	
Horse and cart to get crop .	0 75	
In all	$14 72½	

My income was (patrem familias vendacem, non emacem esse oportet) , from

Nine bushels and twelve quarts of beans sold	$16 94
Five bushels large potatoes	2 50
Nine " small	2 25
Grass	1 00
Stalks	0 75
In all	$23 44
Leaving a pecuniary profit, as I have elsewhere said, of	$8 71½

This is the result of my experience in raising beans. Plant the common small white bush bean about the first of June, in rows three feet by eighteen inches apart, being careful to select fresh round and unmixed seed. First look out for worms, and supply vacancies by planting anew. Then look out for woodchucks, if it is an exposed place, for they will nibble off the earliest tender leaves almost clean as they go; and again, when the young tendrils make their appearance, they have notice of it, and will shear them off with both buds and young pods, sitting erect like a squirrel. But above all harvest as early as possible, if you would escape frosts and have a fair and salable crop; you may save much loss by this means.

This further experience also I gained. I said to myself, I will not plant beans and corn with so much industry another summer, but such seeds, if the seed is not lost, as sincerity, truth, simplicity, faith, innocence, and the like, and see if they will not grow in this soil, even with less toil and manurance, and sustain me, for surely it has not been exhausted for these crops. Alas! I said this to myself; but now another summer is gone, and another, and another, and I am obliged to say to you, Reader, that the seeds which I planted, if indeed they *were* the seeds of those virtues, were wormeaten or had lost their vitality, and so did not come up. Commonly men will only be brave as their fathers were brave, or timid. This generation is very sure to plant corn and beans each new year precisely as the Indians did centuries ago and taught the first settlers to do, as if there were a fate in it. I saw an old man the other day, to my astonishment, making the holes with a hoe for the seventieth time at least, and not for himself to lie down in! But why should not the New Englander try new adventures, and not lay so much stress on his grain, his potato and grass crop, and his orchards,—raise other crops than these? Why concern ourselves so much about our beans for seed, and not be concerned at all about a new generation of men? We should really be fed and cheered if when we met a man we were sure to see that some of the qualities which I have named, which we all prize more than those other productions, but which are for the most part broadcast and floating in the air, had taken root and grown in him. Here comes such a subtile and ineffable quality, for instance, as truth or justice, though the slightest amount or new variety of it, along the road. Our ambassadors should be instructed to send home such seeds as these, and Congress help to distribute them over all the land. We should never stand upon ceremony with sincerity. We should never cheat and insult and banish one another by our meanness, if there were present the kernel of worth and friendliness. We should not meet thus in haste. Most men I do not meet at all, for they seem not to have time; they are busy about their beans. We would not deal with a man thus plodding ever, leaning on a hoe or a spade as a staff between his work, not as a mushroom, but partially risen out of the earth, something more than erect, like swallows alighted and walking on the ground:—

> And as he spake, his wings would now and then
> Spread, as he meant to fly, then close again,—

so that we should suspect that we might be conversing with an angel. Bread may not always nourish us; but it always does us good, it even takes stiffness out of our joints, and makes us supple and buoyant, when we knew not what ailed us, to recognize any generosity in man or Nature, to share any unmixed and heroic joy.

Ancient poetry and mythology suggest, at least, that husbandry was once a sacred art; but it is pursued with irreverent haste and heedlessness by us, our object being to have large farms and large crops merely. We have no festival, nor procession, nor ceremony, not excepting our cattle-shows and so-called Thanksgivings, by which the farmer expresses a sense of the sacredness of his calling, or is reminded of its sacred origin. It is the premium and the feast which tempt him. He sacrifices not to Ceres and the Terrestrial Jove, but to the infernal Plutus rather. By avarice and selfishness, and a grovelling habit, from which none of us is free, of regarding the soil as property, or the means of acquiring property chiefly, the landscape is deformed, husbandry is degraded with us, and the farmer leads the meanest of lives. He knows Nature but as a robber. Cato says that the profits of agriculture are particularly pious or just (*maximeque pius quaestus*), and according to Varro the old Romans "called the same earth Mother and Ceres, and thought that they who cultivated it led a pious and useful life, and that they alone were left of the race of King Saturn."

We are wont to forget that the sun looks on our cultivated fields and on the prairies and forests without distinction. They all reflect and absorb his rays alike, and the former make but a small part of the glorious picture which he beholds in his daily course. In his view the earth is all equally cultivated like a garden. Therefore we should receive the benefit of his light and heat with a corresponding trust and magnanimity. What though I value the seed of these beans, and harvest that in the fall of the year? This broad field which I have looked at so long looks not to me as the principal cultivator, but away from me to influences more genial to it, which water and make it green. These beans have results which are not harvested by me. Do they not grow for woodchucks partly? The ear of wheat (in Latin *spica*, obsoletely *speca*, from *spe*, hope) should not be the only hope of the husbandman; its kernel or grain (*granum*, from *gerendo*, bearing) is not all that it bears. How, then, can our harvest fail? Shall I not rejoice also at the abundance of the weeds whose seeds are the granary of the birds? It matters little comparatively whether the fields fill the farmer's barns. The true husbandman will cease from anxiety, as the squirrels manifest no concern whether the woods will bear chestnuts this year or not, and finish his labor with every day, relinquishing all claim to the produce of his fields, and sacrificing in his mind not only his first but his last fruits also.

Tropical savannas, a sequence of forest felling and repeated burnings

12

GERARDO BUDOWSKI

The role of fire in man's history of landscape modification is a central theme in cultural geography. This article suggests the profound influence man's use of fire has had on the creation of expansive savanna grasslands. Whereas these open areas on the littoral of tropical rainforests were once thought to be caused by decreasing precipitation poleward from the equator, now Budowski builds a strong argument for man's interference as being the primary factor in the creation of savannas. Fire is the tool which man uses and has used to clear land for planting and hunting in the tropics. This repeated burning initiates a sequence of events which Budowski chronicles as it leads to the destruction of the forest and the emergence of open grasslands with only gallery forests.

In assigning man this dominant role in the creation of a distinctive landscape and in supporting this accusation with data drawn from a wide variety of sources, Budowski has written a minor classic.

Savannas are very extensive within the tropics[1], usually covering large areas within each coun-

Gerardo Budowski, "Tropical Savannas, a Sequence of Forest Felling and Repeated Burnings," *Turrialba*, VI, No. 1–2 (1956), 23–31.

* Forester Renewable Resources Service of the Inter-American Institute of Agricultural Sciences, Turrialba, Costa Rica.

[1] The term tropics is rather confusing as it often implies different meanings or boundaries. One ecological definition, here adopted, would include any point of the surface of the earth with a mean annual temperature of 24°-C or more or if higher than sea level, with calculated mean annual temperature at sea level of 24°-C or more. For the present study, only tropical lowlands will be considered. Their mean annual temperature is above 24°-C and rainfall varies to a great extent but most areas receive between 1000 and 4000 milimeters a year.

try. Their extension has been estimated at about 6,700,000 square miles against only 5,800,000 square miles of the combined surface of rain forest and deciduous (monsoon) forest (48).

In spite of considerable variation in species composition they generally assume a uniform physiognomy. Grass is the main cover, but a variable number of scattered trees may also occur.

Because of the alternation of wet and dry season, climate was once thought to be responsible for tropical savanna formation as an analogy to temperate grasslands or steppes (27). It is certainly true that most of the savannas found in tropical areas prevail in regions where sharp differences between dry and wet seasons occur. However, various tropical deciduous or dry forests may grow in the same region under the same climatic conditions; they are found often intermingled with savannas. Even where rainfall is sufficient to produce moist forest (with more than 2000 milimeters) savannas are often frequent (10, 44). On the other hand, in much drier regions with a long and severe dry season, as may occur in the vicinity of 20 degrees North and South latitudes, instead of finding more savannas, actually thorn forest is the characteristic type of vegetation. Grisebach's assumption was shared by Schimper's ecological conception of the world plant formations (50). Köppen (1931), cited by Petterssen, (42), (pp. 212–213), in his classification of world climates, still widely used in most meteorological treatises, not only adopted the idea but actually listed the tropical savanna climate as one of the main types of climates on earth and drew its theoretical boundaries on an idealized continent.

With increasing knowledge the climatic theory fell into disfavor and is usually not accepted nowadays (5, 6, 10, 44, 55). In its place, two main theories have arisen to explain the origin of savannas:

1. *Savannas are due to edaphic factors like leaching of soil, inherently poor soil, or the presence of an impermeable pan, usually associated with a flat topography.*
2. *Savannas are biotic in origin, that is, due to man's activities in removing the forests and preventing its reestablishment, mainly by the use of fire.*

As a matter of fact, there seems to be hardly a disagreement if it can be properly shown that these pedological characteristics of savanna soils are the result of biotic activities. Considerable evidence seems to confirm this, especially in the light of recent research explaining different iron movements occurring in the soil, once the protecting forest cover is removed.

The actual status of savannas

Savannas are usually flat in topography but may also be present on rolling, hilly and even steep areas. The soil texture varies from very sandy to very clayey even on adjoining areas. Forests may be close or rather far away, frequently burnt and degraded or not. Patches of forest are not uncommon within the savanna area and are usually associated with more moisture. Moreover, they often constitute the last remnants of formerly more extensive forested areas. Water courses interrupt the savanna landscape with usually regular belts of gallery forests. Evidently these are more moist and thus more resistant to the entrance of fire. Isolated trees of rather small size, crooked stems and broad crowns are common features in savannas. Most of them belong to the legume family in Africa, notably *Acacia* spp., while in America the most conspicuous savanna trees are *Curatella americana, Byrsonima* spp., *Bowdichia virgilioides* and *Xylopia* spp. They are very resistant to fire.

Tropical savannas have a common feature: they are regularly burnt. Myers (40) claimed: "I have never seen in South America a savanna however small or isolated or distant from settlement which did not show signs of more or less frequent burning." As an exception Beard (10) reports that the small Aripo savannas (680 acres) in Trinidad have not been known to be burnt in recent times. However, this is rather

difficult to demonstrate and the term "recent" is quite broad. Furthermore, according to Beard's own description and classification, he states that a strict definition of that area would list it as herbaceous swamp rather than a savanna.

Fire in savannas not only reduces substantially the amount of potential organic matter, but for some time after its passage it leaves the soil relatively barren and fully exposed to meteorological elements, a matter of much importance in explaining some of the degrading effects that take place.

The behavior of fire is worthy of mention. The sharp boundary often found between forest and savanna is undoubtedly fire-made. The protection of the forest cover from dessication thus acts as a kind of barrier to prevent the entrance of fire. Although the deciduous forests are often burned at the end of the dry season, the intensity and frequency of these fires is certainly much less than on adjoining savannas, thus the boundary is maintained. As pointed out by many authors and summarized by Mohr and van Baren (39), the top layers of forests and savannas differ in their moisture relations. Savannas will burn after a short exposure while forests take much longer in drying out. This explains the typical nature of savanna vegetation not only resistant against repeated fire but also able to survive drought as has been eloquently demonstrated by Rawitscher (43).

The role of fire in the establishment and maintenance of tropical savannas is acknowledged by virtually all ecologists who have considered the problem. The difference in opinion, however, lies in the assumption by some, notably Beard (10) and Michelmore (38), that savannas have always existed because of edaphic factors, notably topography, inherent soil structure and intermittent waterlogging, and biotic influences could at most only modify these factors to a limited degree. However, the extensive literature all over the tropical world only shows limited support to this theory.

Some examples of savanna formation

While the replacement of tropical forests by savannas through the last centuries and even prehistoric times is extremely well documented (18, 46, 49), the reverse process can also be demonstrated when savannas are protected against anthropogenic activities (8).

In many cases, the substitution process from forests to savannas follows a well known pattern. Patches of forests are cleared and burnt by squatters who cultivate their crops for a few years, abandoning the land when crop yields become unprofitable either because of soil exhaustion or weed invasion. Then the establishment of a mere xeric vegetation where grasses occupy an important place is favored. It will burn with more ease than the adjoining forest during the following dry seasons.

Degradation from forest to savanna can also be achieved by fire alone without the help of clearcutting. Actually, all intermediate stages can and have been found (34, 53, 55).

It is interesting to notice that the macrofauna fits well into this pattern. In the llanos of Colombia there are no highly peculiar savanna animals. The fauna is characterized by its poverty and the apparent recent arrival of its chief components. The deer, rabbits and quails are only slightly differentiated representatives of northern types. The adjoining forests, however, supported a very specialized fauna, giving evidence of antiquity and stability of forest habitat (9). All this points to a relatively recent advent of savannas.

The counter part of the rich grazing fauna of the African savannas could then be the result of much earlier and more intensive activity of fire. Anthropological investigations corroborate a very ancient activity of man in African territory while so far as known, man's influence in tropical America has been relatively recent.

Repeated burning will first have a selective effect favoring fire resistant species, but the constant killing of regeneration will gradually result in the opening of the forest. A subsequent increase of insolation creates severe drying of the soil surface. Fire is thus favored with each new dry season until in the course of time all the original forest disappears and is replaced by fire resistant grass with scattered savanna trees (14). In many places of Asia, Africa and Brazil, *Imperata* spp. is the most aggressive of these grasses (17, 56). The different changes in density and forest composition have been described in detail for the Venezuelan oriental llanos (53). In this region, the presence or absence of forest and its replacement by savannas was in direct relation with the intensity of past agricultural and pastoral uses, and fire was the main tool in achieving both activities. Most

of these savannas were found along old settlements and new savannas were increasing around present population centers and roads. Thus it is rather difficult to agree with Beard's statement (10, p. 162) that transitional bush between forest and savanna is very rare in northern South America when actually many if not most of the deciduous forests of Brazil, Venezuela, Colombia, Central America and the Antilles present more or less an advanced stage of degradation. True, the transition is not of the bush type but rather that of forest which is gradually opened. From Beard's itinerary one may infer that his observations on vegetation of Venezuela llanos were made along roads passing through old settlements and active grazing centers where no more forest was left except along water courses.

In Africa, the actual intermixing between forests and savannas is even more evident, as human activity and fire were both longer and more intense. The literature is extensive and very detailed descriptions of the different stages of degradation may be found (5, 6, 16). Most authors consider fire the chief agent of savanna production, although Bernard (11) still speaks of climatic savannas.

On the other hand it has often been demonstrated that forest will eventually replace savanna only if protection against fire and other man-induced biotic activities like grazing is secured (4, 8, 44). The rate of return to forest depends on the stage of degradation of the soil.

Environmental differences between forests and savannas

At this point it seems advisable to mention some of the differences of temperature and other changes in microclimate which may result according to whether the vegetation over the ground is forest or grass. An abundant literature deals with the microenvironmental differences between forest and grass cover (1, 21, 37, 11, 13, 25, 39, 44, 52). If it is assumed that dense forest cover is being replaced by a sparser vegetation, some of the following changes will take place:

1. *The amount of insolation reaching the soil is increased.*
2. *There is a general rise in the mean temperature of the soil and the air layer above it. More than that, the extremes between maximum and mini-*

mum are much wider. It may also be useful to remember that the rate of chemical reactions approximately doubles for each rise of 10°C. a matter of much importance when the fast oxidation of organic matter for example is considered. Not only is decomposition accelerated but the supply of "raw material" also decreases.

3. *Evaporation is largely increased at the upper horizons because of drier and warmer air and its greater circulation over the surface. Not only does this raise the drying effect but it favors higher oxidation activity at the top of the soil.*

4. *In general, transpiration is decreased but while in the forest transpiration may affect the moisture content of different horizons down to a considerable depth, this is not the case under savanna where plant roots are usually shallow, especially when compact soil conditions are prevailing.*

Some of these processes account for the compacting of the soil. They also will help to explain the formation of the already mentioned indurated pan, a feature of basic importance in the degradation process of tropical soils.

Savanna and forest soils

There is no évidence to believe that in tropical regions a soil may become too poor to support forest growth. In fact, the analyses of many forest soils in the tropics reveal an extremely low amount of organic matter and nutrients (33, 39, 44). The upper horizon of savannas may even contain a larger amount of organic matter than forest soils. The explanation is simple: under the forests, most of the nutrients produced by mineral decomposition and especially by the rapidly decomposing humus are immediately taken up to enter the plant cycles or are leached out (44). It has been shown that if compared to temperate regions, a very large amount of organic matter is produced by the tropical forest. However, this same organic matter is also very rapidly decomposed (30). There is consequently a very intensive circulation of organic compounds, further facilitated by the porous soil structure under the forest. Considerable leaching of these organic compounds takes place and may be revealed by the extensive amount carried away by the rivers. Under a savanna soil no such intensive circulation of organic compounds takes place. This difference will be very significant in explaining other soil processes.

In brief, the very low organic content of tropical forest soils can be related to rapid

uptake by the root systems and to intense leaching.

The difference between soils from savannas and forests may be considerable if physical factors are involved. It seems very logical to conclude with Beard (10, p. 201) : "Natural drainage is a most important characteristic of tropical soils which affects the distribution of the vegetation types such as savannas and forests." Poor drainage, according to Beard, is either the result of very compact soil, or because of the presence of an indurated pan. He did not mention that both of these conditions are engendered when a forest is removed and fire is liberally used.

The compacting of soil after forest removal

In Ceylon a number of experiments with soils of adjacent, contrasting, vegetation types showed how clearing can result in poor drainage (31). Very complete experiments carried over a long period have also been reported from southeastern Brazil (22, 23). It could be clearly established that much smaller pore volumes were found in savanna (12 per cent) than in forest soils (51 per cent). The former are the result of recent human activity. The effect of forest in relation to pore volume was further demonstrated when savannas were later protected and artificially planted with trees. The pore volume immediately increased. After 17 years of observations on the reforested soil it reached 39.8 per cent, thus approaching the pore volume of the undisturbed soil. Other experiments carried out by the same author showed a definite relation of the permeability of the soil to pore volume, which was in turn related to the forest cover. If a value of 1 was assigned to the amount of time it took water to go through a steel cylinder under a certain pressure for a soil sample taken under virgin forest, the value increased to 1.8–2.4 after the forest was felled and burned, and to 3.5–5.2 when ten days later it underwent a second intense fire. A nearby savanna also known to be artificially induced not a long time ago showed values of 2.5–2.8.

The compacting of the soil after the removal of forest cover is usually associated with the lack of large roots or canals reaching a greater depth and with the excessive drying and shrinkage in the upper horizons of the more exposed savanna soils. Severity of shrinkage is related to the amount of clay. The effect may often be seen when cracking takes place, a phenomenon often found on savanna soils with a high clay content. It is not found under the forest.

The formation of ferrugineous concretion, indurated hard pan or "cuirass"

Iron crusts, cemented hard pans or cuirasses are names frequently applied to a very common feature of tropical soils. They all refer to a kind of indurated slag-like concretion that extends more or less parallel to the soil surface. Apparently this is not limited only to a single soil group as it may underlie horizons of bleached sand or clay of variable depth or even appear on the surface. The vegetation that covers soils under these conditions is almost always confined to the savanna type and the effect of impeded drainage is obvious.

A great number of theories and observations deal with the factors that contribute to the formation of these concretions. As will be seen the presence or absence of a forest cover is of capital importance to explain the genesis of these pans.

A current explanation proposed for pan formation in temperate countries relates it to a fluctuating water table (35).

Investigations in tropical soils indicate plainly that although this is an important condition it may not be the main or only factor responsible. Fluctuating water tables are frequent in the tropics especially when pronounced dry and wet seasons exist and their movements may even be increased by felling of the forests (24).

Iron pans have been described in all continents but they have received most attention in Africa where man's activities are most intense. In some places they have deserved special names (e.g. "bovai" in Africa, "perdigón" in Cuba, etc.). According to Aubréville (7) some of them are extremely old. He considered different pans in varying stages of decomposition as relics of prehistoric times. Interestingly, iron pans are almost always found under savannas, rarely under forests, and, so far as known, never under virgin forest.

In Dahomey, West Africa, Aubert (3) described how after being cleared, the soil was subject to erosion resulting in the removal of the upper red lateritic horizons. When the lower horizon gradually became exposed, it hardened to a strong iron cuirass. According to the indigenous people, the clearance of the forest and the upper soil loss dated only 60 years ago. In nearby soil, under similar forest, no cuirass could be found, but only a mottled B horizon where accumulation of metallic hydrates took place. A similar observation was made in the Belgian Congo (32). Here, too, the removal of the vegetation and the repeated effect of the burning were held responsible for the formation and further hardening of these pans. Some of them were "ground water laterites where the massive clay in the lower horizon hardens to slaglike rock upon exposure. Once formed, this hard laterite is exceedingly resistant to weathering. The protective effect of the forest was stressed in preventing the downward movement of clay and subsequent exposure. Maignieu (36) attributed the formation of an iron cuirass in a banana plantation to leaching of metallic bases, their accumulation in the B horizon and further hardening after exposure. The following steps were described by Sudres (51) after the forest has been cleared: a) humus disappears because of less biological activity (meaning possibly a lesser production of organic matter); b) the more soluble bases are leached out after the silicates dissociate leaving the less soluble bases (Fe, Al, Mn); c) the silica originating from the dissociating silicates is leached; d) the metallic bases circulate as hydrogels forming deposits and concretions at upper horizons under special tensions whose depth is less as the soil becomes less protected and e) upon exposure, a hard pan is formed and may cement into a cuirass.

In Madagascar a typical soil profile for the rain forest belt shows only a mottled layer and a gray horizon at the bottom underlying the more or less bleached horizon at the top. No iron cuirass occurs but this may change if anthropogenic factors disturb this equilibrium (39). The same authors cite Blackie's description of the soils of Fiji where concretionary formations have never been observed under tall forest, but as soon as the forest is cut a lateritic hard pan develops. Ehrhardt (cited by Mohr and van Baren, 9, p. 373) ascribes the process to evaporation that follows deforestation. This would result in the ascent of the soil solution loaded with ferruginous and aluminous colloidal miscelles. The surface layers are hardened and cemented by the hydroxides of iron and aluminum. Ehrhardt also noticed that the process has never been observed in the primeval forest.

Mohr and van Baren (39) observe that the theory of fluctuating ground water level may reasonably fit in within these processes. It has been formerly shown that the forest soil remains moist to a considerable depth while the bare soil dries out at the upper level, the evaporation being much greater under the less protected soil. Under the forest, the ground water level is always kept lower than under savanna because of the great amount of transpiration. The forest soils also have a rather uniform moisture throughout its horizons and variations are not so accentuated during the dry and wet seasons. But under soils covered with savanna vegetation, much less water is pumped out through evaporation during the wet season and a rise in water level is produced whereas during the dry season, a considerable tension is exerted on the upper exposed soil which cracks, shrinks and dries to a great extent, all of which may be accounted to sharp fluctuations of the ground water (44). The ascent of the soil solution following deforestation and the hardening process may occur in a very short period. In one place in West Africa within two years a distinct hardening was observed (van Baren, cited by Mohr and van Baren, 39).

This foregoing examples of cuirass formation seem to demonstrate that different water movements in the soil may be responsible for its genesis. The first of them may be principally the descent of the iron and aluminum compounds and their precipitation (oxidation), accumulation and hardening under the influence of fluctuating ground water or simply exposure or a combination of both. A retreating water table during the dry season may well be the start of the process. Exposure is often favored or achieved by erosion processes that follow deforestation, especially when slopes are involved and the soil profile is truncated (2, 19). It has also been suggested that the precipitation of the iron compounds may be facilitated by the presence of local points of neutrality or slight alkalinity such as exist originally in the lower horizons (20).

The process would thus be podzolic in that iron compounds are leached down to lower horizons where they may be indurated or be cemented. The bleached A2 horizon is also present and has been described in numerous tropical soils often overlaying a hard pan (39, 41, 44).

The other movement involves the ascension of the soil solution with iron compounds that are precipitated at higher levels when they come into contact with more oxidizing agents. Evaporation and retreat of the water leaves the iron exposed to the air and ready to be oxidized, deposited and hardened to a pan. Here, the dry season, quite long in many tropical regions, is essential. It is possible that a rising water table during the rainy reason, or following deforestation, may even lift the solution to the top or close to it. The soil remains waterlogged for a time and the retreat of the same water table leaves the depositions subject to hardening after exposure. This is substantiated by the fact that a large number of savannas are regularly waterlogged during the rainy season. Forests of course may also be waterlogged, especially when extreme rainfall takes place, but as formerly mentioned no concretions are likely to form. In the Venezuelan llanos the waterlogged savannas are regular features and receive the name of "esteros." They are very heavily textured and an indurated layer is very common at very little depth. The adjoining not waterlogged savannas are called "bancos." They are somewhat higher and very sandy in their upper horizons. The sand evidently conceals the lower clay pan.

At any rate and in order to explain development of concretions of iron oxide, the mobilization of soluble iron first and its further gradual deposition as oxides seems to be essential (41). Ferrous iron in solution as a complex may be absorbed on the surface of ferric oxide. This may occur during the moist period. During a relatively dry period the ferrous iron will be oxidized and build up the ferric oxide deposits within the pores. Thus, the iron pan is continuously growing and develops best when exposed to alternating dry and wet periods.

In all the foregoing cases the removal of the forest cover has been stressed as a previous condition in the formation of a pan. Actually the forest not only prevents the formation of such a pan but has also been reported to break down a pan if trees replace grasses. In Nigeria after reforestation it was found that a poor red lateritic soil with iron concretions and sparse vegetation cover changed gradually into a yellow clay soil with only a few signs of the lateritic concretions to a depth of one meter (45).

This behavior has been attributed to the strong root activity (28) impeding pan formations, but probably more often to the stabilizing effect of the forest cover on environmental effects, especially in relation with water movements responsible for fluctuations. A further important contribution has recently been reported by Bloomfield (12), in trying to explain the iron movements in the soil. He found that organic solutions extracted from leaves and barks of different plants were able to convert the iron into soluble compounds thus entering the soil solution, even at such a high pH (for iron) as 6.5. He concludes that it seems inevitable that the water soluble products of plant decomposition extracted from the surface soil would cause solution and reduction of the ferric oxides during their passage down the profile. This active role of organic matter in dissolving iron compounds has also been pointed out by Ellis (20) in Rhodesia.

Investigations carried on previously in the Belgian Congo seem to confirm these observations (29). By extracting the soluble iron at different horizons it was found that the transformation of iron into soluble compounds may be rather fast and vegetation has a definite effect on that process. Grass, for instance, mobilized more than forest. Furthermore the loose iron moves in the form of complex molecules with organic radicals and its entrance into the "exchangeable market" may have a great impact on other elements whether anions or cations. The amount of soluble iron gradually decreases with depth and more oxidation takes place at lower levels. At a certain depth however there is a sudden final decrease of mobile iron and below this very few traces are found. Evidently flocculation has taken place at this point.

The effect of forest on preventing the formations of a pan thus becomes clearer. The great amount of organic matter circulating in the ground—"circulate" and not "found" is used to render the idea that it will not accumulate—will prevent the iron from being oxidized. Most of it will probably be leached out together with the organic matter because of good drainage

prevailing under the forest. Of course, the protective effect of the forest is no less important and will certainly prevent the soil from drying out and enable the ferrous iron to become oxidized (as well as the organic matter). The other effect of forest in relation with high pore volume and good drainage is no less important because it facilitates this leaching effect of the iron compounds. This would agree with Vine's opinion (cited by Nye, 41) that "there is a general tendency towards the great concentration of concretions and the formation of iron pan in the savanna and a reduction in the amount of concretions towards the wetter parts of the forest."

The observation that grass will mobilize more iron is certainly interesting and worthy of further investigations. Champion and Griffith (15), already mentioned that the presence of grass leads to soil degradation. Rapid drying of savanna soils and the reduced organic content of their lower horizons will then account for an early oxidation of the iron compounds. This is further facilitated by poor drainage, preventing any leaching.

The role of soil fauna in relation with soil degradation

One interesting point remains: the extensive amount of iron rich clay found in many tropical soils, especially under savanna conditions. The best raw material for the formation of the pans is clay. Following leaching one might suppose that the clay of the top horizon would be exhausted quickly especially on certain sandy soils with deep parent material. That this is not the case has been attributed to the intense activity of the soil fauna of the tropics, the most important being earthworms, and termites. The latter are particularly interesting, because unlike earthworms and ants, some species will choose tropical savannas for their habitats. In Africa they display an amazing activity as has been shown by Grasse (26). "In their need for clay, they will dig down to even four to five meters and revolve all the soil everywhere. Their galleries often run to a radius of 200–300 meters from their nests and these by themselves are large and cover extensive areas." Nye (41) even reports clay extraction to a depth of 12 meters and proposes a name for the horizon of clay on top produced by termites. In some Belgian Congo savannas the nests cover 15–30 per cent of the total area (32). Their mounds often stand more than 4 meters above the ground. One nest has been reported 4 meters high, 60 m. long and 6–7 meters wide (26). The clay used is embedded with saliva and is very plastic. Tons of clay are thus lifted and deposited on the top. These termites occur always on savannas and are absent or rare under the forest.

Beard (10) mentions their occurrence in tropical America. Their mounds are a constant feature of the savannas upon the ancient highlands of Guiana and southern Brazil. They also have been reported elsewhere, yet they are sometimes absent over wide areas. Beard's review of evidence of termites (10) led him to conclude that termite mounds are found only in savanna, never in forest. The clay used for the nests is particularly impermeable and able to solidify under exposure. This explains the vertical, stable structure of these mounds. When they are abandoned, and countings reveal that only one out of every four or five are actually inhabited, they collapse very quickly and clay is spread out over the soil. In one region of Africa it has been calculated that half a ton of earth is thus being deposited on the soil every year per acre (41).

How much these depositions of clay over the top layer may be connected with the formation of an indurated pan is still a debatable question but their presence should certainly be taken into account when studying soil processes especially under savannas. Heinzelin (28) and Nye (41), after observing their activity in different African areas concluded that the fine particles drawn up by these insects may later be leached and will upon exposure form a pan.

Thus the intense activity of termites bringing up clay from lower horizons also fits into the general dynamics of deforestation and the hard pan formation. However, this does not imply that termites may perpetuate savannas. Collapsed termite mounds are actually favorable sites for the reestablishment of tree vegetation if, of course, fire does not interfere.

Summary

Savannas in tropical lowlands can be related to man's activities, notably the felling of forest and especially the repeated use of fire. Such practices produce the following effects: (1) notable changes in microclimate, (2) soil erosion, (3) soil compaction and (4) strongly alternating water movements in the soil profile. The final result is often the formation of a ferruginous hardpan. This degradation process favors the establishment and maintenance of savannas at the expense of forests.

There seems to be ample evidence that forests can and, in fact, do eventually return even under these degraded conditions. If the successional stages leading to the establishment of forests are not made difficult by fire or other destructive anthropogenic activities, all the processes can be reversed. The iron pan may be dismantled, drainage improved and forest conditions will return.

Literature cited

1. Allee, W. C. Measurement of environmental factors in the tropical rain forest of Panama. Ecology 7:273–302. 1926.
2. Asprey, G. F. and Robbins, R. G. The vegetation of Jamaica. Ecological Monographs 23:359–412. 1953.
3. Aubert, G. Observations sur la dégradation des sols et la formation de la cuirasse latéritique dans le nord-ouest du Dahomey (A. O. F.). Fourth International Congress of Soil Science. Transactions 1950:127–128.
4. Aubreville, A. Les brousses secondaires en Afrique équatoriale. Bois et Forêts des Tropiques 2:24–49. 1947.
5. ——— Climates, forêts et désertification de l'Afrique tropicale. Paris, Société d'Editions géographiques, maritimes et coloniales, 1949. 351 p.
6. ——— The disappearance of the tropical forests of Africa. Unasylva 1:5–11. 1947.
7. ——— Erosion et "bovalisation" en Afrique noire française. Agronomie Tropicale 2:339–357. 1947.
8. ——— Les expériences de reconstitution de la savane boisée en Côte d'Ivoire. Bois et Forêts des Tropiques 32:4–10. 1953.
9. Bates, M. Climate and vegetation in the Villavicencio region of eastern Colombia. Geographical Review 38:555–574. 1948.
10. Beard, J. S. The savanna vegetation of northern tropical America. Ecological Monographs 23:149–215. 1953.
11. Bernard, E. Le climat écologique de la cuvette centrale congolaise. Institut National pour l'Etude Agronomique du Congo Belge, 1945, 240 p.
12. Bloomfield, C. Experiments on the mechanisms of gley formation. Journal of Soil Science 2:196–211. 1951.
13. Brooks, R. L. The regeneration of mixed rain forest in Trinidad. Caribbean Forester 2:164–173. 1941.

14. Budowski, G. Los incendios forestales en Venezuela. Caracas, Venezuela, Ministerio de Agricultura, Serie Forestal No. 13. 1951, 12 p.

15. Champion, H. G. and Griffith, A. L. Manual of general silviculture for India. Rev. ed. Calcutta, Oxford University Press, 1948. xiv. 330 p.

16. Chevalier, A. La décadence des sols et de la végétation en Afrique occidentale française et la protection de la nature. Bois et Forêts des Tropiques 16:335–353. 1950.

17. ———— Sur l'origine des campos brésiliens et sur le rôle des Imperata dans la substitution des savanes aux forêts tropicales. Academie des Sciences, Paris. Comptes Rendus 187:977–999. 1928.

18. Cook, O. F. Vegetation affected by agriculture in Central America. U.S. Department of Agriculture. Bureau of Plant Science Industry Bulletin No. 145. 1909. 30 p.

19. Coster, C. Bovengrondsche afterooming en exosie op Java. Tectona 31:613–728. 1938.

20. Ellis, B. G. Genesis of a tropical red soil. Journal of Soil Science 3:52–62. 1952.

21. Forestry nursery surface temperatures. Malayan Forester 14:157–159. 1951.

22. Freise, F. W. Beobachtungen über den Verbleib von Niederschlägen im Urwald und der Einfluss von Waldbestand auf den Wasserhaushalt der Umgebung. Forstwissentschaftliches Centralblatt 56:231–245. 1934.

23. ———— Untersuchungen über die Folgen der Brandwirtschaft aus tropischen Boden. Tropenpflanzer 42:1–22. 1939.

24. Frith, A. C. No man's land. Empire Forestry Review 34:179–187. 1955.

25. Gilbert, G. and Focan, A. De la nécessité d'une nouvelle orientation dans la politique agricole congolaise. Institut Nationale pour l'Etude Agronomique du Congo Belge. Semaine Agricole du Yangambi. Comptes Rendus 1:152–178. 1947.

26. Grasse, P. P. Termites et sols tropicaux. Revue Internationale de Botanique Appliquée et d'Agriculture Tropicale 30:549–554. 1950.

27. Grisebach, A. Die Vegetation der Erde nach ihrer klimatischen Anordnung. 2nd. ed. Leipzig, Wilhelm Engelman, 1884. 2 vols.

28. Heinzelin, J. De. Observations sur la génèse des nappes de gravats dans les sols tropicaux. Institut National pour l'Etude Agronomique du Congo Belge. Serie Scientifique No. 64. 1955. 37 p.

29. Institut National pour l'Etude Agronomique du Congo Belge. Rapport Annuel pour l'exercice 1948:42–46. 1949.

30. Jenny, H. Causes of the high nitrogen and organic matter content of certain tropical soils. Soil Science 69:63–69. 1950.

31. Joachim, A. W. R. and Kandiah, S. Studies on Ceylon soils. XVI. The chemical and physical characteristics of soils of adjacent contrasting vegetation formations. Tropical Agriculturist (Ceylon) 98 (2) :15–30. 1942.

32. Kellogg, C. E. and Davol, F. D. An exploratory study of soil groups in the Belgian Congo. Institut National pour l'Etude Agronomique du Congo Belge. Serie Scientifique No. 46. 1949. 73 p.

33. Kiener, P. Contribución al estudio de los suelos de la Guayana Venezolana. Mérida, Venezuela. Universidad de los Andes. Facultad de Ingenieria Forestal. Boletín 1 (3) :5–12. 1954.

34. Lanjouw, J. Studies on the vegetation of the Suriname savannas and swamps. Mededeelingen van het Botanisch Museum en Herbarium van de Rijks-universiteit te Ultrecht 33:823–851. 1936.

35. Lutz, H. J. and Chandler, Jr., R. F. Forest soils. New York, John Wiley & Sons, 1946. xi, 514 p.

36. Maignieu R. Sols à bananier de la région de Kindia (Guinée française). Agronomie Tropicale 10:60–78. 1955.

37. Mesure de l'humidité. Institut National pour l'Etude Agronomique du Congo Belge. Division d'Agrologie. Rapport-Annuel pour l'Exercice 1950:50–52. 1951.

38. Michelmore, A. P. G. Observations on tropical African grasslands. Journal of Ecology 27:282–312. 1939.

39. Mohr, E. C. J. and Baren, F. A. Van. Tropical soils. New York, Interscience Publications, 1954. 497 p.

40. Myers, J. G. Savannah and forest vegetation of the interior Guiana plateau. Journal of Ecology 24:162–184. 1936.

41. Nye, P. H. Some soil forming processes in the humid tropics. Journal of Soil Science 6:51–83. 1955.

42. Petterssen, S. Introduction to meteorology. New York, McGraw-Hill Book Co., 1941. ix, 236 p.

43. Rawitscher, F. The water economy of vegetation of the campos cerrados in southern Brazil. Journal of Ecology 36:237–268. 1948.

44. Richards, P. W. The tropical rain forest: an ecological study. Cambridge, University Press, 1952. xviii, 450 p.

45. Rosevear, D. R. Soil changes in Enugu plantations. (Abs.) Farm and Forest 3:41. 1942.

46. Saint Hilaire, M. A. De. Tableau de la végétation primitive dans de la province de Minas Gerais. Extrait des Annales de Sciences Naturelles, Cahier de Septembre, 1831.

47. Schnell, R. La forêt dense. Introduction à l'étude botanique de la region forestière de l'Afrique Occidentale avez clef de determination pour les principales espèces arborescentes. Paris, Paul Chevalier, 1950. vii, 330 p.

48. Shantz, H. L. The place of grasslands in earth's cover of vegetation. Ecology 35:143–145. 1954.

49. ———— The use of fire as a tool in the management of the brush ranges in California. California, Department of Natural Resources, Division of Forestry, 1947. 156 p.

50. Schimper, A. F. W. Plant geography upon a physiological basis. Oxford, Clarendon press, 1903. xxx, 839 p.

51. Sudres, A. La dégradation des sols au Foutah Djalon. Agronomie Tropicale 2:227–246. 1947.

52. Thomas, R. De la dégradation du sol, de la nécessité de sa conservation et de la possibilité d'une certaine régéneration. Bulletin Agricole du Congo Belge 32:714–755. 1941.

53. *Turner, M. R. and Veillon, J. P. Estudio de las zonas forestales del Estado Portuguesa. Caracas, Venezuelas, Ministerio de Agricultura, Departamento de Divulgación Agropecuaria, 1949. 65 p.*

54. *Waegeman, G. Introduction a l'étude de la latérisation et des laterites du centre africain. Bulletin Agricole du Congo Belge 42:13–56. 1951.*

55. *Waibel, L. Vegetation and land use in the planalto central of Brazil. Geographical Review 38:529–554. 1948.*

56. *Waltson, A. B., Barnard, R. C. and Wyatt-Smith, J. Silviculture of lowland dipterocarp forest in Malaya. Unsylva 7:19–23. 1953.*

Two types of ecosystems

13

CLIFFORD GEERTZ

In this selection from Clifford Geertz' innovative book, Agricultural Involution, *comparative analysis is given to two diverse modes of ecologic adaption. Though the context for this particular comparison is Inner versus Outer Indonesia, the uses of the land and the associated demographic patterns generated by these two systems occur throughout the tropical and subtropical world.*

This selection also suggests the close relationship between cultural geography, anthropology, and ecology. Geertz has turned to a number of geographical works in the assessment he makes of both the swidden and the sawah agricultural systems. In the same way, numerous geographers make use of Geertz' observations and conclusions regarding these ecologic adaptations.

Swidden

As Conklin has pointed out, much of the inadequate treatment swidden agriculture has received in the literature is a result of the fact that characterizations of it have tended to be negatively phrased.[1] Thus, Gourou outlines as

its four most distinctive features: (1) it is practiced on very poor tropical soils; (2) it repre-

sents an elementary agricultural technique which utilizes no tool except the axe; (3) it is marked by a low density of population; and (4) it involves a low level of consumption.[2] Similarly, Pelzer says that it is marked by a lack of tillage, less labor input than other methods of cultivation, the nonutilization of draft animals and manuring, and the absence of a concept of private landownership.[3] For Dobby, it represents "a special stage in the evolution from hunting and food gathering to sedentary farming," this specialness evidently consisting of such null traits as nonrelation to pastoral pursuits and the production of very little which is of trading or commercial significance.[4] And for many, by far its most outstanding feature is that singled out by Spate—namely, that its practice is "attended by serious deforestation and soil erosion."[5] Aside from the fact that most of these depreciatory statements are dubious as unqualified generalizations (and a few are simply incorrect), they are not of much help in understanding how swidden farming systems work.

In ecological terms, the most distinctive positive characteristic of swidden agriculture (and

Clifford Geertz, *Agricultural Involution: The Process of Ecological Change in Indonesia* (Berkeley: University of California Press, 1966), 15–32.

[1] Conklin, 1957, p. 149. For full bibliographic citations for all notes in this selection, see Geertz's book.)

[2] Gourou, 1956.

[3] Pelzer, 1945, pp. 16 ff.

[4] Dobby, 1954, pp. 347–349.

[5] Spate, 1945, p. 527, quoted in Leach, 1954, p. 22.

the characteristic most in contrast to wet-rice agriculture) is that it is integrated into and, when genuinely adaptive, maintains the general structure of the pre-existing natural ecosystem into which it is projected, rather than creating and sustaining one organized along novel lines and displaying novel dynamics. In the tropics, to which, for reasons we may postpone considering, this form of cultivation is today largely confined, the systemic congruity between the biotic community man artificially establishes on his swidden plot and that which exists there in stable climax independent of his interference (in the main, some variety of tropical forest) is striking. Any form of agriculture represents an effort to alter a given ecosystem in such a way as to increase the flow of energy to man: but a wet-rice terrace accomplishes this through a bold reworking of the natural landscape; a swidden through a canny imitation of it.

The first systemic characteristic in which a swidden plot simulates a tropical forest is in degree of generalization. By a generalized ecosystem is meant one in which a great variety of species exists, so that the energy produced by the system is distributed among a relatively large number of different species, each of which is represented by a relatively small number of individuals. If, on the contrary, the system is one with a relatively small number of species, each of which is represented by a relatively large number of individuals, it is said to be specialized. Put somewhat more technically, if the ratio between number of species and number of organisms in a biotic community is called its *diversity index,* then a generalized ecosystem is one characterized by a community with a high diversity index, a specialized one by a community with a low diversity index. Natural communities tend to vary widely in their degree of generalization, or the size of their diversity index: a tropical forest, and in particular a rain forest, is a very generalized, very diverse community, with an enormous variety of plant and animal species sporadically represented; a tundra is characterized by a very specialized, uniform community, with relatively few species but, at least in the subarctic, a large number of clustered individuals.[6]

Much of the most effective human utilization

of the natural habitat consists of changing generalized communities into more specialized ones, as when natural ponds containing a wide variety of green plants, aquatic animals, and fishes are transformed into managed ones in which the number of types of primary plant producers is sharply reduced to those which will support a few select types of fish edible by man. The rice terrace, which can, in these terms, be viewed as a sort of slowly drained, managed pond focused on an edible plant, is an outstanding example of artificially created specialization. The reverse process, increased generalization, also occurs, of course, as when man introduces into a temperate grassland area (for example, the American prairie) a wide variety of interrelated domestic plants and animals, which, though they constitute a much more diverse community than that indigenous to the area, nonetheless prove to be viable within it.

Still other human adaptations, however, attempt to utilize the habitat not through altering its diversity index, but through more or less maintaining its over-all pattern of composition while changing selected items of its content; that is, by substituting certain humanly preferred species for others in functional roles ("niches") within the pre-existing biotic community. This is not to say that such adaptations do not seriously alter the indigenous ecosystem (as, in a gross sense, most hunting and gathering adaptations do not), or that their general effect on the balance of nature may not sometimes be a radical one; but merely that they alter the indigenous ecosystem by seeking to replace it with a system which, although some of its concrete elements are different, is similar to it in form, rather than by a system significantly more specialized or more generalized. Large-scale cattle herding during the nineteenth century on the previously buffalo-dominated southern and western plains is an example of this type of adaptation within a specialized system. Swidden agriculture is certainly an example of it within a generalized one.

The extraordinarily high diversity index of the tropical forest, the kind of natural climax community which still characterizes the bulk of Outer Indonesia, has already been mentioned. Though there are probably more floral species in this region than any other of comparable size in the world (van Steenis has estimated

---

[6] These concepts are taken from Odum, 1959, pp. ii, 50–51, 77, 281–283, and 435–437.

that between twenty and thirty thousand species of flowering plants, belonging to about
2,500 families, can be found in the archipelago), continuous stands of trees or other
plants are rare, and the occurrence of as many
as thirty different species of trees within a hundred square yards is not at all uncommon.[7]
Similarly, on about a three-acre swidden plot in
the Philippines (detailed field studies are lacking for Indonesia as such) Conklin has seen as
many as forty different sorts of crops growing
simultaneously, and one informant drew an
ideal plot containing at one time forty-eight
basic kinds of plants. The people of the area,
the Hanunóo of Mindoro, distinguish more
than sixteen hundred different plant types
(which is a finer classification than that employed by systematic botanists), including the
astounding number of four hundred thirty
cultivates.[8] Conklin's vivid description of what
a Hanunóo swidden in full swing looks like gives
an excellent picture of the degree to which this
agriculture apes the generalized diversity of
the jungle which it temporarily replaces:

> Hanunóo agriculture emphasizes the inter-
> cropping of many types of domesticated
> plants. During the late rice-growing seasons,
> a cross section view of a new [plot] illustrates
> the complexity of this type of swidden crop-
> ping (which contrasts remarkably with the
> type of field cropping more familiar to tem-
> perate zone farmers). At the sides and against
> the swidden fences there is found an associa-
> tion dominated by low, climbing or sprawling
> legumes (asparagus beans, sieva beans, hy-
> acinth beans, string beans, and cowpeas). As

one goes out into the center of the swidden,
one passes through an association dominated
by ripening grain crops but also including
numerous maturing root crops, shrub legumes
and tree crops. Pole-climbing yam vines,
heart-shaped taro leaves, ground-hugging
sweet potato vines, and shrublike manioc
stems are the only visible signs of the large
store of starch staples which is building up
underground, while the grain crops fruit a
meter or so above the swidden floor before
giving way to the more widely spaced and
less rapidly-maturing tree crops. Over the
first two years a new swidden produces a
steady stream of harvestable food in the form
of seed grains, pulses, sturdy tubers, and
underground stems, and bananas, from a
meter below to more than 2 meters above the
ground level. And many other vegetable, spice
and nonfood crops are grown simultaneously.[9]

The second formal characteristic common to
the tropical-forest and swidden-agriculture ecosystems is the ratio of the quantity of nutrients
locked up in living forms (that is, the biotic
community) to that stored in the soil (that is,
the physical substratum): in both it is extremely high. Though, as with the tropical
forest itself, much variation is found, tropical
soils are in general extensively laterized. As
precipitation in most of the humid, rain-heavy
topics greatly exceeds evaporation, there is a
significant downward percolation through the
soil of relatively pure, lukewarm water, a type
of leaching process whose main effect is to
carry away the more highly soluble silicates and
bases, while leaving behind a dreary mixture of
iron oxides and stable clays. Carried to an extreme, this produces ferralite, a porous, crum-
bly, bright-red, acidic soil which, however excellent the Indonesians find it for making bricks
without straw, is of much less value from the
point of view of the support of plant life. Protected to a certain extent by the shielding
effects of the thick vegetation cover, most tropical soils have not developed such a serious case
of what Gourou has called pedological leprosy.[10]
But the great majority of them, having been
exposed to these ultrastable climatic conditions

---

[7] van Steenis, 1935; and Dobby, 1954, p. 61. This
floral diversity is paralleled by an equally great
wealth of fauna: the industrious as well as famous
naturalist A. R. Wallace found 200 species of beetles
in a square mile of Singapore forest and brought
back a total of more than 125,000 animal specimens
from the general Malaysian region. Robequain, 1954,
pp. 38–59. For a general ecological analysis of tropical forest plant diversity, see Richards, 1952, pp.
231–268. More popular accounts, but which include
some discussion of fauna as well, are Bates, 1952,
pp. 175–211; and Collins, 1959.

[8] Conklin, 1954. Other valuable field studies of swidden in Malaysia include, Freeman, 1955 (on diversity, pp. 51–54); and Geddes, 1954 (on diversity,
pp. 64–65). A brief description of swidden-making
in East Indonesia can be found in Goethals, 1961,
pp. 25–29.

[9] Conklin, 1957, p. 147. Conklin estimates that in
the first and most active year of the swidden cycle
up to 150 specific crop types may be planted at one
time or another.

[10] Gourou, 1953b, p. 21.

over very long periods of time, are markedly leached, and thus seriously impoverished in minerals requisite to the sustenance of life.[11]

This apparent and oft-remarked paradox of a rich plant and animal life supported on a thin soil is resolved by the fact that the cycling of material and energy among the various components of a tropical forest is both so rapid and so nearly closed that only the uppermost layers of the soil are directly and significantly involved in it, and they but momentarily. The intense humidity and more or less even distribution of rainfall, the equable, moderately elevated temperatures, the small month-to-month variations in day length and amount of sunlight—all the monotonous constancies of the tropics—are conducive to a high rate of both decomposition and regeneration of animal and vegetable material. Speedy decomposition is insured by the multiplication of bacteria, fungi and other decomposers and transformers which the humid conditions favor, as well as by the multitude of herbivorous animals and insects who are so ravenous that, as Bates remarks, virtually "every fruit and every leaf [in the tropical forest] has been eaten by something."[12] An enormous amount of dead matter is thus always accumulating on the forest floor—leaves, branches, vines, whole plants, faunal remains and wastes; but their rapid decay and the high absorptive capacity of the luxuriant vegetation means that the nutrients in this dead organic matter are reutilized almost immediately, rather than remaining stored to any great extent or for any great length of time in the soil where they are prey to the leaching process.

The role of humus in creating a topsoil storehouse of nutrient materials in colloidal form to be drawn upon gradually as needed, which looms so prominently in ecosystems at higher latitudes, is here minimized; organic materials rarely extend in significant quantity more than a few inches beneath the forest floor, because the nutrients set free by the rapid decay of dead matter are quickly taken up again by the shallow, splayed root systems of the intensely competitive plants. Thus, despite the heavy rains, loss of nutrients due to runoff in this process of transfer is very slight, so that quite marginal additions of energy from outside the system through nitrogen fixing in leguminous trees and adsorption of minerals released by rock decomposition are themselves enough to compensate for it. The climax community, once established, through still imperfectly understood processes of ecological succession, is thus virtually self-perpetuating. By maintaining most of its energy in the form of living things most of the time, the tropical-forest ecosystem is able to prevent any significant escape of energy across its boundaries and to circumvent the problem of impoverished soil conditions by feeding largely upon itself.

Swidden agriculture operates in essentially this same supernatant, plant-to-plant, direct cycling manner. The burning of the slashed plot is at base a means both of accelerating the process of decay and of directing that process in such a fashion that the nutrients it releases are channeled as fully as possible into certain selected food-producing plants. A significant proportion of the mineral energy upon which swidden cultivates, and especially the grains, draw for their growth comes from the ash remains of the fired forest, rather than from the soil as such, so that the completeness with which a plot is burnt is a crucial factor in determining its yield, a fact of which probably all swidden cultivators are aware.[13] A good burn, in turn, is dependent on the one hand upon the care and thoroughness with which the vegetation has been cut, and on the other upon the dryness of the weather during the cutting-planting period. Over the thoroughness of the cutting the cultivators have a high degree of control and, though different groups of swidden agriculturalists, as any other type of farmers, vary widely in their skills, yet their felling, slashing, trimming techniques, as well as their actual

11 This paragraph and those immediately following are based mainly on Richards, 1952, pp. 203–26; Dobby, 1954, pp. 74–84; and Gourou, 1953b, pp. 13–24. However, much remains to be learned about soil factors in the tropics.

12 Bates, 1952, p. 209.

13 For example, among the Mandaya of eastern Mindanao, those cultivating over 1,700 feet where burning is impossible because of the absence of a dry period harvest about 10 to 15 cavans of rice per hectare, while those cultivating in lower areas where burning is possible average 30–35; Aram A. Yengoyan, personal communication. In general, however, the precise effect of firing as a fertilizing mechanism remains to be investigated experimentally, like so much else about swidden.

firing methods, are commonly well developed. Over the weather they have, of course, no control (though they are usually adept at estimating it), and intense ritual activity is commonly directed toward preventing rain, or at least maintaining confidence, during the anxious, all-important few weeks between cutting and sowing. At any rate, the primary function of "slash and burn" activities is not mere clearing of the land (the use of the term "clearing," with respect to swiddens is actually somewhat misleading) but rather the transfer of the rich store of nutrients locked up in the prolific vegetation of the tropical forest to a botanical complex whose general ecological productivity, in the sense of the total energy flow in the system, may be substantially smaller but whose yield to man is a great deal larger.[14]

General ecological productivity is lower because this transfer is less efficient than that which takes place under natural conditions of decay and regeneration. Here, a large amount of energy does escape across the boundaries of the system. Gourou estimates that between six and nine hundred pounds of nitrogen alone go up in smoke in the burning of a single acre of forest; and, despite the utmost shrewdness in judging the weather and the greatest speed in firing and planting, much ash is inevitably washed away by the rains before it can be utilized by the cultivates, fast growing as they tend to be.[15] Further, as the cultivates are less woody in substance than those indigenous to the forest, they do not form a very appropriate material for the technique of accelerating and channeling nutrient transfer through the deliberate production of ash, and so the firing process is not continuously repeatable. The result is, of course, the well-known drop in fertility on swidden plots (rice output of south Sumatran plots is known to drop as much as 80 percent between a first and second cropping), and the surrender of the plot to natural regeneration.[16]

But, despite the fact that secondary forest growth is, at least in the earlier phases of regeneration, notably less luxuriant than primary, if the period of cultivation is not too long and the period of fallow long enough, an equilibrated, nondeteriorating and reasonably productive farming regime (productive in the sense of yield to man) can be sustained, again to a significant degree irrespective of the rather impoverished soil base on which it rests.[17] The burned forest provides most of the resources for the cultivates; the decaying cultivates (nothing but the edible portions of plants is removed from the plot) and the natural processes of secondary succession, including invasions from the surrounding forest within which plots are usually broadly dispersed rather than tightly clustered, provide most of the resources for the rapidly recuperating forest. As in the undisturbed forest, "what happens" in an adapted swidden ecosystem happens predominantly in the biotic community rather than in the physical substratum.

Finally, a third systemic property in which the tropical forest and the swidden plot tend to converge is general architecture: both are "closed-cover" structures. The tropical forest has often been compared to a parasol, because of the effectiveness with which the tall, closely packed, large-crowned, evergreen trees both deflect the rain and shut out the sun so as to protect the soil against the worst effects of the leaching process, against baking, and against erosion. Photosynthesis takes place almost entirely at the very top of the forest, from a hundred to a hundred and fifty feet up, and so most of the growing things (as well as much of the faunal life) reach desperately toward this upper canopy seeking their small place in the sun, either by climbing, as the thousands of woody lianas and other vines, by finding an epiphytic perch, as the orchids and ferns, or by mere giantism, as the dominant trees and the bamboos, leaving the darkened floor relatively free of living plants.[18] In a swidden, this canopy is, of course, radically lowered, but much of its umbrella-like continuity is maintained, in part by planting cultigens not in an open field, crop-row manner, but helter-skelter

14 This analysis is based on the descriptions of swidden techniques given in Conklin, 1957, pp. 49–72; Freeman, 1955, pp. 40–48; and Hose and MacDougal, 1912. For the distinction between ecological productivity and yield to man, see Clarke, 1954, pp. 482–500.

15 Gourou, 1953b, p. 26.

16 Pelzer, 1945, p. 16.

17 Conklin, 1957, p. 152; Leach, 1954, p. 24; and Geddes, 1954, pp. 65–68.

18 Bates, 1952, pp. 200–203.

in a tightly woven, dense botanical fabric, in part by planting shrub and tree crops of various sorts (coconuts, areca, jackfruit, banana, papaya, and today in more commercial areas rubber, pepper, abaca, and coffee), and in part by leaving some trees standing. In such a way, excessive exposure of the soil to rain and sun is minimized and weeding, exhausting task in any case, is brought within reasonable proportions because light penetration to the floor is kept down to a much lower level than in an open-field system.[19]

In sum, a description of swidden farming as a system in which "a natural forest is transformed into a harvestable forest" seems a rather apt one.[20] With respect to degree of generalization (diversity), to proportion of total system resources stored in living forms, and to closed-cover protection of an already weakened soil against the direct impact of rain and sun, the swidden plot is not a "field" at all in the proper sense, but a miniaturized tropical forest, composed mainly of food-producing and other useful cultivates. Yet, as is well known, though less well understood, the equilibrium of this domesticated form of forest system is a great deal more delicate than that of the natural form. Given less than ideal conditions, it is highly susceptible to breakdown into an irreversible process of ecological deterioration; that is, a pattern of change leading not to repeated forest recuperation but to a replacement of tree cover altogether by the notorious *imperata* savannah grass which has turned so much of Southeast Asia into a green desert.[21]

Swidden cultivation may turn thus maladaptive in at least three ways: by an increase in population which causes old plots to be recultivated too soon; by prodigal or inept agricultural practices which sacrifice future prospects to present convenience; and by an extension into an insufficiently humid environment in which the more deciduous forests have a much slower recovery rate and in which clearing fires are likely to burn off accidentally great stands of timber.[22] The population problem has been much discussed, though exact figures are difficult to obtain. Van Beukering has put the population ceiling for swidden in Indonesia over-all at about 50 per square kilometer, Conklin estimates that the Hanunóo area can carry 48 per square kilometer without deterioration, and Freeman calculates 20–25 as the maximum in his central Sarawak region; but it is not known to what degree the various local population densities in Outer Indonesia now exceed critical limits and are producing grassland climaxes as a result of the need for more rapid recultivation.[23] With the population of the region now increasing at 2 percent or more annually, however, the problem seems likely to become overtly pressing in the not too distant future; glib references to Outer Indonesia as "grossly underpopulated" constitute a simplistically quantitative and ecologically naive view of demography.

The fact that wasteful or inept methods may be destructive to the long-run equilibrium of swidden agriculture not only underscores the wide variation in proficiency with which different groups of shifting cultivators operate, but, even more important, demonstrates that cultural, social, and psychological variables are at least as crucial as environmental ones in determining the stability of human modes of adaptation. An example of such a thriftless use of resources by swidden farmers is provided by Freeman who says that the Iban have been less

---

[19] For an excellent description of the concurrent employment by recent immigrant Javanese farmers of an open-field system and by indigenous farmers of a closed-field one in the Lampong area of south Sumatra, and of the essential defeat of the former by the weeding problem, see, Kampto Utomo, 1957, pp. 127–132. Some forms of partial swidden-farming —i.e., where swidden is auxiliary to other forms of cultivation—are, however, open-field systems; while integral systems—i.e., where swidden is the sole form of cultivation—commonly are not. I owe this point to Harold Conklin.

[20] Kampto Utomo, 1957, p. 129.

[21] Gourou, 1953a, p. 288, estimates that about 40 percent of the Philippines and 30 percent of Indonesia are covered with imperata, presumably nearly all of it caused by man. These figures may be somewhat high, however: Pelzer, 1945, p. 19, estimates the Philippine grassland percentage at 18.

[22] A full consideration of the factors relating to the breakdown of the swidden cycle into a deflected grassland succession would need, of course, to consider topographical and edaphic variables, the role of animal husbandry, associated hunting practices, and so on. For such a micro-analysis, see Conklin, 1959.

[23] Van Beukering, 1947. Conklin, 1957, pp. 146–147. Freeman, 1955, pp. 134–135. These various figures are all somewhat differently calculated.

shifting cultivators than *mangeurs de bois*.[24] Located in a primary forest area into which they have fairly recently expanded at the expense of indigenous tribes, the Iban are well below maximum population densities. But they nevertheless seriously overcultivate, often using a single plot three years in succession or returning to a fallowed one within five years, and thereby causing widespread deforestation. The reasons for this overcultivation are various, including an historically rooted conviction that there are always other forests to conquer, a warrior's view of natural resources as plunder to be exploited, a large village settlement pattern which makes shifting between plots a more than usually onerous task, and, perhaps, a superior indifference toward agricultural proficiency. But, again, to what degree such prodigality exists among the swidden agriculturalists of Outer Indonesia is virtually unknown.

As for the climatic factor, the most highly generalized, evergreen, closed-cover tropical forest, commonly specified as "rain forest" is chiefly characteristic of equatorial lowland areas where a marked dry season is absent; as one moves toward higher-latitude areas with a marked dry season, it shades off, more or less gradually, into a shorter, more open, less diverse, and at least partly deciduous variety of tropical forest, usually called "monsoon forest."[25] The delicacy of swidden equilibrium increases at equal pace with this transition toward a more subtropical environment because of the steadily diminishing power of the natural community rapidly to reconstitute itself after human interference. The greater ease, and uncontrollability, with which such drier woodlands, burn, fanned often by stronger winds than are common in the rain forest areas, only increases the danger of deterioration to grassland or scrub savannah and, in time, by erosion to an almost desert-like state. The southeast portion of the Indonesian archipelago, the Lesser Sundas, where the parching Australian monsoon blows for several months a year, has been particularly exposed to this general process of ecological decline, and in some places

devastation is widespread.[26] All in all, the critical limits within which swidden cultivation is an adaptive agricultural regime in Outer Indonesia are fairly narrow.

Sawah

The micro-ecology of the flooded paddy field has yet to be written. Though extensive and detailed researches into the botanical characteristics of wet rice, its natural requirements, the techniques of its cultivation, the methods by means of which it is processed into food, and its nutritional value have been made, the fundamental dynamics of the individual terrace as an integrated ecosystem remain unclear.[27] The contrast between such a terrace—an artificial, maximally specialized, continuous-cultivation, open-field structure to a swidden plot could hardly be more extreme; yet how it operates as an organized unit is far from being understood. Knowledge remains on the one hand specialized and technical, with developed, even experimental, analyses of breeding and selection, water supply and control, manuring and weeding, and so on, and, on the other, commonsensical, resting on a vast, unexamined accumulation of proverbial, rice-roots wisdom concerning similar matters. But a coherent description of the manner in which the various ecological components of a terrace interrelate to form a functioning productive system remains noticeable by its absence. So far as I am aware, a genuinely detailed and circumstantial analysis of any actual wet-rice field (or group of fields) as a set of "living organisms and nonliving substances interacting to produce an exchange of material between living and the non-living parts" does not exist in the literature.[28]

The most striking feature of the terrace as an ecosystem, and the one most in need of explanation, is its extraordinary stability or durability, the degree to which it can continue to produce, year after year, and often twice in one year, a virtually undiminished yield.[29] "Rice

---

24 Freeman, 1955, pp. 135–141.

25 Dobby, 1954, pp. 62, 65–70. Variation in tropical forest composition is also affected by altitude, soil, and local land mass configurations. For a full discussion, see Richards, 1952, pp. 315–374.

26 See Ormeling, 1956.

27 For an encyclopedic summary of such researches, see Grist, 1959.

28 The quotation is the formal definition of an ecosystem given in Odum, 1959, p. 10.

29 Gourou, 1953b, p. 100; and 1953a, p. 74.

grown under irrigation is a unique crop," the geographer Murphey has written,

> . . . soil fertility does affect its yield, as does fertilization, but it does not appear to exhaust the soil even over long periods without fertilization, and in many cases it may actually improve the soil. On virgin soils a rapid decline in yield usually takes place, in the absence of fertilization, within the first two or three years, but after ten or twenty years the yield tends to remain stable more or less indefinitely. This has been borne out by experiments in various parts of tropical Asia, by increased knowledge of the processes involved, and by accumulated experience. On infertile soils and with inadequate fertilization the field stabilizes at a very low level, as is the case now in Ceylon and most of South Asia, but it does stabilize. Why this should be so is not yet entirely understood.[30]

The answer to this puzzle almost certainly lies in the paramount role played by water in the dynamics of the rice terrace. Here, the characteristic thinness of tropical soils is circumvented through the bringing of nutrients onto the terrace by the irrigation water to replace those drawn from the soil; through the fixation of nitrogen by the blue-green algae which proliferate in the warm water; through the chemical and bacterial decomposition of organic material, including the remains of harvested crops in that water; through the aeration of the soil by the gentle movement of the water in the terrace; and, no doubt, through other ecological functions performed by irrigation which are as yet unknown.[31] Thus, although, contrary to appearances, the paddy plant actually requires no more water than dry-land crops for simple transpirational purposes, "the supply and control of water . . . is the most important aspect of irrigated paddy cultivation; given an adequate and well-controlled water supply the crop will grow in a wide range of soils and in many climates. It is therefore more important than the type of soil."[32]

This primary reliance on the material which envelops the biotic community (the "medium") for nourishment rather than on the solid surface in which it is rooted (the "substratum"), makes possible the same maintenance of an effective agricultural regime on indifferent soils that the direct cycling pattern of energy exchange makes possible on swiddens.[33] Even that soil quality which is of clearest positive value for paddy growing, a heavy consistency which irrigation water will not readily percolate away, is more clearly related to the semiaquatic nature of the cultivation process than to its nutritional demands, and paddy can be effectively grown on soils which are "unbelievably poor in plant nutrients."[34] This is not to say that natural soil fertility has no effect on wet-rice yields, but merely that, as "paddy soils tend to acquire their own special properties after long use," a low natural fertility is not in itself a prohibitive factor if adequate water resources are available.[35] Like swidden, wet-rice cultivation is essentially an ingenious device for the agricultural exploitation of a habitat in which heavy reliance on soil processes is impossible and where other means for converting natural energy into food are therefore necessary. Only here we have not the imitation of a tropical forest, but the fabrication of an aquarium.

The supply and control of water is therefore the key factor in wet-rice growing—a seemingly self-evident proposition which conceals some complexities because the regulation of water in a terrace is a matter of some delicacy. Excessive flooding is often as great a threat as insufficient inundation; drainage is frequently a more intractable problem than irrigation. Not merely the gross quantity of water, but its quality, in terms of the fertilizing substances it contains (and thus the source from which it comes) is a crucial variable in determining productivity. Timing is also important: paddy should be planted in a well-soaked field with little standing water and then the depth of the water increased gradually up to six to twelve inches as the plant grows and flowers, after which it should be gradually drawn off until at harvest the field is dry. Further, the water should not

---

[30] Murphey, 1957.

[31] In addition to the mentioned Grist (esp. pp. 28–49), Gourou, and Murphey references, useful, if unsystematic, material on the micro-ecology of irrigated rice can be found in Pelzer, 1945, pp. 47–51, and especially in Matsuo, 1955, pp. 109–12.

[32] Grist, 1959, pp. 28, 29.

[33] For the distinction between "medium" and "substratum," see Clarke, 1954, pp. 23–58, 59–89.

[34] Pendleton, 1947; quoted in Grist, 1959, p. 11.

[35] Murphey, 1957.

be allowed to stagnate but, as much as possible, kept gently flowing, and periodic drainings are generally advisable for purposes of weeding and fertilizing.[36] Although with traditional (and in some landscapes, even modern) methods of water control the degree to which these various optimal conditions can be met is limited, even at its simplest, least productive, and most primitive this form of cultivation tends to be technically intricate.

And this is true not only for the terrace itself, but for the system of auxiliary water works within which it is set. We need not accept Karl Wittfogel's theories about "hydraulic societies" and "oriental despotisms" to agree that while the mobility of water makes it "the natural variable *par excellence*" in those landscapes where its manipulation is agriculturally profitable, its bulkiness makes such manipulation difficult, and manageable only with significant inputs of "preparatory" labor and at least a certain amount of engineering skill. The construction and maintenance of even the simplest water-control system, as in rainfall farms, requires such ancillary efforts: ditches must be dug and kept clean, sluices constructed and repaired, terraces leveled and dyked; and in more developed true irrigation systems dams, reservoirs, aqueducts, tunnels, wells and the like become necessary. Even such larger works can be built up slowly, piece by piece, over extended periods and kept in repair by continuous, routine care. But, small or large, waterworks represent a level and kind of investment in "capital equipment" foreign not only to shifting cultivation but to virtually all unirrigated forms of premodern agriculture. . . .

[36] Grist, 1959, pp. 28–32. One of the primary functions, aside from nutrition, of irrigation water is, in fact, the inhibition of weed growth.

The tyrant: maize

14

LESLEY BYRD SIMPSON

In subsistence economies the peasant class finds itself focusing on the land and its productivity. Ritual, religion, and virtually all of the expression of these universal farmers reflect this fundamental concern for the crop. In this chapter from an excellent Mexican history, Many Mexicos *by Lesley Byrd Simpson, the primacy of land and crop is described. Simpson does not limit his concern for man and the Mexican landscape to maize but graphically points out the other major vehicles of landscape change in Mexico.*

Simpson explains the complex ecological and social systems generated by the axial position given maize. He also explores the notion of an ecologic basis for the flux of the pre-Spanish kingdoms. He has thus written a significant chapter in the literature of cultural geography.

From remote antiquity the people of Mexico have had a common heritage; that is, wherever maize will grow—and it will grow everywhere save in the out-and-out deserts and the water-logged places I have described—their staff of life is the *tortilla,* that flat, leathery, not unpleasant thin cake which is the Mexican's bread, as well as the simple instrument for conveying to his mouth such dripping and delectable messes as bean soup, fried beans, and *guacamole,* this last a paste made of *aguacate* (avocado) and chili, now happily naturalized in the U.S.A. The dry maize is prepared by soaking it overnight in a solution of lime or wood ashes, which removes

Lesley Byrd Simpson, *Many Mexicos* (Berkeley: University of California Press, 1967, 4th edition), 12–21.

the tough outer skin. It is then ground into a wet meal (*masa*) with a stone rolling pin (*mano*) on that curious three-legged washboard contraption known as a *metate.* The masa may be mixed with water and drunk as *atole,* but its principal use is in the making of tortillas, which are baked on an earthenware griddle (*comal*). From one end of Mexico to the other the grinding of the masa and the patting of tortillas is the morning song of life. It has been going on for such countless centuries, and is so thoroughly a part of immutable *costumbre,* that I suspect that the vendors of labor-saving gadgets and those kindly people who would emancipate the Indian woman from her ancient drudgery will not completely interrupt the rhythm of the *tortilleras.* It may be objected that not all Mexicans are Indians; but to most of them (67 per cent, according to the 1960 census), the tortilla is bread. In the cities, to be sure, and wherever electricity and gasoline are available, the motor-driven *molino de nixtamal* now does the work of grinding the maize, but this machine-made product has to contend with a popular superstition that the masa does not taste quite right unless it is ground with mano and metate, and the tortillas patted as God ordained.

This all-pervading heritage goes back to that distant day when the wandering seed-gatherers of the highlands of Central America (or perhaps Peru) found a luscious grass, with edible seeds growing in a single ear. No one has any idea how long ago it was, nor do we know how long the gatherers were content to collect the wild seeds, until one day the accidental sprouting of a lost kernel or two gave some forgotten scientist the idea of planting them. From that moment dates the civilization of the Western hemisphere. The Inca, the Maya, the Toltec, the Zapotec, the Mixtec, the Tarascan, the Aztec, all the numerous cultures of pre-white Middle America, in short, owed their existence to the discovery of maize. *That discovery was one of the most important achievements of mankind anywhere.*

Maize, like rice, wheat, and most other plant foods, was not merely a discovery; it was an invention. The principle of selection had to be thought of before any progress could be made toward the heavy producers we know today; but, once that principle had been established, the long evolution from the wild grass of Middle America to the stupendous cornstalks of Iowa was assured. Those early American scientists, by careful selection, got the wild maize to yield more and more seeds, until it gave a great many more than were needed for reproduction. They also learned that the seeds would keep indefinitely if guarded from moisture, and they stored them in elevated stone bins against the lean months. They brought the seed to the hot country of the coast and to the semiarid country of the Plateau, and made it grow where wild maize had never been. Maize began to take on a certain esoteric or miraculous quality in their minds and became in time the center of the tribal religion. It was the holy grain, the *teocentli* of the Aztecs. Its planting and harvest became the occasion for the most solemn sacrifices of the year, for it was the bread of life, *and it still is.*

The intelligent people of Middle America discovered and invented many other valuable things. They took the small bitter seeds of a species of lupine and from them developed the infinite variety of beans that we know. A small wild squash, under their patient hands, became the pumpkin. A morning glory with a thick root was metamorphosed into the sweet potato. The "Irish" potato, tobacco, "Sea Island" cotton and the ordinary "Egyptian" cotton, a great many useful herbs, the fibers of the maguey and henequen, cochineal, a native indigo, and Tyrian purple (from sea snails), and the techniques of cultivation and manufacture of all these things were Indian discoveries and inventions. Perhaps, if they had not been disturbed, they would have got round to inventing money, interest, time payments, and gunpowder.

Their useful discoveries, however, exacted a price. They learned to depend on maize for their food supply. With the abundant yield of the new grain a larger population could be supported, and, after it had come into existence, it *had* to be supported. The Indians became the slaves of their own inventions. Maize imposed a severe discipline upon her devotees. Land had to be cleared and prepared for cultivation at one fixed season of the year; the grain had to be planted at another, harvested at another. To learn precisely when those seasons occurred forced them to study astronomy, to invent mathematics and an exact calendar. Rain had to be prayed for and gods and priests propitiated with gifts and sacrifices. One break in the eternal round and a community would be faced with starvation or the anger of the gods. No more moving about as in the old free days of hunting and seed-gathering. Surplus food meant that the Indians could now afford the luxury of parasite classes. Warriors and an elaborate hierarchy of priests, artists, poets, scientists, craftsmen, architects, and engineers lived two thousand years ago in the cities of Yucatan. The discipline of maize spread north and south, to the valleys of the Andes and the villages of the Iroquois. In time it might have reduced the people of the whole hemisphere to civilized immobility. And then came the crowning irony of maize: When the Spaniards arrived, to their amazement and delight they found a numerous agrarian population, long accustomed to the sober responsibility of raising food and, after the defeat of their rulers, not unwilling to exchange one parasite class for another.

Maize would brook no competitors. It made ancient Mexico a one-crop country. The reasons are clear. Maize was the single crop that flourished under the peculiar climatic conditions of the Plateau and the lowlands. The seasonal humidity (June to September) coincided with its growing season. It did not require irrigation. As late as 1930 three-fourths of the maize crop was raised on unirrigated land. The weight of this fact will be appreciated after what we have learned about the nature of the terrain and the rainfall pattern. The thoroughness of the tyranny of maize is best illustrated by a few figures. In 1930 more than two million metric tons of maize were produced, or, say, about sixty million bushels. The next two ranking cereal crops, wheat and rice, totaled 365,000 metric tons, and beans yielded some 87,000 tons. In other words, the production of maize was more than four times as great as that of the three other major food crops put together. To state the problem in another way: the ideal diet would include 150 grams of maize a day (under six ounces), but, according to statistics published by the Bank of Mexico in 1945, the city dweller was consuming 565 grams and the country dweller 852 grams a day.[1]

The immense shift of population to the cities, owing to the mechanization of farming, has, of course, during these past few decades changed the eating habits of the country. There are still, however, large numbers of rural folk to whom maize is the holy grain of Mexico. If the ancient gods of rain and fertility have been baptized and made over into Christian saints and virgins, their functions have not materially changed. The local *santo* is still paraded through the fields at planting time, and is vigorously scolded when the rains fail to come. The growing of maize can never be wholly a business for the peasant. *It is a way of life.*

Maize exacts another and more insidious tribute from her slaves. It is one of the most soil-exhausting of crops, and only in the great haciendas and state-operated farms is the soil's fertility kept up by massive use of chemicals. In primitive conditions, which prevail in isolated communities, a plot of land (*milpa*) is good for two or three seasons at most, after which it is abandoned for several years. The preparation of a new milpa is a laborious task. It is cleared usually with machetes and mattocks, and the brush is piled up to dry. Toward the end of the dry season, usually in March, the new milpas are burned over. Immense areas every spring are cleared by fire, and the country seems to be burning everywhere. The burned-over land, enriched by the potash, is plowed and planted after the first rain, and must be kept reasonably clear of weeds, especially in the more humid parts. If the rains come as they should—and they usually do—and if the frost does not destroy the crop—and it usually does not—the maize matures in ninety to a hundred and twenty days, depending upon the altitude, the grain is harvested, and the round is begun over again.

Now, the endless depletion of the soil and the destruction of its protective cover by fire have had certain obvious and disquieting effects. Recent studies have made it pretty clear that slash-and-burn agriculture and its wicked sister, erosion, have been marching side by side in

---

[1] Of late years the agricultural and dietary picture has changed radically. In 1961 maize was still the ranking crop, with 5,500,000 metric tons; wheat, 1,400,000; rice, 275,000; beans, 600,000. The production of maize was still immense, but had shrunk to twice that of the three mentioned. At the same time the Ministry of Agriculture has encouraged the planting of other food crops with notable success, until the diet of Mexico is far less top-heavy in cereals.

Mexico for thousands of years. Leaving out of the reckoning for the moment the white man's contribution to the process (cattle, sheep, goats, the ox and the plow), and his tendency to appropriate the best lands for his own use, it is evident that, as the population increased, more and more land had to be brought under cultivation, which meant that the milpas moved farther and farther up the mountainsides and that the land was cultivated until it was exhausted beyond the point of recovery. Denuded slopes and abandoned fields were then subjected to the intense battering of the summer rains, and what little soil remained was washed down the barrancas to the sea. It is a melancholy thing to see once-cultivated and once-prosperous countryside now thrusting out its fleshless bones in unheeded protest against the vandalism of man. An example is the mountainous part of Mixteca Alta, in western Oaxaca, which four hundred years ago was a heavily populated province, renowned for its high culture and industry. It is today an almost unrelieved stretch of badlands.

The second effect, then, of the tyranny of maize has been the destruction of the soil. That this process is well along in the highlands no thoughtful person can doubt. The pitiful stands of maize growing in pocket-handkerchief milpas on the tops of mountains, or in the cracks and crevices of their naked slopes, and the undisguised poverty of the communities depending upon them, are fierce reminders that maize is a savage taskmistress. To break her iron rule will require an inventiveness, patience, and fortitude as great as those of the ancients who first harnessed her to the service of mankind.[2]

Among the theories advanced to account for the strange succession of Maya "empires" in Yucatan, the most plausible is the exhaustion of the soil. The peaks of Maya culture occurred at intervals of about five hundred years. The intervening depressions were not caused by conquest, so far as we know. The Aztec invasion during the last "empire" in the fifteenth century could hardly have been more than a raid, given the extreme difficulties of penetrating the jungle barrier. It took Cortés and his army,

equipped with steel tools, six months to hack their way through, and even so they were all but defeated by starvation. There is likewise no record of an invasion by water. Yucatan seems to have been beyond the range of the Caribs, the only pre-Conquest people who might have managed it. Gradual exhaustion of the soil, and political unrest caused by the dwindling food supply, may account for the mysteriously abrupt collapse of the Maya state.

The soil of Yucatan is a thin layer of decomposed limestone. Although originally fairly rich, it will raise only two crops of maize before it begins to fail, and the farmer must clear new milpas. Available agricultural land is sharply circumscribed, and the uncontrolled birth rate must have pushed its carrying capacity to the limit within a comparatively short time. Several generations of abundance and expansion were followed by a period of falling production and depression of the subsistence level, until the bulk of the population revolted, emigrated, or died. An "empire" ended.

Centuries passed, during which the decomposition of the limestone and the accumulation of humus created a new layer of soil. Yucatan was rediscovered by its exiled population, and the cycle was repeated. This theory is supported by evidence of massive migrations back and forth. The extensive ruins of Palenque, Copán, and the Lake Petén district, where the earliest "empire" had its beginning, are all indicative of these wanderings. At the time of the Spanish Conquest Yucatan was in the trough of one of its depressions and had been so for about two hundred years.

Maize is probably the greatest but not the only culprit in the destruction of the soil. When the Spaniards imposed new burdens upon it they accelerated the process. They introduced the ox-drawn plow, which may have done as much damage as any other single factor. In primitive times the planting stick of the Indians did not disturb the mat of roots which bound the soil together and retarded erosion. The plow, on the other hand, not only broke up the root binder but created convenient channels for the water to use in its work of destruction. The reader is reminded that a summer's downpour in the Plateau frequently attains the cloudburst rate of two inches an hour. Immediately after the Conquest, the Spaniards brought in sheep and cattle, which

---

2 Quite aware of the urgency of the problem, the government in the past thirty years has constructed vast irrigation systems, mostly in the west and north, and brought millions of new acres under cultivation, with the encouraging results already noted.

bred so freely that in an amazingly short time they had overrun a great part of the country. By the end of the first century of the Spanish occupation overgrazing and the cutting action of hooves, particularly those of sheep, were disastrous. A sharp competition for survival developed between livestock and the Indian population. Horned cattle discovered a taste for green corn and it was virtually impossible to keep them out of the milpas, although the Indians planted cactus fences and killed the intruders. For three hundred years the law courts were flooded with suits for damages.

In this context the story of sheep may be the most important. In Spain for several centuries before the discovery of the New World wool was a valuable article of international commerce. The sheepmen, encouraged by the government, organized themselves into a great confraternity, called a *mesta,* which operated under its own laws and enforced them in its own courts. The sheepmen became a privileged and arrogant aristocracy. It was natural, therefore, that the settlers of New Spain should go in for sheep raising on a large scale. Thousands of grants for sheep *estancias* were made by the Audiencia of Mexico, and the manufacture of woolen stuffs soon became a major industry. The Indians of the Plateau replaced their traditional cotton *manta* with the warmer and more easily manufactured woolen blanket. Indian communities and *caciques* followed the lead of the Spaniards and turned their idle lands into sheep ranges. There was an immense amount of vacated land available, because something like nine-tenths of the native population died off in the first century of the Spanish occupation. By, say, 1600, sheep and goat estancias occupied an estimated area of 36,000 square miles. The tiny province of Tlaxcala was one of the first to be exposed to European techniques of sheep raising and wool manufacture, and the Tlaxcalans soon became celebrated for their skill in weaving, as they still are. Even today, after a marked decline in the wool industry, Tlaxcala has a sheep and goat population of about 200,000 (for an area of 1,500 square miles, more or less), and the land is good for little else.

Another serious cause of erosion was (and is) deforestation. Wherever a Spanish town was built, the surrounding woods had to supply beams for the roofs and charcoal for the kitchens. The reconstruction of Mexico City after the Conquest destroyed the famous stand of cedars (*ahuehuetes*) which extended over the hills beyond Texcoco to the mountains of Tlaxcala. The Spaniards continued the tradition of the old country, which was so thoroughly denuded of trees that a popular saying has it that a bird can fly over Castile and never find a branch on which to rest. Then, every Spanish household (and soon every Mexican household) did its cooking with charcoal. Although its consumption has fallen off considerably in recent years, owing to the increasing use of petroleum products, Mexico City alone consumes some 450 tons of charcoal a day, which means that 3,000 tons of live trees must be fed into the charcoal burners' ovens.

The destruction of the forests by the cities, however, was a small affair in the early days as compared with the ravages of the mines. Shafts and drifts had to be timbered with heavy beams, and all smelting was done with charcoal. Wherever a mining community (*real de minas*) was established, a diseased spot began to appear, and it spread and spread until each mining town was in the middle of something like a desert. As early as 1543 the Indians of Taxco were complaining to Viceroy Mendoza that all the forests nearby had been cut down and that they were forced to make a day's journey to get timber for the mines. The mountains of Zacatecas, the richest of the mining districts, were once covered with a heavy forest. After four centuries of cutting they are now rocky grasslands where the ubiquitous goat has to scratch for a living. The same story was repeated at all the other mining centers of New Spain: Guanajuato, Ixmiquilpan, Zimapan, Pachuca, Zacualpan, Temascaltepec, Tlalpujahua, Parral, and the rest.

Still another cause of soil destruction is the cultivation of maguey (*Agave americana,* or century plant), from the sap of which pulque, the universal tipple of the highland people, is made. The maguey plant requires a great deal of soil. The enormous consumption of pulque has made the maguey the most typical, or at least the most conspicuous, vegetation of the Plateau, where huge estates are given over to its cultivation. The plants are set out in rows, with wide alleys in between, which must be kept free of grass and weeds: The rains descend and the winds blow, and they wash and blow away the soil, until the alleys become gullies and the land is fit for little else but the growing of more maguey.[3]

Meanwhile, the pressure of population on the soil continues to threaten the food supply. The population has tripled since 1910, and demographers see no letup in its advance.[4] The

heartening success of the government in bringing more land into production, with the consequent increase in foodstuffs, has led enthusiasts to predict that technology will always keep ahead of the food crisis. But the numerous dams and irrigation systems, the much-publicized *ejido* (which was to have saved the country by breaking up the haciendas and giving the land back to the peasants), the greatly increased use of farming machinery, improved seed, and chemical fertilizers—all these intelligent measures are defeated in advance by the prodigious fertility of the Mexican mother and the virility of the Mexican male, for whom a vast family is visible proof of his manhood.[5] It looks as though the stage were being set for a Malthusian tragedy. If, as I suspect, the soil of Mexico will one day break down under the intolerable burden of feeding such a huge mass, and the people are eating themselves out of their own house, then the food problem transcends in importance all others. By comparison, the army problem, the Church problem, the school problem, democracy itself, sink into insignificance if the land rebels and the Tyrant has the last laugh.[6]

---

[3] William Vogt, after a visit to Tlaxacala in 1963, reported some progress there in the control of erosion. "The volcano La Malinche," he writes, "the upper part of which is one of Mexico's typically raddled national parks (pecked away at for potato patches, firewood and grazing), is the source of flash-floods that threaten downstream towns, have stripped away thousands of acres of soil, and cut ravines nearly a hundred feet deep. . . . With a minimum of machinery, and an abundance of the very cheap labor available in the Mexican countryside, the soil conservation technicians have treated a section with a series of diked trenches to hold water as it falls, long earthen dams to retard runoff, and a series of semipermeable dams in the many ravines. They report that the flash-floods virtually disappeared in the first year. . . .

"Between Tlaxcala and Mexico City there are considerable areas in two or three hundred acre farms where broad benches have been laid out, and their edges anchored with maguey. . . . Neighboring farmers had been so impressed that the terracing extended over hundreds of adjoining acres" ("Comments on a Brief Reconnaissance of Resource Use and Conservation Needs in Some Latin American Countries," Conservation Foundation, New York, August, 1963).

[4] The pattern of future population growth accepted as most probable by the geographer Jorge L. Tamayo (*Geografía General de México* [Mexico, 1962], 4 vols., vol. 3, p. 448) is as follows:

1970	49,699,000
1975	57,689,000
1980	66,421,000
1985	76,534,000

A simple arithmetical projection of these points

gives a figure of about 100,000,000 by the end of this century.

[5] Arthur F. Corwin, "Mexico Resists the Pill," *The Nation*, May 11, 1964, pp. 477–480.

[6] The whole distressing problem of people and land in Mexico is thoroughly explored by Robert C. Cook, "Mexico: The Problem of People," in *Population Bulletin*, vol. XX, no. 7, pp. 173–203 (Washington, D.C., November, 1964). Further discussion of the problem will be found in chapter 27, below.

Ancient and medieval tillage

RUSSELL LORD

15

This chapter from Russell Lord's The Care of the Earth *discusses several momentous innovations. Drawing heavily on Gordon Childe, Lord points out the importance to man of the domestication of plants and the subsequent advent of urbanism. The rise and decline of the Roman Empire is related to changing technologies of agriculture; paraphrasing the words of Columella, Lord finds the Roman decision to leave farming to the slaves perhaps the significant factor in the death of the Empire. Lord's discussion of both the technology and the theories of ancient tillage practices provides basic information necessary to any consideration of man's husbandry of the earth, whether historic or contemporary.*

Lapses or periods of arrested growth, each extending twenty centuries or more, are discernible at both the far and near ends of the last seventy-century span. These largely inexplicable spells of a general relapse and inertia are bracketed as to dates by archaeological prehistorians and agricultural historians alike.

Having traced the sum of human achievement through 340,000 years, Professor V. Gordon Childe closes his book *Man Makes Himself* with reflections on "the acceleration and retardation of progress." He finds it a matter of wonder that "comparatively poor and illiterate communities had made so impressive a series of contributions to man's progress." During the undated years before 3000 B.C. men made fifteen major discoveries. They learned how to make rude plows, how to drain and

reclaim swamps, and how to irrigate dry land. They learned how to harness animals to wheeled vehicles. They practiced the fundamentals of horticulture and orchard husbandry. These agricultural inventions had been made and in places put into practice during the two millennia preceding 300 B.C.; and of related arts and crafts Childe lists sailboats, bricks, the arch in building, command of the processes of fermentation in food and drink, the beginnings of glazing, smelting copper and bronze, the use of the solar calendar, and elementary approaches to writing and arithmetic. All these, the outcome of inventions of men and women whose names we shall never know, were part of the preliterate heritage of humankind.

It seems apparent that man could make such inventions only when he no longer needed to spend all this time acquiring food.

. . . The First Revolution that transformed human economy gave man control over his own food supply. . . .

In the civilizations which have contributed most directly and most generously to the building up of the cultural heritage we enjoy, wheat and barley lie at the foundation of the economy. . . . The food they yield is highly nutritious, the grain can easily be stored, the return is relatively high, and, above all, the labor involved in cultivation is not too absorbing. . . . The grain grower enjoys substantial spells of leisure, during which he can devote himself to other occupations. . . .

The yield of crops and of herds soon outstrips the immediate needs of the community. . . . The surplus thus gathered will help to tide the community over bad seasons; it will form a reserve against droughts and crop failures. It will serve to support a growing population. Ultimately it may constitute a basis for rudimentary trade, and so pave the way to a Second Revolution. . . .[1]

Civilization, then, is born of and grows on food surpluses. But the easement of primitive conditions and the greater assurances of security breed a further surplus, a human surplus, and this one soon outruns the food supply.

Childe finds that his Second Revolution in prehistoric times accelerated these processes. This "Urban Revolution," as he defines it, must have brought about a sharp "upward kink in the population curve" prior to 3000 B.C. Almost entirely a product of hand labor, it preceded the Industrial Revolution of our nineteenth century by fifty centuries or more. The boom in births and the overload of consumers was in all probability like that which accompanied the later dawning of the Machine Age of Industrialization, when in Great Britain alone the population increased from about 8,000,000 in 1750 to over 16,000,000 in 1800, and 27,500,000 in 1851.

Childe asks why, in the whole two thousand years after that First Urban Revolution, perhaps only four achievements rank with those enumerated above. They are: the "decimal notation of Babylonia (about 2000 B.C.); an economical method of smelting iron on an industrial scale (1400 B.C.); a truly alphabetic script (1300 B.C.); aqueducts for supplying water to cities (700 B.C.)."[2]

Translating these developments into terms of an hour's time-lapse film proportions, it is striking to note that the plow, reclamation and irrigation practices, definite skills in horticulture and grain culture, and the beginnings of animal husbandry were all in the picture during the First Quarter-Hour, and are definitely preliterate in origin.

Childe's initial period of retarded progress extends through the Second Quarter-Hour. His dating of the dawn of literacy, the invention of an alphabetical script, comes into the picture in the thirty-eighth minute, and the evidence of aqueducts, betokening an advance in urbanization, roughly coincident with the multiplication of city-states with a well-established agricultural

support, does not come into view until around the forty-fourth minute of the hour in terms of the clock.

Then the aqueducts and like advances in civilization, Childe reasons, "must have reduced the mortality among city dwellers, and so added to the total load of humanity." Further, the Urban Revolution, "made possible only by an absolute accumulation of real wealth," was forwarded "also by its concentration in the hands of gods or kings or a small class dependent on these. This meant, in practice, the economic degradation of the mass of the population. The lot of primary producers—farmers, herdsmen, fishers—may, indeed, have been ameliorated by the public works, promoted by the State, and by the security regular Government guaranteed. Yet materially their share in the new wealth was minimal, and socially they were sinking toward the status of tenants or even serfs."

All in all: "The Second Revolution seems to mark not the dawn of a new era of accelerated advance, but the culmination and arrest of an earlier period of growth."[3]

Whatever the system, the production of foodstuffs has been and always will be subject to hazards and an unpredictable output as compared with the production of manufactured goods indoors. The distribution of rations in time of need was a device of government that no king or administrator, however absolute in authority, could handle on a strictly business basis and for long survive as master of his kind. Even the slave hunters had to feed those slaves to keep them alive and working.

But there was more to it than that. There was a sense of ethical or moral compassion or compunction, combined with such elementary thrift and sagacity as led Joseph in Egypt to store the yield of the seven fat years against the need of the seven lean years, and to share of the stored surplus with his hungering brothers who had connived against him.

Equalizing the price of grain is another method of distributing agricultural surplus in time of need. When there is plenty and the price of grain is low, the central government buys at the normal price, thus benefiting the farmers. The grain is stored until a lean year, when it is sold at the normal price to the con-

---

[1] V. Gordon Childe, *Man Makes Himself* (New York, New American Library of World Literature, 1951).

[2] *Ibid.*

[3] *Ibid.*

sumers, who would otherwise have to pay dearly for it.

The Han dynasties in China practiced this system of grain storage and distribution during a period roughly coinciding with the height of the Roman Empire. In the Empire, meanwhile, land was concentrated in large holdings, increasingly detrimental to the economy as a whole.

As Brooks Adams describes this society:

> The husbandmen who tilled this land were of the martial type, and probably for that reason, . . . were ill-fitted to endure the strain of the unrestricted economic competition of a centralized society. Consequently their conquests had hardly consolidated before decay set it. . . .
>
> The Latins had little economic versatility. . . . They were essentially landowners, and when endowed with the acquisitive faculty, usurers, . . . at once more subtle of intellect and more tenacious of life than farmers. . . . At a remote antiquity Roman society divided into debtors and creditors; as it consolidated, the power of the latter increased, thus intensifying the pressure on the weak, until, when centralization culminated under the Caesars, reproduction slackened, disintegration set in, and, after some centuries of decline, the Middle Ages began.[4]

In his ten-volume *Study of History,* Arnold J. Toynbee adds to this thesis with his assertion that in Greece and Rome an improvement in the art of agriculture, coinciding with the improvements in the art of war, brought on a general decline. The first technical advance in agriculture—"from a regime of mixed farming to a regime of specialized agriculture for export—was followed by an outburst of energy and growth." But not for long: "The next step in technical advancement was an increase in the scale of operations through the organization of mass production based on slave labour, . . . impersonal, inhuman, and on a grand scale." On the lands of Rome this transition:

> . . . notably increased the productivity of the land and the profit of the capitalist, but it reduced the land to social sterility; for slave-plantations displaced and pauperized the peasant yeoman as inexorably as bad money

drives out good. The social consequence was the depopulation of the countryside and the creation of a parasitic urban proletariat in the cities, and more particularly in Rome itself. Not all the efforts of successive generations of Roman reformers from the Gracchi onward, could avail to rid the Roman world of this social blight which the last advance of agricultural technique had brought upon it. The plantation-slave system persisted until it collapsed spontaneously in consequence of the breakdown of the money economy on which it depended for its profits. This financial breakdown was part of a general social debacle of the third century after Christ; and the debacle was doubtless the outcome, in part, of the agrarian malady which had been eating away at the tissues of the Roman body social during the previous four centuries.[5]

In every land and time of which we have record the pressures and compulsions put upon farmers of small means and holdings by an advancing commercial order have been severe. Virgil pictures the Roman farmer's plight in his *Book of Husbandry,* in which a "small farmer," the shepherd Tityrun, complains:

>   . . . The city men call Rome
> Hath so upraised her head, as cypresses
> O'er limber withies hold pre-eminence . . .
> I pressed rich cheese for the ungrateful town,
> No heavy price e'er filled my homeward hand. . . .
> [Meliboeus responds] Happy old man! Thy farm is still thine own,
> And shall be aye, and great enough for thee,
> Though barren stone and muddy bogrush spread
> O'er wasted pasture. . . .

Of the classic Roman writers on farming, nature, and related subjects, an approximate chronology provides a framework for comparisons with the works of those who lived before Christ and others who came along later. Cato, the Censor (234–149 B.C.), was the first. Varro, born in Rome in 116 B.C., served as Caesar's librarian, wrote twenty-four books of generally shrewd precepts on agriculture, and became rather a large operator on extended holdings. Lucretius, born in 94 B.C., was a poet, philos-

---

4 Brooks Adams, *The Law of Civilization and Decay* (New York, The Macmillan Co., 1896).

5 Arnold J. Toynbee, *Study of History* (New York, Oxford University Press, 1939).

opher, and author of *De Rerum Natura*. Virgil (70–19) was the son of a small landowner. These men, then, were contemporaries, or nearly so, and contemporaries likewise of Cicero and Caesar.

Not much is known of Columella, the ablest and most germinal farm writer of them all. Some say he was a Spaniard who came to Rome before the year 60 of the Christian era, and began to publish later. He described the agriculture and condition of the country some two centuries after Cato, and a century or so after Varro, Lucretius, and Virgil.

In the present century Vladmir G. Simkhovitch has gathered into his collected essays a vast scope of interim compositions on the ground-line decline of the Roman Empire. He notes that Cato's earliest book, *On Husbandry*, practically disregards grain culture and stresses instead crops that draw mainly on subsoil, notably the vine and the olive. By that time, too, a general turning of arable land into pastures had begun, and not long after that, Cato himself, as a country gentleman and investor in farm properties, announced that he preferred to put his money into drainage projects—into new land, reclaimed and fertile. In the same period, when asked what he thought of money-lending, he replied, "What do you think of murder?" Even so, according to Plutarch, "As Cato grew eager to make money he declared that farming was more of an amusement than a source of income."

"Windshield farmers" is what they call farmers such as Cato in the American South and Middle West today. But Cato was a shrewd operator, and some of his blunt remarks on the condition and prospect of arable cultivation in that land and time reflect the realities of the situation more precisely than the bucolics of Virgil. Cicero quotes him: "Cato, when asked what is the most profitable thing in the management of one's estate, answered: "Good pasturage.' What is next best? 'Fairly good pasturage.' What is third best? 'Bad pasturage.' What is fourth best? 'Tilling the soil.' "

Pliny the Elder, looking backward at the beginning of the Christian era, yearns for "those days [when] the land was tilled by the hands of generals; [when] under the hands of honest men everything grew more gladly, since it was more carefully tended." Tiberius Gracchus, in an attempt to limit the holdings of any one citizen, delivered a memorable oration:

. . . The wild beasts of Italy have their dens and hiding places, while the brave men who spill their blood in her defense have nothing left but air and light. Homeless and without a spot of ground to rest upon, they wander about with their wives and children. . . . The private soldiers are called the masters of the world, but fight and die to maintain the luxury and wealth of others, . . . without possessing a single clod to call their own.

Tiberius was assassinated, and his brother, Gaius Gracchus, continuing the agitation for land reform, came to a like ending.

Simkhovitch finds a rise in actual land allotments from 18 acres in the Gracchian era to 250 acres in the Augustinian colony. At the same time grainland had so declined in virility that large operators and small alike preferred to depend on grazing. Recorded yields were dismally low—of wheat and barley, from four to six bushels to the acre, and more often from two to three bushels to the acre, a gain of but one or two bushels over a bushel of seed. Columella, in his third book, advises going over from grain to vines: ". . . for none in Italy can remember when grain increased fourfold."

By Columella's time some of the farm estates that in the time of Cato averaged about as large as the average American farm in the early twentieth century had widened into ranches of thousands of acres. The change was accompanied by an increase in deserted fields. By 395 A.D., Simkhovitch estimates, the abandoned fields of Campania alone exceeded 330,000 acres.

In the preface of *Rome's Fall Reconsidered*, Simkhovitch acknowledges that a "growing insalubrity of the Italian lowlands," with swampy bogs breeding malaria, may have been an attendant circumstance to depopulation, but he argues that the root cause of that was a faulty agriculture.

. . . Rome permitted its farming population to be wiped out, and then tried to make farmers out of idle city paupers and old army veterans. But army veterans or army rabble would not make successful farmers, even on good soil—and as a rule the land assigned to the new colonies in Italy had already ceased to be paying farming land. . . .

The soil of Italy did not get exhausted overnight. It was a long process and many were the stages. . . .

The expropriation of the Roman peasantry, the concentration of ownership in the hands of a few, . . . is also a very gradual process and runs parallel with the process of soil exhaustion. . . . The transformation was slow and constant, and not only agonizing to the people; it was sapping the very life of Rome as a nation, decreasing its population, undermining its morale and convulsing its political fabric, . . . arousing the outcry of the indebted and bonded farmer. . . .[6]

As her agriculture failed, Rome fell. This has become an oratorical commonplace. But is it not quite as reasonable to come at the question from the other end: As Rome failed, her agriculture failed? Civilization is a condition of working interdependence sustained by government, and if one partner is enfeebled, the other will be affected. Also, the cradlelands of modern agriculture were predominantly arid or semi-arid, yet barbaric invaders deliberately destroyed waterworks or neglected to keep the sources and conduits of irrigation and sanitation in working order. These factors may have contributed to the fall of many an ancient civilization.

It is hard to see where the form of government had, or has, a great deal to do with it. The extent to which self-government, through a decent respect of the individual for land that comes into his charge, can be expected to insure a permanence of productivity and national security remains to be determined; but there is certainly no evidence that the slave states of the past did any better in this regard than did states that nourished as best they could free choices and a free spirit. Neither history nor prehistory offers proof or indication that the democracies now must embrace absolutism or perish at source. France has not. Nor has Sweden. Nor Holland. Nor Great Britain.

Reviewing the transition from ancient through medieval agriculture the known world over, we may note, in terms of our hour-long time scale, a general lapse in sound husbandry followed by a sharp recovery of comparatively recent date. The record is mixed, but in the first five-minute sequence of this final quarter-hour, Act IV, *Scene 10,* centering on the lands of Rome from 200 to 800 A.D., a decline from the peak is evident. Throughout *Scene 11* (800 to 1400 A.D.) , the Old World over, we observe little change, save for the worse. The full flowering of a Scientific Revolution in farming will not become greatly evident until *Scene 12,* in the last five minutes of the picture.

And yet, when all has been said as to the faults of Old World ancient and medieval husbandry, compared with our more dashing American record since Columbian times, it must be added that most of the soil of Europe has been brought through to the present relatively intact and in reasonably good productive shape. One reason for this, no doubt, derives from no particular skill and virtue of these earlier farmers, but from their very lack of power and equipment to do soil endless harm. Nor is the climate there, in general, as likely to tear down and move soil off as it is here.

There are indications, too, that in Europe, as later in America, the first waves of farmers passed over the land lightly, practicing a primitive scratch culture that did not vastly disturb the balance of nature; and that whenever an overdose of cultivation on a boom-and-break basis led to widespread abandonment of holdings—this, while bad for the people, may well have been good for the land. It may not even have been so bad for the people and for their country in the long run, as an incessant demolition of topsoil and a fouling of water sources degrades and impoverishes the whole landscape and those who are a part of it. Until quite recently in history there has been no more generally practiced way of restoring beauty and fertility than simply to let the land alone for a spell or permanently, and let nature effect a cure.

The plows of Alexander the Great's time and those of the Romans had not such power to harass raw earth and rip it open to the weather as do modern tractor rigs of iron with blades of steel. In early Britain, even after horseflesh crept into draft use, the invention and use of harness had been so slowly developed that beasts about the size of ponies drew loads by crudely improvised yokes, or sometimes were hitched to light plows and harrows by their tails. More advanced examples of medieval harness put the draw on a garrote strap that choked the horse and checked pulling power accordingly. Horseshoes to firm hooves and

---

[6] Vladimir G. Simkhovitch, *Toward the Understanding of Jesus; and Two Additional Historical Studies* ("Rome's Fall Reconsidered," and "Hay and History") , new ed. (New York, The Macmillan Co., 1937) .

footings were altogether unknown until the eighth century A.D.; and the work-collar, or broad-breast collar, which allows the animal to draw from the shoulders without pressing upon the windpipe, did not come into general use until two centuries later.

Indeed, once this harness was invented, man was on his way to changing the face of the world. Before that, the earth was given a great deal more rest. When scratched-over fields failed to return enough grain to justify reseeding, they were customarily allowed to lie fallow as a stay against further depletion, or to go over to grass. The cultivation of grasses was then unknown. The natural growth that came in was probably thin and weedy, but it did cover the ground; and when herds or flocks were put to graze upon this cover, there is no record of the sort of calamitous overgrazing which, along with the march of the conquering plow, raised dust storms and gritty flash floods centuries later on our Great Plains. Most early European farmers did not have enough livestock to do severe damage to ground cover by hoof and tooth.

The British and most of the mainland farmers of Europe were not, it should be added, operating under as sudden an alteration of torn ground cover as in our semi-arid West. Crude as they were, the early European systems of alternation between tillage and fallow, with general access to grassy commons, provided a reasonable extent of continuous cover; and in the recurring recorded cycles of widespread abandonment the periods of disuse and natural regeneration were often quite long.

Early in the Christian era, in the second of his twelve books *On Husbandry,* L. Junius Moderatus Columella wrote: "*. . . the Earth neither grows old, nor wears out, if it be dunged.*" He goes on to say:

> . . . For land, which, from being all covered with wood, has been lately reduced to corn-land—ought not therefore to be reckoned the more fruitful because it has lain untilled and is younger, but because, being fattened, as it were, with the more plentiful nourishment, which it received from the leaves and herbs, which it naturally produced, during the course of many years, it has strength to bring forth, educate and bring to perfection the fruit that grew upon it. But when the roots of the herbs, which are torn up and broken with the spades, and plows, and the woods which are cut down with an axe, have left off nourishing their mother with their leaves—it follows that the ground being deprived of its former nourishment, grows lean.

It may be that the Romans, Columella in particular, wrote about farming better than they farmed; but there can be little doubt that the principles they laid down and the practices they developed and advocated represent revolutionary advances for the enduring foundation of a conservative agriculture. The best of the Romans knew how to work land and build soil at the same time. They knew how to farm for sustained yield. They developed rotations that included leguminous grasses, such as at once draw nitrogen from the air and store it in the soil as free fertilizer and thrust deep roots down into subsoil to draw up further raw fertility into use. They grew clovers and, later, lucerne, or alfalfa. . . .

The modified earth

GEORGE P. MARSH

16

Though there are passages decrying man's abuse of the landscape in both Plato and Mencius, it was not until the middle of the nineteenth century that serious concern began to be shown over man's casual destruction of nature. In 1864 George P. Marsh published the first edition of Man and Nature, *in which he called attention to the critical nature of the landscape changes which were set in motion by man. Marsh suggested then, as he does later on in this 1885 edition, that man could no longer be seen as only a passive animal, akin to the large quadrupeds, in considerations of landscape modification. Marsh gave full focus to the role of man as a dominant agent of change and destruction of the earth's mantle.*

This short essay, the introductory note to his 1885 edition, focuses on the deterioration of the territory of the Roman Empire and suggests that there is much blame to be placed on man as a careless farmer and woodsman. Though the examples are obviously particular to Marsh's Mediterranean view, his sense of concern anticipates by approximately a century today's disquietude over man as a modifier of nature.

Natural advantages of the territory of the Roman Empire

The Roman Empire, at the period of its greatest expansion, comprised the regions of the earth most distinguished by a happy combination of physical conditions. The provinces bordering on the principal and the secondary basins of the Mediterranean enjoyed, in healthfulness and equability of climate, in fertility of

Marsh, George P., *The Earth as Modified by Human Action* (New York: Charles Scribner's Sons, 1885). 1–7.

soil, in variety of vegetable and mineral products, and in natural facilities for the transportation and distribution of exchangeable commodities, advantages which have not been possessed in an equal degree by any territory of like extent in the Old World or the New. The abundance of the land and of the waters adequately supplied every material want, ministered liberally to every sensuous enjoyment. Gold and silver, indeed, were not found in the profusion which has proved so baneful to the industry of lands richer in veins of the precious metals; but mines and river beds yielded them in the spare measure most favorable to stability of value in the medium of exchange, and, consequently, to the regularity of commercial transactions. The ornaments of the barbaric pride of the East, the pearl, the ruby, the sapphire, and the diamond—though not unknown to the luxury of a people whose conquests and whose wealth commanded whatever the habitable world could contribute to augment the material splendor of their social life—were scarcely native to the territory of the empire; but the comparative rarity of these gems in Europe at somewhat earlier periods, was, perhaps, the very circumstance that led the cunning artists of classic antiquity to enrich softer stones with engravings that invest the common onyx and cornelian with a worth surpassing, in cultivated eyes, the lustre of the most brilliant oriental jewels.

Of these manifold blessings the temperature of the air, the distribution of the rains, the relative disposition of land and water, the plenty of the sea, the composition of the soil, and the raw material of the primitive arts, were wholly gratuitous gifts. Yet the spontaneous nature of Europe, of Western Asia, of Libya, neither fed nor clothed the civilized inhabitants of those provinces. The luxuriant harvests of cereals that waved on every field from the shores of the Rhine to the banks of the Nile, the vines that festooned the hillsides of Syria, of Italy and of Greece, the olives of Spain, the fruits of the gardens of the Hesperides, the domestic quadrupeds and fowls known in ancient rural husbandry—all these were original products of foreign climes, naturalized in new homes, and gradually ennobled by the art of man, while centuries of persevering labor were expelling the wild vegetation, and fitting the earth for the production of more generous growths. Every loaf was eaten in the sweat of the brow. All must be earned by toil. But toil was nowhere else rewarded by so generous wages; for nowhere would a given amount of intelligent labor produce so abundant, and, at the same time, so varied returns of the good things of material existence.

Physical decay of the territory of the Roman Empire

If we compare the present physical condition of the countries of which I am speaking, with the descriptions that ancient historians and geographers have given of their fertility and general capability of ministering to human uses, we shall find that more than one-half their whole extent—not excluding the provinces most celebrated for the profusion and variety of their spontaneous and their cultivated products, and for the wealth and social advancement of their inhabitants—is either deserted by civilized man and surrendered to hopeless desolation, or at least greatly reduced in both productiveness and population. Vast forests have disappeared from mountain spurs and ridges; the vegetable earth accumulated beneath the trees by the decay of leaves and of fallen trunks, the soil of the alpine pastures which skirted and indented the woods, and the mould of the upland fields, are washed away; meadows, once fertilized by irrigation, are waste and unproductive, because the cisterns and reservoirs that supplied the ancient canals are broken, or the springs that fed them dried up; rivers famous in history and song shrunk to humble brooklets; the willows that ornamented and protected the banks of the lesser watercourses are gone, and the rivulets have ceased to exist as perennial currents, because the little water that finds its way into

their old channels is evaporated by the droughts of summer, or absorbed by the parched earth before it reaches the lowlands; the beds of the brooks have widened into broad expanses of pebbles and gravel, over which, though in the hot season passed dryshod, in winter sealike torrents thunder; the entrances of navigable streams are obstructed by sandbars; and harbors, once marts of an extensive commerce, are shoaled by the deposits of the rivers at whose mouths they lie; the elevation of the beds of estuaries, and the consequently diminished velocity and increased lateral spread of the streams which flow into them, have converted thousands of leagues of shallow sea and fertile lowland into unproductive and miasmatic morasses.

Besides the direct testimony of history to the ancient fertility of the now exhausted regions to which I refer—Northern Africa, the greater Arabian peninsula, Syria, Mesopotamia, Armenia and many other provinces of Asia Minor, Greece, Sicily, and parts of even Italy and Spain—the multitude and extent of yet remaining architectural ruins, and of decayed works of internal improvement, show that at former epochs a dense population inhabited those now lonely districts. Such a population could have been sustained only by a productiveness of soil of which we at present discover but slender traces; and the abundance derived from that fertility serves to explain how large armies, like those of the ancient Persians, and of the Crusaders and the Tartars in later ages, could, without an organized commissariat, secure adequate supplies in long marches through territories which, in our times, would scarcely afford forage for a single regiment.

It appears, then, that the fairest and fruitfulest provinces of the Roman Empire, precisely that portion of terrestrial surface, in short, which, about the commencement of the Christian era, was endowed with the greatest superiority of soil, climate and position, which had been carried to the highest pitch of physical improvement, and which thus combined the natural and artificial conditions best fitting it for the habitation and enjoyment of a dense and highly refined and cultivated population, are now completely exhausted of their fertility, or so diminished in productiveness, as, with the exception of a few favored oases that have escaped the general ruin, to be no longer capable of affording sustenance to civilized man. If to this realm of desolation we add the now wasted and solitary soils of Persia and the remoter East that once fed their millions with milk and honey, we shall see that a territory larger than all Europe, the abundance of which sustained in bygone centuries a population scarcely inferior to that of the whole Christian world at the present day, has been entirely withdrawn from human use, or, at best, is thinly inhabited by tribes too few in numbers, too poor in superfluous products, and too little advanced in culture and the social arts, to contribute anything to the general moral or material interests of the great commonwealth of man.

Causes of this decay

The decay of these once flourishing countries is partly due, no doubt, to that class of geological causes whose action we can neither resist nor guide, and partly also to the direct violence of hostile human force; but it is, in a far greater proportion, either the result of man's ignorant disregard of the laws of nature, or an incidental consequence of war and civil and ecclesiastical tyranny and misrule. Next to ignorance of these laws, the primitive source, the *causa causarum,* of the acts and neglects which have blasted with sterility and physical decrepitude the noblest half of the empire of the Caesars, is, first, the brutal and exhausting despotism which Rome herself exercised over her conquered kingdoms and even over her Italian territory; then, the host of temporal and spiritual tyrannies which she left as her dying curse to all her wide dominion, and which, in some form of violence or of fraud, still brood over almost every soil subdued by the Roman legions.[1] Man cannot

struggle at once against human oppression and the destructive forces of inorganic nature. When both are combined against him, he succumbs after a shorter or longer struggle, and the fields he has won from the primeval wood

---

to travel fifty leagues with their carts whenever they required it; he labored for them three days in the week, and surrendered to them half the product of his earnings during the other three; without their consent he could not change his residence, or marry. And why, indeed, should he wish to marry, when he could scarcely save enough to maintain himself? The Abbot Alcuin had twenty thousand slaves, called *serfs,* who were forever attached to the soil. This is the great cause of the rapid depopulation observed in the Middle Ages, and of the prodigious multitude of monasteries which sprang up on every side. It was doubtless a relief to such miserable men to find in the cloisters a retreat from oppression; but the human race never suffered a more cruel outrage, industry never received a wound better calculated to plunge the world again into the darkness of the rudest antiquity. It suffices to say that the prediction of the approaching end of the world, industriously spread by the rapacious monks at this time, was received without terror."—*Résumé de l'Histoire du Commerce,* p. 156. See also Michelet, *Histoire de France,* Vol. V., pp. 216, 217.

The abbey of Saint-Germain-des-Prés, which in the time of Charlemagne had possessed a million of acres, was, down to the Revolution, still so wealthy that the personal income of the abbot was 300,000 livres. The abbey of Saint-Denis was nearly as rich as that of Saint-Germain-des-Prés.—Lavergne, *Économie Rurale de la France,* p. 104.

Paul Louis Courier quotes from La Bruyère the following striking picture of the condition of the French peasantry in his time: "One sees certain dark, livid, naked, sunburnt, wild animals, male and female, scattered over the country and attached to the soil, which they root and turn over with indomitable perseverance. They have, as it were, an articulate voice, and when they rise to their feet, they show a human face. They are, in fact, men; they creep at night into dens, where they live on black bread, water, and roots. They spare other men the labor of ploughing, sowing and harvesting, and therefore deserve some small share of the bread they have grown." "These are his own words," adds Courier, "and he is speaking of the *fortunate* peasants, of those who had work and bread, and they were then the few."—*Pétition à la Chambre des Députés pour les Villagecois que l'on empêche de danser.*

Arthur Young, who travelled in France from 1787 to 1789, gives, in the twenty-first chapter of his *Travels,* a frightful account of the burdens of the rural population even at that late period. Besides the regular governmental taxes and a multitude of heavy fines imposed for trifling offences, he enumerates about thirty seignorial rights, the very origin and nature of some of which are now unknown,

---

[1] In the Middle Ages, feudalism, and a nominal Christianity whose corruptions had converted the most beneficent of religions into the most baneful of superstitions, perpetuated every abuse of Roman tyranny, and added new oppressions and new methods of extortion to those invented by older despotisms. The burdens in question fell most heavily on the provinces that had been longest colonized by the Latin race, and these are the portions of Europe which have suffered the greatest physical degradation. "Fedualism," says Blanqui, "was a concentration of scourges. The peasant, stripped of the inheritance of his fathers, became the property of inflexible, ignorant, indolent masters; he was obliged

relapse into their original state of wild and luxuriant, but unprofitable, forest growth, or fall into that of a dry and barren wilderness.

Rome imposed on the products of agricultural labor, in the rural districts, taxes which the sale of the entire harvest would scarcely discharge; she drained them of their population by military conscription; she impoverished the peasantry by forced and unpaid labor on public works; she hampered industry and both foreign and internal commerce by absurd restrictions and unwise regulations.[2] Hence, large tracts of

---

while those of some others are as repulsive to humanity and morality as the worst abuses ever practised by heathen despotism. But Young underrates the number of these oppressive impositions. Moreau de Jonnès, a higher authority, asserts that in a brief examination he had discovered upwards of three hundred distinct rights of the feudatory over the person or the property of his vassal. See *État Économique et Social de la France*, Paris, 1870, p. 389. Most of these, indeed, had been commuted for money payments, and were levied on the peasantry as pecuniary imposts for the benefit of prelates and lay lords, who, by virtue of their nobility, were exempt from taxation. The collection of the taxes was enforced with unrelenting severity. On one occasion, in the reign of Louis XIV., the troops sent out against the recreant peasants made more than 3,000 prisoners, of whom 400 were condemned to the galleys for life, and a number so large that the government did not dare to disclose it, were hung on trees or broken on the wheel.—Moreau de Jonnès, *État Économique et Social de la France*, p. 420. Who can wonder at the hostility of the French plebeian classes towards the aristocracy in the days of the Revolution?

[2] Commerce, in common with all gainful occupations except agriculture, was despised by the Romans, and the exercise of it was forbidden to the higher ranks. Cicero, however, admits that though

land were left uncultivated, or altogether deserted, and exposed to all the destructive forces which act with such energy on the surface of the earth when it is deprived of those protections by which nature originally guarded it, and for which, in well-ordered husbandry, human ingenuity has contrived more or less efficient substitutes.[3] Similar abuses have tended to perpetuate and extend these evils in later ages, and it is but recently that, even in the most populous parts of Europe, public attention has been half awakened to the necessity of restoring the disturbed harmonies of nature, whose well-balanced influences are so propitious to all her organic offspring, and of repaying to our great mother the debt which the prodigality and the thriftlessness of former generations have imposed upon their successors—thus fulfilling the command of religion and of practical wisdom, to use this world as not abusing it. . . .

---

retail trade, which could only prosper by lying and knavery, was contemptible, yet wholesale commerce was not altogether to be condemned, and might even be laudable, provided the merchant retired early from trade and invested his gains in farm lands.—*De Officiis*, lib. i., 42.

[3] The temporary depopulation of an exhausted soil may be, in some cases, a physical, though, like fallows in agriculture, a dear-bought advantage. Under favorable circumstances, the withdrawal of man and his flocks allows the earth to clothe itself again with forests, and in a few generations to recover its ancient productiveness. In the Middle Ages, worn-out fields were depopulated, in many parts of the Continent, by civil and ecclesiastical tyrannies which insisted on the surrender of the half of a loaf already too small to sustain its producer. Thus abandoned, these lands often relapsed into the forest state, and, some centuries later, were again brought under cultivation with renovated fertility.

Starlings for Seville

17

JAMES J. PARSONS

James Parsons *writes here of a particular migratory pattern and trapping system developed in southeastern Spain for the capture of starlings. These 3- to 4-ounce creatures are gathered by the thousands and sold for their meat in certain market towns. This reaping of the wind is a highly regional, ingenious example of man's harvest from the earth. Parsons' commentary upon it, mentioning the trait's antecedents which lie well back into Roman times, creates an excellent example of the cultural landscape as a reflection of both the past and the present. One of the article's distinctive elements is the strong sense it imparts of the geographer in the field; one conjures up the image of Parsons with a dozen* pajareros *in the pre-dawn hours, awaiting the setting of the moon in a Spanish cane field.*

One of the more fascinating examples of Spain's inexhaustible cultural diversity and the persistence of its folkways is the large-scale capture and consumption of *pajaritos*, or small wild birds. In Andalucía the species principally involved is the common European starling or *estornino (Sturnus vulgaris)*, come south from Central Europe to spend the winter in a milder climate and to feed on ripe olives and the fruits and berries of the *monte bajo* of the Iberian wildlands. The visitor to the public markets of Seville during the winter months is struck by the abundance of these tiny birds offered for sale in the meat and poultry sections. Weighing little more than three ounces, innards and all, they are piled high on the vendors' counters and, at two to three pesetas (3½ to 5 cents) apiece, business is lively.

To supply the Seville demand they are netted

James J. Parsons, "Starlings for Seville," *Landscape*, Vol. 10, No. 2 (Winter 1960–1961), 28–31.

in amazing numbers on dark winter nights at half-a-dozen widely separated points in Andalucía, Extremadura, and, recently, in Aragon. It is estimated that anywhere from one million to two-and-a-half million of them may be consumed in Seville alone in a season, both as a substitute for more expensive forms of poultry and as traditional snacks that are served in the city's unnumbered wine bars and cafés, where chalkboards proclaim, *"Hay Pajaritos."*

In Seville everyone eats *estorninos* from November to February, when they are in season, yet nowhere else in Spain or perhaps the world are they a significant human food. Even at nearby Cádiz, Córdoba, Jerez and Huelva these birds are seldom seen in the market place. When they are, they are likely to be outnumbered by the sparrows, larks, thrushes, woodpeckers and partridges, all usually taken individually, either for pets or to be marketed as food. Tradition ties the eating of starlings to *Sevillanos* alone, but after centuries of such intensive exploitation the wonder is that the birds continue to arrive each winter in apparently undiminished numbers.

The case against them

If such a mass slaughter of wild things tends to rouse our indignation, it is tempered by the realization that these little birds provide a cheap and needed protein food. In the cold logic of the Spanish countryman the starling is deserving of no more sympathy than a White Leghorn or an acorn-fattened pig. In any case sympathy for wildlife is not one of the stronger Spanish character traits. The starling is not a much loved bird at best and on balance it must be considered a detriment to agriculture, for a large flock may quickly and completely ruin a crop. From a practical point of view it seems

reasonable enough to make an economic resource of such an interloper.

The netting of starlings is the traditional
activity of the men of the white-washed village
of Villaverde del Río, on the right bank of the
Guadalquivir river, some thirty miles above
Seville. During the present century the activity
has been extended from Villaverde to several
distant canebrakes and reed swamps, but per-
sonnel and techniques are from Villaverde, the
traditional town of the *pajareros,* or "birdmen."

In the first months of 1624, Don Gabriel de
Santana, traveling through Andalucía, visited
Villaverde and described the taking of starlings
there in words that would apply almost as well
today.

"At this place," he wrote, "the Count of
Cantillana owns a piece of property which he
rents for 500 ducats a year for the taking of
starlings. These birds are taken with nets on
the dark nights of November, December and
January in a canebreak on the banks of the
Guadalquivir, one-quarter league from the
town, which has the length and breadth of a
musket shot. The fewest taken in a night are
100 dozen, but the night before the pre-Lenten
carnival they ordinarily kill a thousand dozen
and there have been nights when they have
taken 2,500 dozen. They carry them to Seville
where they are sold for 1½ *reales* a dozen, a
single buyer taking all of them."

Villaverde still has its canebrakes where starlings are taken in nets for a single Seville buyer,
and there are others at nearby Cantillana, but
since the turn of the century the starlings have
been flocking here at night in considerably reduced numbers. Still, in a good year, these
canebrakes may still supply more than 10,000
dozen birds for export, while many more are
consumed within the two villages. Local opinion
attributes the decline in numbers of the Villaverde starlings more to the clearing of the
monte bajo of the adjacent Sierra Morena foot-
hills, where the birds fed, than to any overdraft
by the nocturnal netting parties (*cazerías*) of
the past. In any event there are starlings in
abundance elsewhere.

Plumage and meat

Although the starling is today valued only for
its meat, as it apparently was three centuries
ago, there was a time in the last years of the

19th Century, and the first years of the present
one, when its plumage was in high demand as
ornamentation for women's hats. French buyers
came to Andalucía in search of bird skins for
the Paris market. It is said that the meat left
from the birds caught for their skins was offered
on the Seville market at very low prices and
that it is from this time that the custom of
eating starlings, and the taste for them, became
firmly established among the city's population.
As the heavy draft on the Villaverde canebrakes
could not meet the demand, the residents of
that town turned their attention to other areas
where starlings were known to be abundant
during the winter months.

It was then that the present eleven-hectare
canebrake at El Cueávo, fifty miles south of
Seville and just inside the Province of Cadiz,
was first planted, on rolling hill land watered
by two springs where *junco,* or rushes, had
originally grown and to which bands of starlings had nightly come to roost in season. The
property is still known as the Huerta del
Juncal. Men and nets were from Villaverde.
Somewhat later, *cazerías* were begun in a stand
of Phragmites, or *carrizo,* at Aguilar de la
Frontera, Córdoba, and also near Valencia de
Alcántara, Cáceres, where the present canebrake was planted by a citizen of Villaverde in
1928.

A wild stand of *Phragmites* in the Ebro valley
of the far northeast of Spain, near Almacellas,
Lérida, where clouds of starlings come each
winter night to sleep, began to be exploited in
the 1958–59 season for the first time, again by
Villaverde men working on shares. As at Aguilar, the standing water makes the work more
arduous than in the drier canebrakes, but the
product of this new *cazería* has been extraordinary. In early January, 1960, a record 5,700
dozen birds were taken in the net in a single
night, to be trucked south to Seville in a 24-
hour, non-stop run. The yields from Almacellas
may be explained by the newness of the *cazería,*
but the establishment of a second *cazería* near
Zaragoza is being contemplated in view of the
singular success of this venture. In the markets
of Catalonia and Aragon, however, starlings are
unmarketable.

The common cane in which the starlings
roost is a commercial crop in Andalucía.
Planted along irrigation ditches and in other
moist places, it is used as a building material,

for fences, broom handles, basket-making, and in many other ways. The cane from El Cuervo and Villaverde, cut annually at the end of the starling season, has been sold in the Canary Islands in recent years for staking the early tomatoes that, along with bananas, are the islands' principal export. New stands of cane are sometimes planted to attract roosting starlings in areas where the birds are known to be plentiful. In early 1960 I heard of such plantings at Castilblanco (Sevilla), Coto Doñana (Huelva) and Torrejón del Rubio (Cáceres), none of which had as yet attracted sufficient quantities of birds to be worth exploiting. All of the canebrakes now being worked have been planted with the specific aim of developing a starling *cazería*. It would appear to be a profitable business. A cane stand such as that at El Cuervo or Valencia de Alcántara may yield an income of perhaps 600,000 pesetas ($10,000 U.S.) annually from starlings alone. And if the birds do not come there is still the cane to be harvested and sold.

The net or *maquina* used for taking starlings was developed in Villaverde. It was patented in its present form by Señor Manuel Benitez Fernández about twenty years ago, so that wherever starlings are taken in Spain today it is with such a net. Of cotton and linen, it is generally about 100 feet on a side. It can be used only on moonless nights or after the moon has set, for the birds scare easily. In the first days of 1960, for example, a net was unfurled at El Cuervo at 3 a.m. on January 7, and at 5 a.m. two days later, each time within minutes after the disappearance of the moon below the horizon. One or two hours of total darkness seem to be as satisfactory as twelve. Cloudy or rainy nights are especially favored. During the day preceding a *cazería* the net is placed in position, rolled up at the foot of six poles, each about twenty feet high, placed in a line along a trail cut through the cane or reed. Long ropes are stretched taut from each of the six posts to six similar posts on the far side of the tract to be covered. On signal, with the setting of the moon, the net is hoisted and unfurled by a system of ropes. The net, once in place, clears the top of the cane or reed, where the birds are roosting, by two or three feet. It also has sides, perhaps fifteen feet high, reaching to the ground along trails cut in the dense growth. When the net is being opened out, many birds

are disturbed and escape. Hence, after it is in place one side is left open and into this birds from adjacent roosts are slowly driven by the workers, who rustle the cane and whistle in the darkness to move them along. Then the fourth side flap is brought down and the crew retreats to the warmth of an inside fireplace to await the dawn.

Some ten minutes before sunrise the loud whistling chorus of the awakening birds is suddenly stilled and a cloud of starlings arises from the cane, circles, and is off for distant feeding grounds. All except the fortunate ones, seldom ten percent of the total population present that night, find themselves surrounded by the net. As they flutter desperately about, some become entangled in the webbing by a leg or a wing, but most remain in the cane tops. Now a giant net sleeve, some thirty feet long and the same height as the net, is sewn into one corner of the *maquina* with the fibers of the dwarf fan palm, and is supported at its extremity by a tall pole with a short crossbar at the top. Once the sleeve is in place, the workers enter the cane and from the far corner of the net begin to drive the hapless birds toward it. When the sleeve is sufficiently full—perhaps 600 dozen were in it on the first round when I witnessed the operation at El Cuervo—it is collapsed and the birds, now piled twenty or thirty deep, are quietly and systematically dispatched, one at a time, by squeezing their heads between the index finger and thumb. Considerable force is needed and for most workers the task requires two hands. When all have been killed, they are sacked and removed from the sleeve to be spread out on a shaded concrete floor for three hours to cool before being crated for trucking to the refrigeration units in Seville. This operation may be repeated two or three times, or until all of the starlings have been removed from the net. For this work a team of twelve or fourteen men is generally employed most of the day.

A single dealer, Manuel Gallegas Aguilar, holds a monopoly of the wholesale starling market in Seville. As did his father before him, Gallegas owns and operates the El Cuervo canebrake and has purchase contracts with each of the other *cazerías*. From his stall in the wholesale market the birds are distributed in crates to retail outlets. Demand generally reaches its peak during the Christmas-Epiphany season, for *pajaritos* are traditionally a fiesta food among Sevillanos. Although the netting of starlings after the first week of February without special government consent is forbidden, as a measure to insure their reproduction, they generally are available in the markets until early March. Under refrigeration the unplucked, undressed birds may be kept thirty days or more.

Their habits

Perhaps because their principal foods are the ripe fruits of the cultivated olive and the small wild olive, along with the bitter berries of the lentisco, the dark meat of the wintering starling is rather strongly flavored and not particularly attractive to those not accustomed to it; but at least it contains no buckshot. The average bird weighs some three and one-fourth ounces as caught, reaching to three-and-a-half ounces at the end of the season. It takes at least three of them, fried in olive oil, to make a respectable plate. More commonly, perhaps, they are stewed with rice and pimiento as *arroz con pajarito,* a traditional wintertime dish in Seville homes. In this the birds go into the pot head and all.

The daily flight range of the wintering starlings from their habitual roosts is believed by local observers to exceed forty or fifty miles. Their extraordinary navigational ability, which permits them to return to the same stand of cane or reed night after night, cannot but evoke awe in anyone observing the great clouds of birds that descend on these resting places at sunset each night, in rain, fog, wind or fair weather. It is widely but erroneously held that the birds return nightly to their roosts with an olive in each claw and another in the mouth and that in the morning half-eaten fruit and their pits lie thick on the ground at the base of the cane or reed.

On rare occasions a white starling may be taken in the net. When this occurs the bird is always set free, as these are popularly thought to be the guides that bring the flock back at night. Although most of the birds have black feathers specked with white or buff and with green and purple irridescence on the male's breast, some are jet black all over. The latter, known as *tordos* in Andalucía, belong to another species, *sturnus unicolor,* which is in permanent residence, breeding in these south-

ern latitudes. Indeed, the Benítez patent on the net described it as for taking *"tordos ó estorninos."* In Lérida the term *tordo* is often used synonomously with *zorbal* (lark).

European starlings have two main wintering areas, the western Mediterranean and the British Isles. From recoveries of marked birds it is possible to draw a line east-west across the North German Plain dividing the populations with a WSW standard direction, wintering in the British Isles (the northern and western populations) and those with a SW standard direction, wintering in the Mediterranean basin, especially Iberia (the central and eastern European populations). According to Robert Spencer of the Bird-Ringing Committee of the British Trust for Ornithology, no starling ringed in Britain has ever been recovered in Spain or Portugal. However, birds ringed at Helgoland are occasionally taken, indicating the presence of at least some north European representatives in the migrants to the western Mediterranean.

Their origin

That the Spanish starlings are immigrants from Central Europe is abundantly proven by the numerous bands that are taken in every netting operation. Germany is the country best represented by these bands, followed by Poland, the U.S.S.R., Austria, Czechoslovakia, Switzerland, and, more rarely, France and Hungary. There is no systematic collection and return of the metal bands, however, and only a small part of those taken find their way back to their point of origin. Although probably more starlings have been ringed in Europe than any other species, there has been almost no interest in such activities in Spain. I was told, however, that the director of a prominent wine house in Jerez de la Frontera planned to purchase some of the live birds taken in the last *cazería* of the 1959–60 season at El Cuervo for banding and release, thus initiating marking activities at the southern end of the migration route. No comprehensive study of the seasonal migrations of starlings to Spain seems to exist, although the *cazerías* described above would provide abundant and easily accessible materials for such an investigation. It is widely believed that the birds return to the same roosting place not only every night during the season but year after year, perhaps until caught. Yet, there are years of few starlings and years of many; and there are numerous unexploited starling roosts at various points throughout the peninsula. It would be worth knowing whether years of abundance and of scarcity in other wintering areas, such as Italy, southern France, and North Africa, correlate with those of Spain and Portugal.

Starlings do considerable damage in Spain, especially to olives and to newly sown grain fields, and any reduction in their numbers would probably be welcome by the rural population. Yet despite the heavy and continuing drain imposed by the *cazerías,* the 1959–60 season was described by the Andalucía *pajareros* as the "best" within memory. Learning that starlings had become a nuisance in parts of eastern North America, where they were introduced in 1890, the owner of the Villaverde *maquina* patent recently offered his services to the United States government. Instead of taking only a small part of the pestiferous birds from their communal resting places he would take them all. The well-known preference of many American starlings for city halls and office buildings as roosts is but one of several and considerable complications to such a scheme of extermination, but he would like to try.

Their future

It is their geographical localization that makes both the starling *cazerías* and the starling market of Spain unique. Is there anywhere else on earth where 60,000 wild birds may be taken at one fell swoop in a single net? We are reminded of the netting of migrating pigeons and other birds in the passes of the Pyrenees and the Alps, but the techniques are rather different and the numbers involved certainly fewer. However, *The New York Times,* under the headline, "Bird Slaughter Stirs Italy Again," recently stated that 800,000 hunters and 60,000 netters were expected to kill 100 million birds during the year, some legally, others not. Professor Erhard Rostlund, in calling my attention to this, observes that the breeding power of these little birds must be terrific and points out that this netting and killing has been going on at least since Roman times. They still provide an inexpensive and not insignificant seasonal source of protein to the expanding, meat-hungary population of southern Europe, but one wonders how much additional pressure they can withstand. If starlings were as popular a culinary item elsewhere as they are in Seville their story, at least, would be a quite different one.

Between two seas

CHIH-CHUAN JU

18

One of the most practical aspects of the study of the cultural landscape is the consideration of the development of marginal lands. Economic, agrarian, and social factors must be sorted out by a researcher who knows something, not only of the land and its capacities, but also of the dynamics of social interaction within a develop-

Ju, Chih-chuan, "Between Two Seas," *Chinese Literature Monthly,* No. 6 (1965) , 76–81.

ment scheme. This short article from the Chinese Communist periodical Chinese Literature *is an excellent analysis of a developmental scheme created by ambitious commune populations in the late 1950s. The target area is a tidal flat of saline soils and lacking in fresh water. The seemingly simple solution arrived at by the youth of this particular team illustrates the zeal and optimism of groups determined to make marginal land productive, for such inhospitable land has historically bent the will of farmers.*

My destination was the East Sea coast, due south of Maleh Bay, and here I was.

Before I came here I was told that you could walk that eastern coast in the rain without leaving footprints and after the rain a layer of frosty salt soon appeared on the surface. It was barren alkaline land, an expanse of white all year round, white for scores of years. But whether white or black it was still land, a vast tract stretching as far as eye could see. How many farmers it fired with daring dreams!

And twenty years ago a farmer named Li-pen, driven by famine from his native home, brought his old parents and six children here. The landlord told him, "Till this land, and I won't charge you rent for the first three years." Li-pen looked at this vast white expanse, his heart beating fast, his face flushed in anticipation. Three years without having to pay rent! If he could improve the soil a little the first year, in the second year and the third he could do better. Beautiful visions of his six children's future flashed before his dazzled eyes. He was well aware that others before him had failed here. Still he stooped to taste a pinch of the soil, which was salty and bitter. However, he was strong and determined enough to take a gamble on this vast pitiless stretch of white coast. He pulled down his old house and rebuilt it by the seaside. Nearly everyone in his family worked on the land. He sold whatever they had of value to get a little money to buy fertilizer. In a word, he staked the lives and property of their family of ten on this land. He brushed aside all warnings and advice, trusting to his own hard work, convinced that any land warmed by the sun and washed by the rain and dew must produce good crops if only enough hard work was put into it.

The tides ebbed and flowed. In quick succession three years came to an end. The eastern coast was still a stretch of white. The only difference was that a small plot of land bore cotton stems no thicker than chopsticks. Li-pen was reduced to skin and bones. For three years the whole family had had to subsist on the crabs and rhubarb roots which Hai-ta, his fifth son, caught and dug up on the sea-shore.

When the three years were up, Li-pen and his family pulled down their house and moved away. Before leaving, Li-pen gazed at the coast with tears in his eyes and said: "My strength and money are gone, I can do no more. But I'm sure this land could grow crops."

Now a pioneer team made up of young members of the people's commune was farming this stretch of coast. Apart from growing cotton, wheat, melons and paddy on the white alkaline soil, they had raised fish and planted fruit trees. Last of all I was told that the team leader was Hai-ta, Li-pen's son, who had once again rebuilt his house, the only property his father left him, by the seaside. The young folk had set up a new village there.

A flock of white seagulls suddenly took flight nearby and whirred with slanting wings over my head. In front of me glittered a white belt— the sea. I half ran to the shore and there I saw two seas. One with dazzling waves and white sails in the distance, the gulls overhead looking like stars that somebody had scattered in the sky. These faithful companions of all navigators were drifting with wings unfurled from this sea to another: a rippling green sea of wheat. It was early spring. The wheat had not ripened yet. Nevertheless, the field was a sea of green stretching to the azure sky. Clouds were scudding before the wind. The East Sea seemed to be booming: "This land could grow crops." No, it was not the voice of the sea but that of Li-pen and Hai-ta, the voice perhaps of two generations of peasants.

I wanted to meet Hai-ta and the rest of his team to see if they were as husky as I imagined. But where did they live? Was that an island beyond the green sea? No, it was a shelter belt, behind which a mass of peach blossom or apricot blossom showed pink.

In front of the blossoming trees I found the team's headquarters. But nobody was in. It happened to be their day off. The few stockmen who had stayed to feed the animals told me that Hai-ta and the others would be back that evening and led me inside a very small office. I sat down behind a desk by the window, my head touching the loudspeaker hanging on the wall. It occurred to me that this small house might be the very one that had been pulled down three times and rebuilt by the seaside. Through the window one saw the boundless sea. Looking at the green sea in the dusk, my mind turned to Li-pen and Hai-ta. I wondered what magic Hai-ta had that he was able to make the goal for which his parents had vainly risked all they had, including their lives. The green sea became a dark blur and a solemn march struck up, softly but clearly. I found it was coming from the loudspeaker behind me;

the commune was broadcasting the day's last programme of music. Just then, bicycle bells rang outside the gate. The members of the pioneer team were back, Hai-ta among them. A short young fellow with full lips and a lock of hair falling forward over one eyebrow, Hai-ta did not quite fit my conception of him. And I bombarded him with so many questions that at first he was at a loss as to where to begin. After a while he said in all seriousness: "In the autumn of 1958 the Youth League of our commune called on us to organize a pioneer team. More than forty young men volunteered. Later they elected me to be the team leader. . . ." When he started, his comrades listened to him out of curiosity, but soon enough they went to another table and started a game of cards, since Hai-ta's account held nothing new for them.

"When we arrived here, we planted wheat. The next year we reaped an average yield of. . . ." He took out his notebook to check up the figure. He was giving me an accurate, detailed survey when the "battle" at the other table reached a climax. The onlookers were shouting advice, some were even grabbing at cards. The packed office was seething. Those originally seated had leapt to their feet and their places had been promptly seized by others. It was difficult to distinguish the players from the onlookers. A gay party was under way.

It was hard to concentrate on what Hai-ta was saying, but I could hardly drop the subject I had just raised. I asked: "What was your biggest difficulty when you started reclaiming the wasteland?"

"The biggest difficulty?" Hai-ta had no answer ready. Smiling at me and scratching his head he began to think hard. He looked as if this were the biggest difficulty he had yet faced.

"Believe me, two extra batteries will make the sound louder," said one young fellow to another. The two of them were fiddling with the loudspeaker.

"I know how to do it. Just tighten that thing there and it will improve the volume," said a youngster with tousled hair. And no sooner said than done. After a sudden shriek the loudspeaker was silent. Though nobody had seemed to pay any attention to the music before, now that the loudspeaker had ceased to make any sound everybody noticed it. All turned to look at the youngster with tousled hair who flushed in embarrassment. Silence reigned in the room.

"Oh, I know the difficulty." Hai-ta had found

one at last. "When we first came here there was no fresh water. Our porridge tasted bitter."

"How did you get round that?" I asked.

"Get round it? By digging a canal." Hai-ta seemed surprised that I should not know how to solve this problem of water. And he added, "By bringing in fresh water from Maleh Bay. We killed two birds with one stone—got ourselves drinking water and a good means of transport." He spoke of digging a canal as if it were the easiest thing in the world, like building with toy bricks. So that difficulty was no difficulty at all. I asked, "Had you no other difficulties?"

"Of course we had," said a tough-looking young man who had just been defeated in the card game, before Hai-ta was ready to reply. "Soon after we arrived here there was a typhoon and downpour. The straw on our thatched huts was blown off like willow-down. We stayed indoors holding up umbrellas."

"The cooking was the best part to watch," put in another.

"Ha, at that time we had this wretch as our cook." The tough cardplayer patted the head of the lad who had been trying to repair the loudspeaker. "He behaved like the king of all cooks. When it rained he made three men hold umbrellas for him. One for the cooking pan, another for the firewood, and the third for His Majesty's head. Imagine what a lively time we had."

I was so impressed by their youthful, revolutionary optimism that I wanted to spring to my feet and pay tribute to these fine youngsters. But they had talked only about their living conditions. How about the land? How had they made it yield?

"How could it help but yield?" said the tough young fellow quickly before any of the others could get a word in. "Tractors came round the beach and roared up and down the whole farm. When we wanted fertilizer, boatfuls came. Sheep and cattle were grazed here to give us more manure. Now we have all the fertilizer we need, chemical or natural. A small heifer we brought with us then will soon be a grandmother."

Suddenly the loudspeaker came to life again and the first line of the song it broadcasted was: "The people's commune is fine."

"The people's commune is fine." The volume had certainly increased. Everybody cheered. The young repairer smiled, wiping the sweat from his forehead, happiness written on his face. Hai-ta nodded at me, grinning, as if to say, "You see what we are like here. Nothing else to speak about."

Outside the wind was sweeping over the green sea. The wheat was shooting up, the fruit trees were blossoming. A voice seemed to be saying, "This land could grow crops." Another feeble voice said, "My strength and money are gone, I can do no more." Above both these voices I heard the song growing louder and clearer: "The people's commune is fine."

Forest clearance in Northwest Europe

CLARENCE J. GLACKEN

19

There is a Swedish proverb that Clarence Glacken cites which says, "the forest was the mantle of the poor." Not only has the common man traditionally been close to the forest, but he has made substantial use of it. Besides being a source of construction material, fuel, and animals, forests have provided man with lands to grub his swine and browse his herds. Man seems to have seen their ultimate value, however, in reserve farmland. To capitalize on this reserve, man had only to clear the land. This selection chronicles the clearing and use of the forests of northwest Europe during and following the Middle Ages.

The strength in this selection lies not so much in the inventory of the techniques and instances of clearance and the lands gained, but rather the multitude of perspectives Glacken has marshalled to illustrate this process of landscape modification. The range of sources incorporated into just this small section explains why this tome is already noted as one of the classics of the literature of cultural geography.

If monasteries and settlements were to be created, a start in the removal of forest (using fire and the axe or both) and in the drainage of marshes had to be made. The woods of northwest Europe were, of course, infinitely greater in extent, different in species, and finer in quality than those of the Mediterranean, whose trees and scrub, the product of the distinctive Mediterranean climate, had been exposed to destructive activities dating from the immemorial past.

Northwestern Europe in the Middle Ages was a civilization of wood to a far greater degree than the Mediterranean region had been. A substantial part of economic life revolved around the elaborate rights of forest use, with demands on the one hand for clearance to provide the arable with demands on the other to save the forest in order to protect old rights of usage or to prevent torrents and soil erosion. One cannot read the history of the period without becoming aware of the pivotal importance of the forest and its close ties to town and country life. In western Europe, there was the unique combination of an environment requiring great changes for the continuance of civilization there, and a conscious interest in the tools, techniques, and technology necessary for accomplishing this purpose: "L'Antiquité n'a pas eu l'idée d'un mechanisme général. Il est probable que cette nouvelle conception de la technique est véritablement née au Moyen Âge."[1]

The publication in 1931 of Lefebvre des

Clarence J. Glacken, *Traces on the Rhodian Shore* (Berkeley: University of California Press, 1967), pp. 318–22.

[1] Gille, "Les Développements Technologiques en Europe de 1100 à 1400," *JWH*, Vol. 3 (1956), pp. 63–108. Refs. on pp. 65–66, quote on p. 77.

Nöettes' *L'Attelage et Le Cheval de Selle à Travers les Âges* greatly stimulated interest in invention and its relation to social and environmental change in the Middle Ages. Let us set forth his thesis in broad philosophical terms, omitting the technical discussions and illustrations upon which they rest for proof. In the front rank of man's conquests of nature, he says, is his ability to use animal power; controlling and directing the energies of animals like the horse and oxen, in order to use them as draft animals, has been one of the most difficult problems that man has had to solve in his struggle for existence. There is, he continues, a fundamental difference in the use of draft power in the ancient world and in the age beginning in about the tenth century. Animal power in the ancient world was very inefficiently used, the reason being in the method of harnessing animals. Of key importance is a change in the role of the horse. In ancient times, collars of soft leather were placed around the horses' necks in such a way that they pressed on their windpipes, interfered with their breathing, and severely restricted their efficiency and their ability to pull heavy loads. In about the tenth century (dating is by no means precise) the horse began to replace the ox as a draft animal because of the invention of a new, stiff collar resting on the shoulder. The transition, he thought, took place under the first Capetians; he regarded the invention as an immense boon to humanity because he thought the vastly increased efficiency in the use of draft animals had a direct bearing on the disappearance of slavery. This idea has been the most controversial of his findings.

The invention immensely increased men's ability to modify the landscape, making construction, clearing, cultivation, and the transportation of heavy materials over long distances easier.[2]

It is true that inventions were brought in from elsewhere, but a distinction must also be made between the place where an invention is made and the place where it is applied to greatest effect. Water mills possibly originated in the Mediterranean region despite unfavorable conditions for their year-round use; most of its rivers either are very low or dry up entirely in the summer. The environment of northwestern Europe provided much better conditions for the use of this invention. (The water mills of late Roman times are mentioned in the charming verses of Ausonius [died about 395] on the Moselle.)[3] It was an important addition to a civilization in which wood was an indispensable raw material and source of energy (for heating, cooking, charcoal making, mining, etc.), in which the forest was the locale for such diverse activities as grazing, hunting, beekeeping. Recent studies of medieval technology point, moreover, to the so-called Dark Ages as a period of greater technological competence and activity than had previously been thought.[4] Particularly intriguing is the invention and the dispersion throughout northwestern Europe and Scandinavia of the hydraulic saw. To my knowledge little detail is known of the origin of this great invention which was to become so powerful an agent in changing the environment, especially long river-banks.[5] Finnish, Swedish, and Norwegian historians have stressed the decisive changes its introduction brought about in the economic history of their countries. Marc Bloch believed the hydraulic saw went back to the third century A.D. at least,[6] although admittedly the first drawing of the valuable invention is in the album of Villard de Honnecourt (composed about the middle of the thirteenth century); moreover,

---

2 *L'Attelage et Le Cheval de Selle*, pp. 2–5, 122–124. On its relation to environmental change, *AMA*, p. 446. Discussion of the origin and diffusion of this invention and modern critiques of the slavery thesis (including Marc Bloch's) are outside the scope of this work, but see *AMA*, pp. 444–449, and Bark, *Origins of the Medieval World*, pp. 125–135 and the references there cited.

3 Bloch, "Avènement et Conquêtes du Moulin à Eau," *Annales d'Histoire Économique et Sociale*, Vol. 7 (1935), p. 541. Ausonius, *Mosella*, V, 362, and now White, *Medieval Technology and Social Change*, pp. 80–84.

4 See Forbes, "Metallurgy," in Singer, *et al.*, *History of Technology*, Vol. 2, pp. 62–64; Salin and France-Landlord, *Rhin et Orient*, Vol. 2, Le Fer à l'Époque Mèrovingienne (Paris, 1943). Gille, "Notes d'Histoire de la Technique Métallurgique. I. Les Progrès du Moyen-Âge. Le Moulin à Fer et le Haut-Fourneau," *Métaux et Civilisations*, Vol. 1 (1946), p. 89, on the effects of the Norse invasions in bringing in new metallurgical techniques from Scandinavia. See also White, *op. cit.*, pp. 82–83.

5 Gille, "Le Moulin à Eau," *Techniques et Civilisations*, Vol. 3 (1954), pp. 1–15; ref. on p. 12.

6 Bloch, *op. cit.*, p. 543.

the first mention of the saw, in Du Cange's dictionary, is later than the date of the album.[7]

Fire, the small tools like saws and axes capable of making rapid changes in a landscape, and the larger installations like the hydraulic saw, the water mills, the use of navigable waterways on a scale unknown to the peoples of antiquity, to say nothing of the artisans and their techniques,[8] were the technological resources with which environmental change, especially in the twelfth century and onwards, was accelerated.

Why must one regard the forests and attitudes toward them as the crucial element in our theme? Because they were involved in both the need for change and the need for stability. Their disappearance might not grieve either the agriculturalist or the Alpine shepherd; their preservation might be the hope of the lowland shepherd, of another farmer, of the royal or noble hunter. But we cannot identify attitudes with occupations; too much depended on local interests. The monks at one place might favor a clearing; at another, they might oppose any clearing or draining, and ferry people over the marshlands whose waters abounded in precious fish.

The uses of the forest

Attitudes toward forests are derived from the uses—religious, economic, or aesthetic—to which they are put. The old Swedish proverb that the forest is the mantle of the poor suggests its closeness to the life of the ordinary man.

From the Merovingians through the end of the Middle Ages, forests had so many uses that for the moment it is better to consider them in broad categories as sources of food and household needs; for grazing, hunting, and beekeeping; as the locale of small industries and of charcoal making; as valuable primitive areas in their own right. The intimate relationship is clear in the numerous customs relating to forest use, in the alarms heard in many countries regarding misuse of the forests, and in the forests as places of work.

In the period (roughly from the Merovingian through the Carolingian age), the list of the uses of the forest in the old German economy is already impressive—and worth summarizing in detail. The people gathered acorns and beechnuts. They used the broadleaved trees (like the oak and the aspen) and the conifers (like the Scotch-fir, fir, larch, yew) for building houses; the oak, beech, pine, and fir were used for shingling, the conifers for interior finishing and partitions. All woods were burned for fuel. Benches, tables, chairs, chests, boxes, cupboards, were made out of oak, ash, mountain ash, maple, birch, wild apple; humbler people used fir. Owing to a lack of potter's clay in quantity, dishes and kitchen utensils, baking troughs, vats, barrels, dippers, racks, were made of oak, beech, fir, linden, and the finer products, especially spoons, of common maple. Winnowing and grain shovels, wheel rims (fellies), axles, barrows, flax-breakers, winepresses—later, oil stampers and presses—came from the beech; and from the elm, wagons, axles, hubs, rims, ladders, harrows, paddles for the mill wheels. The birch was used for cart shafts and ladders, the privet for spokes, while the roots and the lower end of the trunk of the red beech were made into the tubs carried on sleds. Hoops and bands around barrels and tubs came from the birch and the willow, rope and cord from the bast of the linden. The light alder furnished flailing sticks; it and the conifers, well borers and the wooden conduits. The alder was also used for this purpose and for piles in the swampy ground. From the forest came the wood for the winepress, the plow, the wagon, the stave, the plow handle, the wooden rim of the wagon wheel, the fence. Twigs of birch, through age-old custom, were the brooms; pine torches and glowing chips served for illumination. Dugouts were made of oak trunks, the boat mast of fir, the rudder of beech. From the ash were made the spear and the shaft of the axe; from the linden the shield and boilers; from the yew, the bow; from the alder, bows, lances, arrows, and bolts. Drinking vessels came from the rooty wood of the maple and from other trees. Tannin and various dyes were derived from wood bark; the foliage of various trees supplied litter and fertilizer, and ash leaves were used for fodder. One could get a refreshing drink from the trunk of the birch, food from the wild apple and the wild pear. The linden, ash, birch, alder, aspen, and larch

---

7 Gille, *op. cit.*, p. 12.

8 Gille, "Des Dev. Technolog. en Europe," *JWH*, 3 (1956), pp. 65–66, 91.

furnished charcoal. Resins were in demand for calking household wooden vessels. And the master of the house was laid in his coffin—a hollowed-out tree.

The forest was used for the hunt and the pasturing of cattle and smaller livestock; it was the place for gathering acorns, beechnuts, and berries. When the witty Heriger, Bishop of Mainz (913–927), was told of a false prophet "who with many good reasons had advanced the idea that Hell was completely surrounded by a dense forest," he laughingly replied, "I would like to send my swineherd there with my lean pigs to pasture."[9]

The classification of trees according to their grazing value apparently was an early practice among the barbarian peoples of the Latin West. Trees were classified as productive (*fructiferi*) or nonproductive (*infructosi, steriles*) most likely because of their mast; and the Scotch-fir and the pines were included among the fructiferi in the Law of the Burgundians because their usefulness was equivalent to that of the mast-producing trees.[10]

In the laws of the Visigoths and the Langobards there were detailed regulations about swine grazing in the forests, the German tribes giving less attention to it. There is fuller mention in the *Capitulare de villis et curtis imperialibus* of Charlemagne and in the rules of the cloister of Prüm. During the mast season, the bonded freedmen of that cloister could graze their swine in turn—to each a week at most.[11] In a notice from the ninth century, the number of swine that could be fed with mast in a forest becomes the measure of its size.[12]

Beekeeping was also an ancient tradition. Customary law included provisions for the rights of ownership to a swarm that was discovered, and to a swarm that had flown off and lodged itself in a tree hollow. Beekeeping was important up to the end of the Middle Ages: honey was used as a sweetener and in the preparation of mead, and beeswax was indispensable for illumination, especially in the churches. Barbarian laws mentioned honey and wax before wood among the products of the forest. In France there is a long and interesting relationship between bees and the oak. Swarms of bees were hunted in the forests; the kings of France and the ecclesiastical and lay nobles had officers especially charged with traversing the forest in search of swarms. The desire for bees was so intense that it was necessary to prohibit the cutting of trees, especially of oaks which harbored them. "Au moyen-âge on n'hésitait pas à abattre les plus beaux arbres pour s'emparer des essaims."[13]

The use of fire in clearing and of charcoal in industry are characteristic of all countries and of all periods in the Middle Ages. Firing was a traditional means—often forbidden—of clearing land. Charcoal making was closely related to smelting, to glassmaking. Forests might have, as in the Harz, their tar boilers.[14] Wood or charcoal was used in salt cooking, iron smelting, tar boiling, as in Norway even before the introduction of the water-driven saw. . .[15]

---

[9] Examples are taken from Heyne, *Das Deutsche Nahrungswesen*, pp. 148–151. The passage relating to Bishop Heriger is quoted in part, p. 151, footnote 153. The poem has been translated from the Latin into English by Helen Waddell, *Medieval Latin Lyrics*, p. 161.

[10] Schwappach, p. 46.

[11] *Ibid.*, p. 48.

[12] *Ibid.*, p. 48, footnote 14.

[13] Huffel, Vol. 1:1, p. 5, footnote 1, and general discussion, pp. 4–7; see also De Maulde, pp. 227–229. On beekeeping, *AMA*, pp. 528–534.

[14] Schwappach, p. 166.

[15] Best survey in A. Bugge, *Den norske Traelasthandels Historie*, Vol. 1, pp. 12–14 and *passim*; on the water-driven saw in Norway, see pp. 5–6. See also Sandmo, *Skogbrukshistorie* (of Norway), pp. 48–73.

On charcoal burning, and the role of the charcoal burner

J. E. SPENCER

20

As mentioned elsewhere in this anthology, man's destruction of forest cover by means of fire and the subsequent encroachment of grasses is a well-pursued theme in cultural geography. However, the fire utilized in swidden is not the only forest-destroying human agent in landscape change. J. E. Spencer, in this paper, suggests the introduction of another vehicle for forest destruction: the gatherer of charcoal. He elaborates on the uses of charcoal, the sources for the raw material, and the longevity of this use pattern. Concluding with a series of questions and tentative inferences about the role of the charcoal burner, this paper gives a good view of the processes involved in the creation of a particular cultural landscape.

At some point in time after the cultural control of fire was learned by early man, a subsequent advance in cultural development led to the knowledge of, and the controlled technology for, production of charcoal as a fuel material. When this controlled technology accrued is probably impossible to determine, where it developed first is equally uncertain, and what the first purposeful uses of charcoal may have been is undeterminable. Charcoal remains are found in many of the oldest Paleolithic sites, but there is no way of knowing when the accidental production of charcoal was first replaced by purposeful production of charcoal which, then, became an agent in the furtherance of some specific technologic process. It seems certain that the learned technology of

J. E. Spencer, "On Charcoal Burning, and the Role of the Charcoal Burner," a working paper given at the Toronto Meetings, Association of American Geographers, 1966.

charcoal production far predates the historic era, even though we have no way of dating it precisely. Whether through independent development in several regions, or through diffusionary processes from a single or small number of centers, charcoal burning did become purposeful at an early date, and it did spread almost world wide in quite early time. It is an initial assumption of this paper, therefore, that charcoal burning has been a purposeful fuel-producing activity in most parts of the world to a major or lesser degree for a long span of time.

That charcoal burning continues in many parts of the world today makes charcoal burning one of the historic technologies of importance in any discussion of the fuels and the fuel-producing industries. There is a theme here that could be followed in terms normal to economic geography. Charcoal burning, however, has been an activity through which man has long made an impact upon the vegetative cover of the earth, and it is this aspect which is followed in this particular paper. Charcoal burning is here considered one of the cultural processes having to do with the development of the earth. Much of my long term research interest has been directed toward the identification and understanding of the cultural procedures involved in the human occupation and development of the earth. More specifically, this interest has concerned itself with the origins and evolutionary development of the cultural technologies significant to the occupance, alteration, and modification of the different species of "natural landscapes," which technologies have been important in the creation, development, and redevelopment of particular species of "cultural landscapes." The concern for process has the ultimate objective of understanding a present particular landscape and being able to account for the manifestations of human occupance therein; the concern for process is in terms of a tool and not as an end product in itself. This paper is devoted to the consideration of a particular technology and the general significance of that technology in the modification of the vegetative associations of the earth as one aspect in the development of cultural landscapes. To this end the paper concerns itself with charcoal burning, the uses of charcoal, and the role of the charcoal burner, and ends in suggesting some tentative questions which may be of significance in the creation of particular cultural landscapes.

It is possible to suggest that there are many parts of the earth wherein charcoal burning no longer is a significant matter because charcoal has been replaced by other kinds of fuels. It is also possible to suggest that there are many parts of the world wherein charcoal burning cannot be carried on today owing to the very scarcity of plant materials suitable to the making of charcoal. In both kinds of situations, however, it is possible to suggest that charcoal burning has been important in the past, and that the process of charcoal burning has been one of the procedures assisting in the development of the particular patterns of wild vegetation existing today. In point of fact, it is really only in the regions truly barren of woody and reed-like vegetation in which today the making of charcoal is not possible. The historic pattern of charcoal burning may well be one of the cultural technologies which helped to create particular vegetative associations, or vegetative barrens, which dot the map of world vegetation today. Although contemporary American reference to charcoal as a fuel has reference to charcoal produced from particular types and sizes of wood (such as "genuine hickory lump charcoal" or "briquet charcoal made from oak"), it remains true that good quality charcoal may be produced from an amazingly wide range of plant materials. Faced with scarcity of raw materials of larger size, preferred qualities, and particular types, charcoal burners range very widely in their acquisitonal activities designed to procure suitable substitute materials. The very history of charcoal production suggests that almost any plant material other than leaves and very thin twigs and fine rootstems may be turned into charcoal by the application of appropriate techniques.

The uses of charcoal as a fuel

Throughout the literature which does refer to charcoal it is customary to refer to the use of charcoal in metal smelting. But that, today, activated charcoal is becoming significant as a filter for nicotines and tars in the cigarette industry is just one suggestion that man has used charcoal for many different kinds of purposes. This section reviews some of the historic uses of charcoal in order to broaden the frame of reference for the world-wide consideration of the subject.

One of the primary uses for charcoal has long been for simple heating purposes, with the charcoal being placed in a simple device which provided what may be termed space-heating. We can only speculate, so far, on the origins of the device commonly known as the brazier. In varied forms it was known almost all over the Old World at a very early date, although many of the simpler cultures did not use it until rather late times. A brazier serves to hold a small volume of burning material and it constitutes a portable fireplace or hearth. Charcoal came to be the chief fuel burned in the brazier and, in addition to space-heating, the brazier came to be used for cooking, for religious rituals, and for several other but related uses. Braziers came to be made in large sizes, to hold several pounds of fuel at one time, and in very small sizes, able to hold only a few ounces of fuel at any one time. Whereas the large ones served for space-heating, the quite small ones could be carried about as utensils for the warming of hands, feet or the body as a whole. The historic record for the brazier seems to be related to the Classical Near East, with many illustrations of the specific forms in which it was made. In northern latitudes and in northwestern Europe other forms of fire-holding devices came to be used in time, replacing the brazier, resulting eventually in the built-in fireplace, the fire grate, and the device now termed the stove. From the western Mediterranean to Japan, however, the charcoal brazier has remained the chief device in which to burn charcoal for heating right down to contemporary times.

Space-heating by other and differently structured devices is widespread throughout the region in which the brazier was employed, though not every people used such devices. Such devices were employed to spread warm air or warm water through, under, and around baths, sleeping platforms, or ceremonial halls. The Roman *hypocaust* was such a device, as is the Chinese sleeping platform or *k'ang*. Wood could frequently serve as fuel in these space-heating arrangements, but there were many situations in which banked masses of charcoal served better and for longer periods prior to the technologies employing coal, coke, and other modern fuels.

The cookstove of the ancient world, and several portions of the modern world, is a raised and solid-structured, fire proof unit on which a group of stones, bricks, or a grate arrangement holds cooking pots above a fire. Wood is, of course, a common fuel around the world for cooking, but also very widespread was, and is, the use of charcoal as a fuel, antecedent to the process which produces the modern charcoal-broiled steak. There long have been many cooking operations in situations in which charcoal was much to be preferred to smoky, soot-yielding wood, and throughout portions of the Mediterranean Basin, the Near and Middle East, and the whole of Eastern Asia charcoal still is the preferred cooking fuel when it can be afforded or procured.

The pottery kiln, of course, has been another user of charcoal with a long history. Although wood fuel often served quite adequately to fire simpler forms of pottery, temperatures often could not be raised high enough to fire efficiently some of the more complex pottery and porcelain manufacturers. Coke, coal, and other fuels came late into the pottery-porcelain industries.

Metal smelting, forging, and foundry operations, perhaps, become the first thought in regard to the use of charcoal, but such uses were probably late in comparison with some of those mentioned above. The use of charcoal in the metals industries became common wherever the metals technologies spread, but the knowledge and technology of charcoal burning must already have been common in most such areas.

The concern of this paper is not to bring the uses for charcoal up to date by a cataloguing of the modern applications. Some of the uses for charcoal in the field of chemistry date rather far back in time, and today are wide-ranging in their technologies. It is not likely, however, that such operations ever have been the users of large volumes of charcoal, in the comparative sense. The modern uses of charcoal probably range more widely than in the ancient world, and taken together probably use a considerable volume of charcoal. It must suffice here to suggest that charcoal remains one of the important fuels in the world today, beside having a wide range of uses as an agent, tool, or medium.

The raw materials for charcoal production

Charcoal, essentially, is the carbonaceous residue of plant materials fired under conditions in which an inadequate supply of oxygen prevents total combustion of the raw materials. Dependent upon the temperature attained during the firing process, a larger or lesser share of the volatile constituents of the raw materials will be driven off as gases; some tar-coke residues, a share of the original water content, and a variable share of the other chemical constituents will remain within the carbonaceous residue. Charcoal burning can be carried on with any plant materials having sufficient size and texture that total combustion may be prevented. Generally leafy, fine stemmed, and fine rooted materials cannot easily be turned into useful charcoal, but almost any densely structured materials can be turned into charcoal even though the sizes of the fragments or pieces of raw material are quite small. Twigs and small branches of some of the fine-grained hardwoods can be made into good charcoal, whereas even larger pieces of coarse-grained, porous, and soft-textured materials can be turned into charcoal only with difficulty. Fine-grained and densely structured root materials often make very excellent charcoal. Such items as date pits, olive pits, walnut and almond shells, coconut shell (not husk), and various of the hard shells of the stone fruits can be made into good charcoal. The record indicates throughout the Classical Near East that olive pits and date pits often were used for charcoal burning for specific purposes. The sources for charcoal, therefore, are extremely varied around the world, and the charcoal burner has found innumerable kinds of plant materials in particular regions which are acceptable raw materials for charcoal burning with relatively simple technology and devices. In the modern period, with efficient technology and devices, the range of source materials is even greater than it was in early times.

The simplest of all procedures for making charcoal requires only that a supply of raw materials be piled on the ground and fired. When the fire has attained close to its maximum strength dirt may be thrown over the burning pile to prevent the free access of oxygen to the materials fired, or the fire may be quenched with water. After the pile has cooled the residue will be charcoal of some quality grade, dependent upon the raw materials used and the skill of the charcoal burner in securing a good but incomplete firing. Often a shallow pit provided a more easily controlled firing site, and the dirt removed from the pit provided the cover.

It is not the object of this paper to follow the evolution in charcoal burning technology. The modern vertical-process steel retort accomplishes no more than does a shallow pit, in producing charcoal, although it does handle larger volumes, saves the distillation products, renders out a larger share of the percentage of charcoal (against the volume of raw material fired), and saves human labor in the process. The object in mentioning the process is but to indicate that the technology is so simple that early man could employ it from very early times right down to contemporary time in almost any portion of the world containing sufficient raw materials.

Regionally, and technologically, of course, there clearly developed preferences for particular sources and types of raw materials, dependent upon the use to which the charcoal was to be put. Charcoal made from fir was preferred over charcoal made from oak by the early Greek ironsmiths because fir charcoal burned with an even, hot fire, whereas oak charcoal produced many sparks and required the almost constant application of the bellows to maintain the fire at the proper heat. Certain gummy woods contain volatiles hard to drive off in simple charcoal burning, and these produce smoky fires in later burning, which makes these woods less desirable for cooking purposes. These same qualities, however, early lent a useful aura to the fire burned for purposes of religious ritual. In general soft woods produce charcoal which burns out very quickly at a temperature but little above the temperatures attained by burning wood. The early ironsmiths who counted on case-hardening their forged products much preferred quite pure charcoals containing few volatiles and few chemical impurities, since the case-hardening process involved absorption of the carbon into the molecular structure of the surface skin of the product being forged. The rise of steel-making very greatly increased the demand for high quality charcoal owing to the early technique of carbonizing the iron in producing hard steel products.

Quantitative comment on charcoal production

It is almost impossible to suggest accurately the annual production of charcoal for any particular region in the past, and almost useless to make a quantitative comment on the volume of forest timber turned into charcoal for any one region. Some suggestive notations may be set down, however, to indicate that the volume of charcoal cut out of the vegetative cover for a populated region must have been significant in the past. A pound of charcoal represents close to four pounds of wood by weight, on the average, and it represents about two-thirds of the original raw material by volume. A pound of charcoal burned in a small brazier will raise the temperature in a small room for several hours, it will cook a meal for several persons, and it will smelt about a half-pound of pig iron (the proper ratio is about two tons of charcoal to a one-ton yield of pig iron). To turn such data into a regionally quantitative total, the following somewhat speculative estimates are set down for mid-18th century China, prior to the development of modern technologies. The annual production of pig iron during the 18th century ranged a little below 100,000 tons, with a little over half the volume probably produced with charcoal as the smelting fuel. The annual charcoal requirement, then, might have been about 120,000 tons. The Chinese metal smelters and fabricators working in copper, brass, zinc, bronze, gold, and silver and the fabricators of iron products chiefly used charcoal as a fuel. Many of the pottery and porcelain kilns throughout the country used charcoal as a firing fuel. I suggest a speculative figure of about 300,000 tons of charcoal per year as used in all such activities. The fifty million families then resident in China normally cooked not quite three meals a day, on the average, and from about a fourth to a third of the cooking operations may have involved the use of charcoal. Assuming a total of 40,000,000 charcoal fires per day, using about a pound of charcoal per fire, the annual requirement for cooking charcoal totalled over 7,000,000 tons per year. In north China, of that day, some 10,000,000 families might well have used a pound of charcoal per day in personal and space heating (even the wealthy Chinese never have heated their houses effectively) during a period of about four months each year. This very crude estimate would yield an annual requirement of about 600,000 tons of charcoal per winter. These data, in sum, suggest an annual consumption of charcoal at between eight and nine million tons per year for the 18th century, and it is clear that the domestic usage far outranks that of the metals industries. Even if these specific figures are wide off the mark, the annual impact of the regional share of total consumption upon the wild vegetation of north China would have been a considerable one, since it was a region of slow plant growth and extended agricultural landscapes in the 18th century. In modern China the scarcity of fuel wood for domestic uses is a striking fact, and in many local regions puts a heavy drain upon all forms of plant materials.

The charcoal burner at work

The lonely charcoal burner working deep in a heavy forest is one of the folk characters in the fairy tales of both Grimm and Anderson; the situation reflected is that of northwestern Europe at a time at which the culture patterns, and the landscapes, of northwestern Europe were those of the pre-industrial era. The charcoal burner draws his chosen plant materials from the vegetative cover of a region where and as he can. In a landscape chiefly containing much heavy cover he may be selective and carry out his burning operations close to the sites at which charcoal will be used. As patterns of occupance fill out a landscape the charcoal burner either must scavenge or move his operations to localities retaining much of the vegetative cover. With usage patterns which demand particular grades of charcoal, the cutting of wood for charcoal tends to move outward and away from the occupied landscapes. The process is one of selecting out those kinds of woody materials which can be turned into the best, or the desired, grades of charcoal within a distance range from which the finished product can be transported to its markets. Historically the charcoal burner has moved ahead of the agriculturist, as an advance agent in the broad process of reducing natural vegetation to patterns of tolerated wild growth which marks the developed agricultural landscape.

In heavily forested landscapes of mixed species made up of numerous hardwoods the migration of the charcoal burning sites away from developed landscapes may be relatively slow, but its selective impact through time may be effective. On the other hand, on the dry margins and the arid fringes, in which good charcoal-producing materials may be somewhat scant at best, the migration patterns and the scavenging patterns may require the charcoal burner to work over a large territory. In such cases the selective impact upon the wild vegetation of a region may be very marked, since the selection process in time may well reduce or clean out selected species from the vegetative association. In the short run of time these effects may not seem severe, but when such selective operation ranges for centuries, or millennia, they probably have a marked impact upon the distribution of species in the broad definition of a vegetative association.

It has been fairly well documented for England in the 15th to 18th centuries that the charcoal burner worked through much of the plant cover of the Weald, in the south of England, providing charcoal as a fuel for the iron smelting industries; and that iron smelting gradually shifted northward into the Midlands as the good charcoal sources of the Weald were exhausted. In 16th and 17th century England the charcoal burner competed with the shipbuilder for raw materials to the end that charcoal burning was prohibited within fourteen miles of the coasts and the banks of navigable rivers. It was, in fact, the scarcity of good charcoal and the high prices of charcoal which led to the development of the English coke industry as a source of fuel in the iron and steel working industries in the late 18th century. Northwestern Europe in general is the zone in which the wood-burning fireplace, used both for heating and cooking, evolved. It also is the region in which the closed stove, connected to a chimney to remove smoke, developed. As these devices evolved they replaced the open fire hearth and the charcoal brazier. Northwestern Europe from late Roman times onward burned less and less charcoal as a cooking-heating fuel, but came to employ it more exclusively in the metals industries. This forms a strong contrast to the continuing use of charcoal from the Mediterranean Basin eastward to the Pacific Ocean.

Throughout the whole of North Africa and the Middle East the charcoal burner has had to range widely within recent centuries, leading to rather long distance transport patterns in some areas; charcoal remains a preferred cooking fuel in most of this region, as well as finding other kinds of uses. The charcoal resources of the whole broad region have been steadily reduced to the end that the charcoal burner today often is a scavenger now having an even more emphatic impact upon species distributional patterns. Regional scarcity of good charcoal is not new in the Mediterranean and Near Eastern area for, in Roman Empire times, Macedonia regularly shipped charcoal to southern Greece and to the Italian Peninsula, and the Central zone regions of the empire imported charcoal from several outer sectors; historically many different regions have overworked their sources of charcoal during the period since Roman times.

It is in the populated but seasonally dry, semiarid, and arid sectors of the earth that the long term impact of the charcoal burner may well be a major one in the matter of vegetative change, for scavenging goes as far as digging out roots of shrubs and trees (often producing superior quality charcoal). The removal of rootstocks may have an even more devastating effect upon the vegetative association than does the prevention of reseeding by the cutting of top growth.

Concluding questions

This paper has dealt chiefly in speculative inferences, while presenting certain basic generalizations about charcoal burning as a technological process. The chief thought of the series of inferences is that the charcoal burner, intent upon supplying a widely used fuel material, may well have been one of the chief agents active in the process of deforesting the earth, altering the vegetative association, and creating the broad category of patterns described as cultural landscapes. How important was he?

Around the earth as a whole the causes of deforestation often have been laid to pastoralists whose animals either browse off the plant growth, or whose fires burn off the old growth so that their animals may browse fresh new growth. Timber cutters have been held responsible for a selective role in deforestation in many regions. Shifting cultivators have been accused of the ruination of the vegetative landscape in many regions. The woodcutters who cut firewood to be used as wood fuel have sometimes been accused of a heavy hand in deforestation, although they often have not been highly selective in their operations. And, of course, the sedentary crop growers, interested in cleared fields for their ease of handling and higher productivity, have shared the blame for deforestation. Where does the balance of impact lie among these several kinds of operations?

It should be very evident that no single answer may be given for all parts of the world. Even if the data are inaccurate in specific terms, it should be evident that the charcoal burner of China provided a different market than the charcoal burner of England, and that the total effect of charcoal burning in the two regions must be assessed differently. That charcoal today is the chief fuel used in cooking and handicraft manufacturing in such a region as the Sudan certainly means that the impact upon the vegetative landscape is both significant and differs from the contemporary impact of charcoal burning upon the landscape of such a region as Norway, in which electrification has become highly developed. But what of the impact of the charcoal burner upon the wild vegetation of Norway over the last two thousand years?

In that the charcoal burner normally has been documented as chiefly serving the metals industries, his role as an agent in producing vegetative change, I suggest, has been under-described. In that the charcoal burner often has served the general public as a supplier of a preferred fuel for many different purposes, his role in the creation of cultural landscapes and degraded wild landscapes, over several thousands of years, has probably been more significant than has been recognized. The key question remains, of course, how significant has the charcoal burner been as an agent of modification in any particular landscape?[1]

[1] No formal documentation is provided in this brief and speculative paper. Much of the background material may be gleaned from the two volumes by R. J. Forbes, *Studies in Ancient Technology*, Vol. VI (Leiden: Brill, 1958), and *Man The Maker* (New York: Schuman, 1958). The journal *Unasylva* (New York: United Nations) contains a series of articles dealing with different parts of the world and with the manufacture of charcoal, and various of the forestry journals do the same. Several technical journals deal with modern refinements in charcoal burning technology.

Culture and ecology in prehistoric Africa

J. DESMOND CLARK

21

The level of tool sophistication in preliterate or pre-historic societies is an important determinant of the cultural configuration of that society. In this article from Ecology and Economic Development in Tropical Africa, *J. Desmond Clark explores the various stages of man's early tool making capacities in African prehistory. The cultural concerns become more evident as dissimilar tool technologies lead to varying modes of ecologic adaptation, with consequently differing population densities.*

Clark's interest in "marginal" areas, as well as his discussion of plant and animal domestication, extends the focus of this article to additional themes pertinent to the cultural landscape.

Early man was a hunter and a food gatherer. As such he was entirely dependent upon the immediate resources of his environment—water, game, and vegetable foods—to support life. His manner of behavior, the social and economic structure of his group organization, probably did not show much variation between groups, taking the broad view. He must have resembled a member of recent hunter-gathering groups, though ways of life differed much in detail according to the richness of the environment and the efficacy of the technology being used to exploit it.

Prehistory provides the record of man's steadily increasing ability to make greater and more effective use of the resources of his habitat. At first this ability was little greater than that with which the chimpanzee exploits its environment. Also like the chimpanzee, man was at this time, it would seem, considerably restricted as to the type of surroundings in which he could live successfully.

Although biology knows of several tool-using species—Darwin finches, parrots, sea otters, digging wasps, for example—only the chimpanzee among the higher primates, as we now know

J. Desmond Clark, "Culture and Ecology in Prehistoric Africa," in *Ecology and Economic Development in Tropical Africa*, ed. by David Brokensha (Berkeley: Institute of International Studies, University of California, 1965), 13–28.

from the work of Jane Goodall in Tanzania,[1] actually *manufactures* tools, albeit in the lowest category of tool-making. Benjamin Franklin's definition of man as "the tool-making animal," a definition that has remained unassailable for so long, now requires modification. For it is now apparent that it is not so much tool-making as such but the ability to envisage the use of one tool for improving the efficiency or contributing to the manufacture of another to achieve a desired end, more often than not connected with food getting, that is the essential characteristic of man. In this respect the working of stone was of the greatest importance. In fact, it may not be going too far to say that it was stone-working that started our hominid ancestors on their long road to civilization.

Up to now, Africa has produced most of the fossil evidence for a knowledge of the earliest stage of hominid evolution. Moreover, it also provides a wealth of material for later periods and great potential for studying the interrelationship of biological and cultural evolution, biome, and habitat. It was the interrelationship between these factors, in the ecologically very different regions of the continent, that contributed to produce the characteristics of the indigenous populations of present-day Africa.

Prehistory, at least Pleistocene prehistory, has all too often been reduced to detailed classificatory systems for stone tools, largely because it is generally only stone that has survived. But prehistorians are now becoming increasingly conscious of the need to study early man in relation to ethology and the environment in which he lived. Consequently, in recent years, interdisciplinary investigations have been initiated with most promising results that have demonstrated the great importance of such studies, not only for the prehistorian, but for all who are concerned with the palaeo-ecology of Africa. Much of what was previously obscure to prehistorians regarding certain cultural distributions, to botanists or zoologists regarding discontinuous habitats, or to pathologists concerning certain tropical diseases becomes appreciably clearer in the light of the team studies that have been carried out. We hope to see many more of them in the future.

In this paper I want to examine the evidence for the biological and cultural evolution of man and the changing relationship between him and his environment, in particular where it concerns sub-Saharan Africa, from the earliest evidence of tool-making up to the coming of husbandry and metal-working into the sub-continent.

The importance of the physical environment

Prehistoric culture cannot be interpreted effectively without first knowing the nature of the environment in which it was practised. Very varied environments exist in Africa today—desert and semi-desert, low and high altitude grasslands, savanna, woodland and montane forest, and the Mediterranean and Cape macchia. All these environments were equally present in the Pleistocene and, indeed, must have been in existence since at least the Miocene. Their zones of distribution have varied, however, in accordance with the climatic changes—increases or decreases in rainfall, temperature, winds, etc.—which were contemporary with the advances and retreats of the continental glaciations in the temperate and higher latitudes, as in Europe and North America.

Attempts have been made to assess the degree of change that took place in Africa during the Pleistocene. Without considerable additional evidence such studies cannot, of course, be considered precise or of general application, yet they do suggest that rainfall may have fluctuated by as much as 40–45 per cent from the present, and that temperature varied between the present and a climate of 5-6°C. lower. It is probable that temperature change was the more important. Such conclusions have been obtained from studies of the mineral composition of sands, of mechanical and chemical weathering of soils, and of the pollens present in certain horizons in relation to the chronological framework based upon stratigraphy and an absolute time scale.

Since the food supply is always the chief concern of hunter-gathers, the area of greatest population density may be considered to be that providing the best continual, all the year

1 "Tool-using and Aimed Throwing in a Community of Free-Living Chimpanzees," *Nature*, CCI (1964), p. 1264.

round, supply of meat, vegetable foods, and water. In the case of Africa, it was the savanna and the grasslands that were best suited to man's physiological needs. This is, in fact, the area in which the earliest human remains and the earliest cultural evidence occur, dating to approximately 1.75 million years ago. Until somewhere between 100,000 and 50,000 years ago this would seem to have been the *only* type of environment that was *permanently* occupied, but as climatic change brought about modifications of the ecological zones, the human and animal populations would have made related adjustments, moving into country that would previously have been unfavorable, or vice versa.

Attempts have been made by H. B. S. Cooke and others to construct vegetation distribution maps to show the vegetation changes brought about by Pleistocene climatic fluctuation.[2] R. B. Lee has shown how the regions which were ecologically favorable, marginal, or unfavorable for early hominid occupation might have changed in response to the changes in the vegetation pattern.[3]

Today the hunter-gatherers live in some of the most unfavorable and inaccessible areas of the globe. This is certainly true of the Bushmen, Bergdama, Pygmies and certain Batwa groups in Africa. This pattern, however, represents a survival distribution. The physical and cultural evidence is considerable, certainly in respect of the Bush type, that peoples who were physically of that stock occupied much of the permanently favorable region of southern Africa during final and post-Pleistocene times. They continued to do so until subsequent events and peoples removed and replaced them. So long as the population remained small enough, there can have been no need for man to occupy the unfavorable or even the marginal areas. As I shall show, there is good evidence from cultural distributions and chronological data that such regions were avoided until the end of the Later Pleistocene, except at times when climatic change made places like the Sahara attractive to settlement.

The present-day population density of the

northern Kalahari !Kung Bushmen is estimated at 17–25 persons per 100 square miles,[4] that of the Hadza in the savanna of northern Tanzania at perhaps 40 persons per 100 square miles,[5] and that of the Bushmen in the southwest corner of the Northern Rhodesian savanna at around 16 persons per 100 square miles.[6] In North America the population densities of hunting-collecting groups varied between 6 per 100 square miles in the arid Great Basin to 250 per 100 in parts of California.[7] Lee estimates for the human population of southern Africa during the early Upper Pleistocene a density of 25–100 persons per 100 square miles for favorable areas and 1–25 per 100 square miles for marginal zones.[8] Lee's estimates, however, are based on the population densities of recent hunter-gatherers, who have advanced a great deal further physiologically, intellectually, and technically than had the hominids of 100,000 to 50,000 years ago. Indeed the *Mesolithic* population of England and Wales in the period 7000 to 5000 B.C. is estimated at about 12 persons per 100 square miles.[9] The population density of tropical Africa during the earlier Pleistocene is much more likely to have been close to that of the hunter-gatherer populations living in the unfavorable zones today, since the prehistoric people would have been incapable of such a successful exploitation of the resources of their environment as would the specialized *Homo sapiens* hunters of later times. Even with the higher estimates, however, it is apparent that the favorable zones were easily capable of supporting all the human population of Africa

---

[4] L. Marshall, "!Kung Bushman Bands," *Africa*, XXX (1960), pp. 326–27.

[5] H. A. Fosbrooke, "A Stone Age Tribe in Tanganyika," *South African Archaeological Bulletin*, XI (1956), pp. 3–8.

[6] P. V. Tobias, "On the Survival of the Bushmen," *Africa*, XXVI (1956), pp. 174–86.

[7] A. L. Kroeber, *Cultural and Natural Areas of Native North America* (Berkeley: University of California Press, 1939), pp. 137–43. [U.C. Publications in American Archaeology and Ethnology, XXXVIII.]

[8] *Op. cit.*, pp. 253–55 (see note 3).

[9] R. J. Braidwood and C. A. Reed, "The Achievement and Early Consequences of Food Production: A Consideration of the Archaeological and Natural-Historical Evidence," *Cold Spring Harbor Symposia on Quantitative Biology*, XXII (1957), pp. 19–31.

---

[2] F. C. Howell and F. Bourliere, eds., *African Ecology and Human Evolution* [Viking Fund Publications in Anthropology, 36 (1963)], pp. 606–10.

[3] "The Population Ecology of Man in the Early Upper Pleistocene of Southern Africa," *Proceedings of the Prehistoric Society*, XXVI (1960), pp. 235–57.

until the closing stages of the Pleistocene, when technological efficiency enabled man to transcend environmental restrictions.

The effects induced by Pleistocene climatic change *in the marginal zones* are, I believe, of the greatest importance for explaining intellectual and cultural evolution. Especially important were the effects of the changes that altered the habitat from favorable to unfavorable in the regions of lower rainfall. It is true that, during periods of ecological stability, natural selection would favor the populations living under optimum conditions. However, at times of ecological instability, the stimuli to survival and the resulting response in populations trapped in these marginal zones would have produced the greatest improvement in technical skill among those groups that did not succumb.

The oldest fossil remains of tool-making hominids and the associated artifacts come from East and South Africa.[10] The earliest are of creatures who lived 1.75 million years ago at the Olduvai Gorge in northern Tanzania during the later part of the Lower Pleistocene. The occurrence of these hominid fossils in the same tectonically unstable region as that of the much older Miocene apes, the *Proconsulidae,* suggests that this region must have been an extremely favorable one for primate evolution and tool using. It was a habitat of limited stands of forest—on the slopes of the volcanoes and in galleries along the stream courses—but where wide use could also be made of intervening savanna. The deterioration of climate during the later Tertiary would have destroyed some of these forest microclimates, and thus may have been responsible for producing fully savanna-dwelling forms and for the evolution of the Tertiary primates to the fully bipedal, erect walking Australopithecines during the Lower Pleistocene. There can be no doubt that for a very long time these latter creatures had been adapted to using tools and, on the evidence of the chimpanzees, to *making* simple tools also, before they took to working stone.

The Lower Pleistocene hominids may or may not all fall within the range of the Australopithecines, but they all occupied a semi-arid en-

vironment that would today be considered marginal-to-favorable park savanna and grassland with plenty of permanent water and large quantities of game for meat. This was the environment of Olduvai, of the Transvaal/Sterkfontein group of caves, and of Taungs in the northern Cape. It was much the same then as it is today.[11]

The development of tools

There were at least three hominid forms living at this time in Africa that were capable of making stone tools. These were *Australopithecus africanus, Australopithecus robustus,* and the recently discovered *Homo habilis.* It is possible that all three of them actually did make tools, although only one can have given rise to *Homo sapiens* through the *Homo habilis* stage. At Olduvai the tool maker lived close to the margin of the lake. His occupation sites (for such one may truthfully call them) were, judging from the one that has been completely excavated and in part described, small—15 feet in diameter—the limits being determined by the distribution of bone and stone. He ate a variety of small and juvenile animals—frogs, snakes, lizards, tortoises, young antelopes, gazelles, and pigs—and the bones lay broken and scattered among his stone artifacts. There are no large animal remains. The stone tools belong to what is known as the Oldowan Culture, and consist of natural stones, numbers of hammer and bashing stones, some choppers, and numerous flakes. There is not much evidence of intentional retouch, though some good examples of small tools have been found, and the tools represent mostly stones that were utilized, rather than purposefully shaped implements. The commonest form of utilization was bashing and hammering, and it is apparent that the flakes are the result of (on the one hand) unintentional and (on the other) unskilled but intentional stone working.

From the earliest Australopithecine sites in South Africa the stone tools are missing, but some utilized bone certainly occurs. The re-

[10] L. S. B. Leakey, "Very Earliest East African Hominidae and Their Ecological Setting," in Howell and Bourliere, *op. cit.,* pp. 448–57 (see note 2) .

[11] C. K. Brain, *The Transvaal Ape-Man-Bearing Cave Deposits,* Transvaal Museum Memoir XI (1958) ; R. L. Hay, "Stratigraphy of Beds I through IV, Olduvai Gorge, Tanganyika," *Science,* CXXXIX (1963) , 3557, pp. 829–33.

mains of small creatures, including crabs, occur at Taungs, and the remains of small to medium-sized antelopes are commonly associated with the Transvaal ape-men. It is, of course, not yet proven that these animal remains represent the food debris of the hominids. No doubt there were several factors contributing to these bone collections in the caves, but it seems more and more probable that the main one of these was, in fact, the hominids.

It is significant that the animal remains in these and the Olduvai deposits are selected, and that only portions of the animals are represented. The limbs and the skulls are most commonly preserved, and much less often the body parts. This strongly suggests that scavenging was one of the main sources of the meat supply, and it may be supposed that the earliest hominids were but another of the scavengers that hung around the kills of the larger carnivores, as is still the practice of some peoples even today. It might be asked why they did not also scavenge large animals naturally dead. They probably did on rare occasions—witness the chalicothere and hippopotamus at Makapan—but it is possible that they had not any equipment that would penetrate the thickness of hide of an elephant or a hippopotamus, and so had to rely on the help of the carnivore with his teeth. Physiologically these early hominids were hardly equipped to be successful hunters of larger game, and the smaller creatures in the faunal lists probably represent the limit of their hunting efficiency.

Most of their food may with certainty be considered to have been vegetable, which was also the traditional diet. On the basis of evidence concerning present-day hunter-gatherers, it can be estimated that vegetable foods comprised 70–80 per cent of the total diet. That *Australopithecus robustus* was primarily a vegetarian can be seen by the wear on his teeth. *Australopithecus africanus* and *Homo habilis* were omnivorous. It is likely that the sudden appearance of stone tools in the geological record was connected as much with an improved vegetable diet as with meat eating. A stone chopper for pointing a digging stick would have meant that man could increase greatly the variety as well as the quantity of his vegetable foods by using the tool to obtain more deeply buried articles of food, which could then often be rendered more palatable by

being softened or pulped by bashing between two stones. In the same way this simple stone equipment would have been effective for breaking long bones to get at the marrow, and the flakes would have greatly facilitated skinning, or scraping the meat from bones.

The hominid makers of the Oldowan Culture evolved physiologically very slowly in their favorable dry savanna environment. However, because of their cultural ability, even though it was so rudimentary, they were able to exploit more of their potential food resources than had been possible without any tools at all, and their physiological development was thus correspondingly more rapid than would have been possible without culture. By 500,000 years ago, even perhaps as early as one million years ago, *Homo habilis* had evolved genetically into a form clearly within the *Homo erectus* pattern, and from sites not much later in age in northwest Africa come jaws and jaw fragments belonging to an African version of *Pithecanthropus*. The most characteristic large tool was then the handaxe, though at first it was very rare, and the majority of the large tools consisted of bashing stones, choppers, and polyhedral stones. With these there are numbers of small tools, often showing careful retouch, made on irregular flakes and nodules. Some of these were very small and must have been used for fairly delicate work.

The occupation sites were still close to water, along the edges of lakes and rivers, and are notable for the quantities of artifacts and remains of large animals that are found associated with them. These animals include elephants, rhinoceroses, hippopotamuses, giraffids, and large antelopes, as well as smaller animals, including horses and pigs. One such site at Olduvai is associated with a stream course, and it appears that the animals had been driven in, bogged down, and butchered. Such an activity implies group organization for hunting purposes as well, no doubt, as for protection, just as does the increased size of the occupation area. In the base of Bed II at Olduvai there are Oldowan Culture choppers associated with the articulated bones of an almost complete deinothere. Even so, these tools at best must have been inefficient for dismembering an animal of that size, and it is not unlikely that the handaxe and, later, the cleaver were developed for skinning and cutting out the meat from the larger mammals that occupied the African savanna during the Middle Pleistocene, which was a period that saw much proliferation of mammal species and the appearance of giant forms.

More is known about the Acheulian cultural stage in the later part of the Middle Pleistocene and the early Upper Pleistocene between approximately 200,000 and 50,000 years ago. The tool kit then was comprised of handaxes, cleavers, knives, choppers, picks, spheroids, core and flake scrapers, and grooving tools. To this one should add wooden spears (known from Europe) and probably a number of other wooden tools. The skill of the stone worker is now clearly seen in the large cutting tools—the handaxes, cleavers, and knives—which are often very fine, and go, perhaps for aesthetic reasons, far beyond the bounds dictated by utility alone. Acheulian occupation sites have a wide distribution throughout the savanna but avoid the lowveld of southeast Africa, the semi-desert country of the Horn, and the lowland rain-forest of Equatoria and West Africa. A few sites do occur in these marginal or unfavorable zones, but they are extremely rare in comparison with the profusion of sites in the savanna and grasslands. Country now desert in southwest Africa and in the Sahara was also occupied when climatic amelioration permitted these now arid regions to support a thicker vegetation and a richer fauna.

It might be expected that the pattern of hominid behavior would be different in the north and the south, but one of the most outstanding features of Middle Pleistocene culture is its homogeneity. It is true that some four or five variants can be observed in the stone culture of these times, but these are all connected with special activities rather than with regional differences. The evidence is now quite clear that stone tools were being made and used for individual specific purposes by Acheulian man,[12] but it is equally clear that these same forms occur throughout all the vast area of the Old World where the Handaxe Culture was practised. Handaxe man used a greater variety of raw materials than had been used at any other period of the Stone Age, and from the faunal lists it would seem that in his dietary

habits, at least as far as meat was concerned, he was equally diversified.

The pattern of hominid behavior of this time is now beginning to become clear. Settlements seem to have consisted of several family groups, probably totalling about 25 individuals. One living floor which has been discovered is 30 feet in diameter. (For comparison, one !Kung Bushman band of 32 persons—8 family fires—occupied an area 40 feet by 20 feet for maximum warmth, light, and protection.) The settlements were still tied to sites immediately adjacent to water, and the groups might have come together for seasonal foraging and hunting. The people ate a very wide variety of foods, and their technology, though it showed a mastery of the principles of stone flaking, was yet restricted to a low level of efficiency by their inability to exploit to more than a very limited degree any of the natural resources. If the ability to do even crude stone working enabled the Australopithecines to obtain the advantages of a meat and buried vegetable diet, then the skill that produced the Acheulian handaxe and cleaver would seem to be connected with the better exploiting of the meat supply offered by the large animals.

The tool kit of Middle Pleistocene man was restricted and, within broad limits, still unspecialized. There were large cutting tools, heavy duty implements for chopping, bashing, gouging, adzing or shaving, and light duty—scraping, grooving, and small cutting—tools. All these are present in a normal Acheulian assemblage in Africa and southwestern Europe. The so-called "flake, chopper, and handaxe traditions" present at that time in the Old World can better be explained as the most favorable adaptations permitted by the ecological extremes in which his behavioral limitations enabled man to live.

The first evidence for the use of fire in Africa dates to the closing stages of the Acheulian Culture, during a period of climate like that of the present day, but later changing to cooler and wetter conditions. At the Kalambo Falls site there are charred logs, charcoals, and wooden tools—digging sticks, clubs, and machettes—worked by fire which have been dated to approximately 58,300 years ago.

A considerable change in the distribution of culture then took place, and there is evidence for broad regional adaptation within the favor-

---

[12] M. R. Kleindienst, "Variability within the Late Acheulian Assemblage in East Africa," *South African Archaeological Bulletin*, XVI (1961), pp. 35–52.

able savanna and grassland zones and also in the forest. This behavioral change was accompanied or induced by climatic variation—lowered temperatures and increased rainfall, that corresponded to the period of the early Würm in Europe—which brought about considerable modification of the favorable zones. The regular use of fire also contributed to the change, since it vastly increased the efficiency of the cultural equipment, permitted the use of materials other than stone for the manufacture of tools, and led to very greatly improved methods of wood working.

About this time also there was a revolution in social behavior. Man began to make permanent use of caves and rock shelters as regular places for habitation. Occupation sites were no longer invariably by the water side, and from this time onward tools became increasingly specialized. Whereas it had taken some 1,700,000 years to reach the stage of technical efficiency of Later Acheulian man, it required only 60,000 to 50,000 years to go the rest of the way and to achieve full urbanization. The reason for this must surely lie in man's ability to organize his social structure and economy with improved efficiency, once his technical skill has assured the basic dietary requirements of the group.

Three main cultural traditions

Between 60,000 and 40,000 years ago prehistoric culture in the African continent could be divided into three broad traditions:

(1) *A continuation of the Acheulian handaxe tradition in the grasslands and dry savanna of the south and southwest (known as the Fauresmith or Acheulio-Levalloisian Culture);*
(2) *A tradition with many heavy duty tools—core-axes, picks, choppers, etc.—and a number of light duty tools with denticulated edges in the savanna grassland/forest margin region of Equatoria, following the retreat of the lowland humid forest and the advance of the montane elements (called the Sangoan Culture); and*
(3) *A tradition of light flake tools present in Africa north of the Sahara, which may or may not be intrusive from Europe or southwest Asia (known as the Mousterian or Levallois-Mousterian Culture).*

Each of these three traditions must be expected to have developed the technology best suited to the pattern of life and food resources of its makers. The difficulty comes in trying to assess the relative importance of the stone equipment in a material culture from which usually the remains of all the more perishable elements are missing. However, if the site at Hajj Creiem in Cyrenaica is any indication, the North African Mousterian population were skillful hunters, since a small temporary camp site, which can have provided living space for a small group for a few days only, yielded the remains of five to ten Barbary sheep, three or four zebra, two or three buffalo, and a gazelle.[13] The delicate flint scrapers and points found there support the belief that hunting was of prime importance to this North African Mousterian population.

In the higher rainfall, thicker vegetation region of the Sangoan Culture, enhanced importance must have been given to vegetable foods, since game is not so plentiful in such areas, and the vegetable potential is much greater. More emphasis was here placed on wood working, and the Kalambo Falls site shows that man had already learned how to work wood by charring and scraping. In the savanna, however, game must always have been very plentiful and man's taste unselective, as the long faunal lists from the Broken Hill cave show.

The remains of the Fauresmith or Acheulio-Levalloisian Culture are found in what today is grassland, often high altitude or semi-arid steppe country, sometimes even desert, seemingly the result of the continuation of the traditional ecological conditions of Middle Pleistocene times.

The makers of these prehistoric cultures were of early *Homo sapiens* stock—Neanderthaloids in North Africa, Rhodesioids and others in sub-Saharan Africa. These cultures of the early Upper Pleistocene became differentiated because they were adapted to different ecological conditions. The technological level from locality to locality in each of the cultural zones seems to show little individual variation, however, and one is forced to the conclusion that, although regional specialization in Africa had already begun at this time, it was based on only a comparatively shallow level of unselective

---

[13] C. B. M. McBurney, *The Stone Age of Northern Africa* (Baltimore: Penguin Books, Inc., 1960), pp. 167–68.

efficiency in exploitation of the natural resources.

By the later stages of the Upper Pleistocene the pattern of prehistoric culture is very different, and there was then a variety of specialized regional forms. Their makers belonged to the modern *Homo sapiens* stock which, from 35,000 years ago, began to replace everywhere the older Neanderthaloid and Rhodesioid populations. These regional culture forms seem to have had their origin in the three earlier complexes—the Levallois-Mousterian, the Sangoan, and the Fauresmith—producing in turn the Aterian, the Lupemban, and the Stillbay/Pietersburg traditions, which date from between about 35,000 to about 12,000 years ago.

Within these broad cultural divisions quite a variety of secondary differentiation existed, and a host of regional cultural stages can be distinguished, the characteristics of which are likely to be related to the resources of the local environment. There was a much larger range of specialized stone tools present in the equipment of the Later Pleistocene hunter-gatherers than in the equipment of their Early Pleistocene predecessors. In addition, the relative importance of one form of tool over another, seen in the percentage variations of Middle Stone Age times, could be due only to the interaction of cultural tradition and ecology selecting for greatest efficiency. That cultural tradition was of importance by this time is shown not only by the clear evolutionary development of the local Middle Stone Age cultures from their earlier Upper Pleistocene antecedents, but also by the way the intrusive Upper Palaeolithic Blade and Burin cultures maintained their individuality unaffected by the autochthonous African cultures of the northwest and south.

The Later Pleistocene saw movement into the Sahara from both north and south activated by the spread southwards of the Mediterranean flora, probably as far as Chad, and the northward transgression of the Sudanic vegetation belt to make the Sahara a favorable region for hunter-gatherers. By 20,000 years ago the makers of the Aterian Culture had penetrated into the southeastern Sahara to Wanyanga and probably to the Nile. Contemporaneously, the bearers of the Lupemban Culture moved north from the Guinea and dry savanna, so that in such areas as far removed as Adrar in the west and Kharga in the east there took place a blending of these two traditions.

Regional adaptation and cultural development

The greater degree of specialization in the material culture at this time is probably to be connected with the greater specialization in the diet. The source of meat was most often medium-sized animals, and, while the range of species at any site is still fairly wide, it is usual that one or two species predominate—wildebeests, hartebeests, zebra, or pigs, for example—depending on the local ecology. Bones of large animals are rarely found in the cave and rock shelter sites. This is not because these animals were no longer eaten, but because from the time that semi-permanent occupation of sites was possible, only the meat was carried back to the camp, and the band no longer had to camp around the meat.

The enormous number of Middle Stone Age sites in Africa, even in such unfavorable areas as the Namib desert or the Lybian Sand Sea, show that, during the cooler, optimum climate of the Later Pleistocene, man in Africa was capable of occupying, though probably only seasonally, regions that today are among some of the most inhospitable on the continent. That man found it attractive to do this must surely imply a considerable population in the optimum zones during this period.

From the evidence of many new cultural traits it is also apparent that the appearance of *Homo sapiens* produced a quickening and intensification of regional adaptability. Groups or bands now used camping places which could be seasonally, or perhaps semipermanently, occupied and regularly revisited. From the occupation of caves and rock shelters, it would also seem that they were able to live continually in these sites for much longer than had been possible to Middle Pleistocene man. To such places the proceeds of the hunt were regularly carried back, and the maintenance of a semipermanent home must have encouraged specialization of activities as between man and woman. Aesthetic and magico-religious beliefs are attested to by the presence of personal adornment, pigment, art, and ritual burial. Technical improvements, especially in hunting

weapons such as the spear and knife, resulted
from the regular hafting of tools, and it is
probable that the bow and arrow made its appearance in the northwest at this time. All this
goes to show that, by the close of the Pleistocene 10,000 years ago, the organization of prehistoric society in the continent is unlikely to
have differed in many essential respects from
that of recent hunter-gatherers. There is also
good reason to believe that by this time the
indigenous racial groupings—the Khoisan, Ne-
groid, and Afro-Mediterranean—had already
made their appearance.

At the close of the Pleistocene there is evidence for climatic deterioration and a swing to
aridity which had a concentrating effect upon
the human and animal population, emptying
the unfavorable areas and scattering the population of the marginal zones. That man was
able to maintain himself in these marginal
zones throughout Later Stone Age/Mesolithic
times after 8000 B.C. shows that his technical
ability had reached a higher level of efficiency
than at any time previously.

The period from about 6,000 to 2,500 B.C.—
known in Europe as the Climatic Optimum—
was one of increased rainfall in Africa and resulted in another expansion of the favorable
zones and a repopulation of the Sahara from
both directions. Either population explosion,
the climatic deterioration terminating the Pleistocene, or cultural diffusion—probably a combination of the three—was responsible for the
establishment of large, near permanent or permanent settlements adjacent to lakes, rivers,
and the sea shore. These were made possible by
the exploitation for the first time on a significant scale of fresh water and sea foods. Such
sites are found near waterways in the Congo
Basin, up the Nile, around the lakes of East
Africa, and in the Sahel and Sudanic belts of
the Sahara. In addition, around the Mediterranean and southern African coasts, middens,
composed largely of the fossil refuse from sea
foods, accumulated up to thirty feet in thickness. Around the fringes of the forest also, the
wild *Dioscorea,* oil palm, and other near permanent sources of vegetable food probably led
to the development of a vegecultural way of
life.

In the savanna at this time were a large
number of regionally adapted groups who were
capable of making what is probably the maxi-

mum use of the material resources for a hunting-gathering way of life. Their food included
large and small animals in near equal amounts,
and there can be no doubt that improved hunting techniques, particularly in the use of the
bow and poisoned arrow, permitted a reduction
in the territorial range of the hunting area. The
Saharan, or Makalian Wet Phase, as this period
is called, must have been an extremely advantageous time for the hunting populations of the
favorable zones, so much so that, when cultivated wheat and barley were introduced into
the Nile valley during the early fifth or sixth
millennium B.C., farming was unable, until two
millennia later, to compete successfully with the
hunting-gathering way of life south of the
Sahara. Something of this living pattern can be
gathered from the rock art of the period.

By 3,500 B.C. the new cereal plants and domestic cattle, sheep, and goats had spread
rapidly throughout the Mediterranean littoral
and north Atlantic coast as well as in the
marginally favorable but winter rainfall region
of the Sahara. In the oases and river valleys
cereal cultivation must have been of major importance, but the emphasis in the Sahara was
on pastoralism, particularly cattle raising.
When the climate again deteriorated, after
2,500 B.C., there was a general movement out of
the Sahara, and the evidence suggests that it
was at this time that the populations in the
Sudanic belt began, or intensified, experimentation with local food plants, since in the tropical
summer rainfall regions the north African
winter rainfall crops only grow well under
irrigation.

It was not, however, until a further 2,000
years had elapsed that the benefits of the agricultural way of life began to penetrate to the
sub-continent, though some of the regions of
West and northeast Africa—Senegal, Guinea,
Ghana, Nigeria, and Ethiopia—saw the establishment of local Neolithic communities. These
groups lived on the margins of the West African rainforest and in the savanna and grasslands of the East African high plateau, showing
that by this time culture was able to cut across
several very different ecological zones by reason
of the success achieved with the local domesticates. Perhaps 2,000 years were necessary to
develop these domesticates; certainly the equipment of the Neolithic slash-and-burn cultivators
was fairly inefficient for any large scale agricul-

tural activity, and this method cannot have had the appeal to the populations of the game-stocked, well-watered tropical savanna that it had for the occupants of the semi-arid North African region where it was the sole means of maintaining population growth and stability. The detailed history of domestication in Africa can, however, only be learned from properly controlled, stratigraphic archaeology and, as yet, there is little of this available.

Whatever the reason or reasons, it was not until a knowledge of metallurgy, with its resultant immeasurably more effective metal tools, spread south of the Sahara during the last half of the first millennium B.C. that agriculture and domestic stock spread into southern Africa with immigrations from the southern Sudan. These seem to have started about the beginnings of the Christian Era, and the crops that were introduced were the Sudanic ones—sorghum, bullrush millet, and finger millet—along with cattle, sheep, and goats. From this time on (and the stages now begin to be better documented by radiocarbon dating) the superiority of the mixed farming way of life shows itself in the disappearance of the hunting-gathering economy, though both these activities have remained of considerable importance in the life of the Bantu populations of central and southern Africa. For example, in the savanna country of the Luapula District of Northern Rhodesia, 46 adults spent 4.6 per cent of their time collecting, 4.3 per cent fishing, and 1.6 per cent hunting—the last a small percentage because there is little left to hunt.[14] Among the Valley Tonga on the Middle Zambezi, the source of relish for midday and evening meals for three households on 169 days indicates that gathering accounted for 547 meals, and hunting and fishing for 12 each, totalling 571 out of a grand total of 712 meals.[15]

With the coming of domestication, the most favorable ecological zones were, on the one hand, the marginal, drier habitats, where disease of cattle and other stock was reduced to a minimum, and, on the other hand, the marginal rainforest country where, though disease

might eliminate most livestock, this was compensated for by the agricultural richness of the environment, especially after the Asian food plants of the humid tropics had reached Equatoria in the early centuries A.D.

From this time onwards man's activities began to have a more permanent effect on his environment in the tropics, as they must surely have done in the Sahara during Neolithic times. It is probable that intensified and regular burning by man at this time began the replacement of forest by tall grass savanna in the higher rainfall zones. At this period, also, the thorn thicket probably began to encroach on grassland in the semi-arid zones where overstocking and regular burning preceded soil erosion and, indeed, must have hastened the desertification of the Sahara.

Because of its sparseness, the hunter-gatherer population is unlikely to have affected significantly the distribution and density of the game. For example, an !Kung Bushman band kills an average of 15–18 large animals (i.e. large antelopes and giraffes) in a normal year. No doubt, under optimum conditions, the number of animals killed by earlier hunter-gatherers would have been greater, but, even if doubled, it can have had no appreciable effect on game distribution. Significant reduction of the game can only have begun with the coming of food production and the establishment of large permanent settlements by Bantu and Negroes. In regions where disease excluded domestic stock, the growing scarcity of game, and thus of a balanced protein diet, must have been one of the causes of population pressure leading to migration.

Summary

Ecology has played a major role in the distribution and evolution of man and his culture in Africa. It provided the basic stimulus for tool-making. Knowledge of palaeo-environments shows that the striking differences that exist today between North, West and East Africa began at least 50,000 years ago. It shows, moreover, if we are interpreting the data correctly, that climatic change was capable of producing a variety of responses in the human population—movement of peoples and thus cultural and genetic diffusion, stimulus to more intensified technical efficiency, population increase (espe-

---

14 G. Kay, *Chief Kalaba's Village* (Manchester: 1964), pp. 51–60. [Rhodes-Livingstone Paper No. 35.]

15 T. Scudder, *The Ecology of the Gwembe Tonga* (Manchester: Manchester University Press, 1962), p. 202.

cially after colonization of empty environments), and isolation, which gave increased
opportunity for genetic drift.

Environmental factors alone, however, could
at best have had only a stabilizing effect on
human groups, but the steady growth of new

technical skills keeping pace with intellectual
evolution permitted populations to increase
and develop ever more efficient livelihood patterns, and so to reach the realization that the
most efficient are those who make the best use
of the resources of their habitat.

Landforms made by man

BERL GOLOMB AND HERBERT M. EDER

22

*If man has indeed shaped much of the land-
scape about him, then should we not give
serious study to the genesis and morphology of
these "Anthropogenes"? If man-initiated processes produce topographic modifications which
rival whole suites of natural processes, then is it
not time that academics should make up a
methodology and jargon to study such activities? Berl Golomb and Herbert M. Eder
consider these questions in this discussion of
the geomorphologic role man has had in Earth
history. From mining to farming and marshes
to mountains, process and landscape are surveyed with the intention of drawing attention
to man's unstudied powers. When read with
Ian Narin's The American Landscape selection
below, the reader comprehends the scope of
concern of the landscape student as he sees
man's dominant mark on field and city.*

The activities of humankind, whose numbers
now exceed three billion, constitute an increasingly important agency of landscape change.
Unlike other organisms, man adapts to different
environments less through direct biological
modification than through specialized developments of his culture. Our species has thus been

able to inhabit and to exert varied ecological
influences over the greatest range of environments. Human modification ranges over a complex interplay of extension and intensity, from
faint but noticeable pollution of all the world's
oceans to the highly localized but wholly artificial environment of a space capsule in orbit—
with temporary clearings of bush for shifting
cultivation in the tropics, permanently de-
forested agricultural landscapes of the mid-lati-
tudes, or the artificial landscapes of cities distributed appropriately on the continuum. The
modifications may involve the micro-climate,
the eco-climate, the biological balance of species, geologic weathering processes and even the
creation of artificial landforms.

Many of man's activities result in modifications of the actual earth surface. Where such
modifications become perceptible, they may be
considered man-made landforms. The exact
compass of the term "landform" admits debate.
The present discussion holds to a limited definition, restricting landforms to features of soil
and rock. Even so, man-made landforms cover
an ever-larger area of the surface of the earth.
The Netherlands, where more than a thousand
square miles of land have been reclaimed since
Roman times, may be one of the largest deliberately fashioned man-made landforms. Millions of tons of earth have been moved in creating the agricultural terraces of eastern Asia

Berl Golomb and Hebert M. Eder, "Landforms
Made by Man," *Landscape*, XIV, No. 1 (Fall,
1964), 4–7.

during the past several thousand years. Elsewhere in the world extensive plains have been corrugated into hills and hummocks in the construction of agricultural mounds. The embayments called by the English "broads," by the French "claires," and by the Dutch "meers," are flooded coastal depressions created by the excavation of peat. The examples of landform creation and modification by man are highly varied in form, in scale and in process of formation.

In terms of the amount of work done, man is just now beginning to operate at the same order of magnitude as "natural" forces. In the mine dumps of the Witwatersrand, some 165,-000 tons are accumulated daily. At the Ruth open pit mine near Ely, Nevada, 100,000 tons of rock are moved each day. Some 118,000 tons a day were excavated from the Mesabi Range in 1962. In the Rhineland coal fields brown-coal extraction reaches 150,000 tons per day. These examples compare favorably—or alarmingly—with the 700,000 tons of silt the Colorado River deposits each day in the Lake Mead reservoir behind Hoover Dam. In any one day, over an area comparable to that of its watershed, the Colorado undoubtedly far outstrips man in amount of earth-moving. And the Colorado is far from being the world's major river. Nature, however, generally operates through steady accumulation of small amounts of work over large areas. The sediment deposited in Lake Mead may represent only minute lowering of the average ground surface over thousands of square miles. In contrast, man's work is locally concentrated. The surface of the ground is scraped out, filled, pushed or otherwise molded far more noticeably than would result from comparable expenditure of energy by "natural" forces.

An interesting problem here is the satisfactory distinction of directly and indirectly created landforms. Accelerated erosion in a gully or a landslide along Los Angeles' Pacific Palisades may be as much due to human activity as a road cut along a freeway. But while the latter was purposely created, the former were accidental and undesired. Landforms indirectly created by man are formed by natural processes to which man has contributed only the initial, triggering force. These examples of indirect morphogenesis are a link between the landforms of "natural" geomorphology and those of artificial "anthropogeomorphology."

If the indirectly created landforms qualify as "man-made," man's geomorphic scope is of greater magnitude than previously described. Erosion initiated by human activity must account for a large share of the 2,000,000 tons of sediments daily swept out by the Mississippi to its mouth, to say nothing of the tonnage deposited enroute. Since around 3000 B.C., the head of the Persian Gulf has receded nearly 150 miles, and some 2000 square miles formerly under water are now alluvial land. A large if undeterminable part of this alluviation resulted from intensive agricultural activity in Mesopotamia, accompanied by over-grazing and deforestation of the upper Tigris and Euphrates watersheds. These relations hold for the vast Hwang Ho delta, where the river has frequently shifted course and alluviated an area of several thousand square miles, transforming the Shantung island into a peninsula within historic times. A similar development, though at a smaller scale, has taken place at the head of the Adriatic Sea, attributable at least in part to human activity within the Po River's watershed. Diversion of waters for irrigation has converted some 10,000 square miles of the Aral Sea into dry land. Irrigation and diversion of waters for navigation canals have taken their toll of the Caspian Sea. Some 15,000 square miles formerly under water have become dry land, and shoals have developed throughout the northern Caspian as water level dropped some six feet.

Taken in gross, no one would deny that these developments are "anthropogene," caused by human activity. But if the wholes are "anthropogene," what about the parts? Are the shoals of the Caspian, the mudbars of the Hwang Ho or the Venetian *lido* to be considered man-made landforms? They match the typical "natural" landforms, and differ markedly from landforms which man has deliberately shaped, such as road cuts, strip and open-pit mines or agricultural terraces. Herein lies a conceptual problem still to be resolved.

Among the surfaces deliberately fashioned by man, agricultural landforms are the most venerable, the most extensive and in many ways the least known and the most ignored. Certainly among the most spectacular are the terraced landscapes of the world. Over thousands of square miles in the Orient, the earth surface has been worked into terraces—flat-lying flood plains, broad, gentle interfluves and steeply sloping rugged hillsides are terraced. The intricately delicate terracing of the Ifugao in the rugged mountains of northern Luzon is the common textbook example. Other such landscapes are characteristic of the Western Andes or of the Mediterranean Basin. In a pioneer paper in *Pacific Viewpoint,* J. E. Spencer and G. Hale have recently called attention to the importance of terracing as a human imprint on the surface of the earth, and offered a tenfold classification of forms. The geomorphic significance of terraces varies with the environment of the terraced landscape. As well as transforming the natural slopes, terracing may alter patterns of natural drainage, modify the development of soil profiles, interrupt natural cycles of erosion and alter rates of weathering. An abundance of other agricultural landforms, modern as well as ancient, await study.

Since urban areas are foci of human activity, intensive landform modifications are often characteristic of city sites. The Los Angeles Basin and the San Francisco Bay Area are replete with excellent examples. In both regions, man is cutting, leveling and filling for residential, industrial, recreational and communication purposes. In the Hollywood Hills, spurs are terraced for house sites. Artificial residential islands are built up out of fill in the salt marshes of Seal Beach. On sloping hillsides, houses are built on compacted artificial scree-cones. Earth sculpturing is carving high-rise building sites out of the hills of San Francisco, and leveling pads for "ticky-tacky" tract housing all around the Bay. The transportation function produces a variety of forms. Raised freeway beds twist through the lowlands like artificial eskers and great freeway cuts truncate mountain spurs like fault scarps. Need for sheltered harbors and increased docking space resulted in dredging basins in Southern California or a ship canal in the Bay. San Pedro's important Terminal Island is an artificial bar created from the accumulation of dredgings. Artificial flats of dredgings are shoreside features of Mission and San Francisco Bays. In response to the demands of recreation, great sand beaches have been artificially accumulated

along the shores of Santa Monica Bay. Provision of recreational facilities has led to the formation of pocket embayments in the several marinas. Mining activities have also left their mark on the surface of coastal Central and Southern California. Expressions vary from borrow pits opened for gravel, clay and diatomaceous earth to the inexorable industrial erosion of a limestone hill for the cement mills of Colton. Destruction by gold-dredging of the alluvial landscape on the margins of the Sacramento Valley is a large scale example of surface alteration by mining. With efforts to combat air pollution restricting incineration, burial has gained importance as a means of refuse disposal in the Los Angeles and San Francisco Bay regions. Open pit mines are being filled, and whole canyons are being leveled. San Francisco Bay is being constricted; human accretion in the form of "sanitary fill" has been advancing toward the center of the bay at an estimated rate of one foot per year.

Like any other phenomena, man-made landforms may be studied through a variety of approaches. At least three systems of classification can be suggested:

First, *man-made landforms could be classified descriptively in terms of the forms they assume, or in terms of similarity to natural landforms that they approximate.* For example, embankments, terraces, fills and cuts could constitute classes. This descriptive approach of form analysis would avoid consideration of the underlying generative processes.

Second, *man-made landforms could be grouped genetically, according to the agency that formed them.* The analogy with "natural" geomorphology would be classification of landforms created by agents such as moving water, wind or mass wasting. In the case of man-made landforms, the agents would be tools and machines. The term "bull-dozogenesis" has often been used informally in the U.C.L.A. Geography Department to refer to the dynamic impact of the bulldozer in creating and destroying landforms throughout the Los Angeles Basin. Many similar terms come to mind, although with less felicitous results. With the application of nuclear technology as in the Atomic Energy Commission's "Project Plowshare," new tools and new terms may develop. The genetic approach has been the most fruitful in geomorphology, but it does not seem promising for the study of man-made landforms. This is, by and large, a result of our burgeoning technology and the proliferation of machines and techniques. Furthermore, given machines are capable of causing a large variety of morphologic expressions on the landscape.

Third, *man-made landforms could be classified in terms of the major functions or human activities that led to their formation.* Major categories of man-made landforms would be associated with functions such as transportation, shelter, agricultural activity, mineral extraction, etc. A second order of classification could comprise the purposes the individual landforms serve. This approach may permit more meaningful analysis than the other two systems.

The study of man-made landforms need not be limited to the geomorphic aspect or to cataloguing and identification. Historical and comparative studies are certainly of interest, and can shed light on problems in adjacent fields of knowledge. Middens, often imposing topographic features, are associated with settlement sites in human archeo-geography; their study has yielded knowledge of the home environments of early man. Middens, incidentally, are still being formed, whether as "sanitary fill" or as non-sanitary municipal dumps, such as Lima's notorious "El Monton." Less obviously, changes in the space-time pattern of Mesoamerican earthmounds, the terraced landscape of the Rhine Graben, the earthworks of the Mojos Savannas of northeastern Bolivia, would tell much about regional changes in nature and culture. These may be speculative jobs, but challenging and rewarding to those of inquisitive bent. Problems in the more usual areal- and time-perspective of historical geography abound in the wake of our modern mining activity and urban expansion. Refinement of problems in a cultural-geographic orientation could result from a comparative line of inquiry. Tools, techniques, attitudes and motivations are cultural variables. Comparable man-made landforms in various culture regions might show significant differences. Have Southeast Asian and West Andean terraced landscapes been compared? Or Polynesian taro pits and the mulch-pits of coastal Peru? And might not a scheme of classification be devised to encompass landforms such as the *chinampas* in permanently inundated marsh in the Mexican basin, the "earthworks" of the seasonally flooded Mojos, and the canal-ringed cultivation plots of the arid Viru Valley? Such a scheme would parallel classification of terraces but involve landforms designed for control of moisture rather than slope. Schemes of landforms for other functions, as well as problems of overlap and multifunctional forms, can be expected.

Given its scale, variety and intensity, the importance of man's landforming activity is obvious. A geomorphic agent of such significance deserves study as much as do wind, ice and moving water. In effect, man's activities approximate the gamut of "natural" agents. These processes and their resulting landforms may come to be studied as something distinct from but equally as important as "natural" geomorphology.

Study of man-made landforms has had a curious history. Comments on environmental and land-surface alterations by man have been recorded since classical antiquity. In the early 19th Century, Alexander von Humboldt commented on the force of habit that made Spaniards recreate the arid landscape of Castile in the initially lacustrine environment of the basin of Mexico. In 1864 came publication of *Man and Nature,* George Perkins Marsh's study of man's alterations of landscape and of the impact of human activity on physical geography. Recognition of man's importance as an environmental modifier has accompanied the rapid increase in technologic capabilities. The 1955 symposum called by the Wenner-Gren Foundation led to the compilation of a thousand-page volume, *Man's Role in Changing the Face of the Earth.* Man's impact on environmental resources has become alarming in many quarters. Awareness of the magnitude and pace of change is now apparent in popular discussions, and the mixed feelings toward this change are reflected in Richard Armour's short verse:

"Out with trees and don't lament;
  Fill the valleys with cement."

A considerable volume of literature has thus accumulated on the subject. Most of the contributions have been of an ecological orientation, focused on the disturbance in the balance of nature that human activities have brought upon the impact on the general environment of man's increasing numbers and expanded enterprises. Only a relatively small part of this literature has stressed man's role as a geomorphic agent, exerting a noticeable effect on the earth's crust. Geologists seem to have been the principal contributors to this geomorphic orientation.

On the whole, specific attention to this geomorphic rather than ecologic aspect has been neglected. This relative neglect is true even of the aforementioned symposium volume itself. The study of man's geomorphic activities, then, is one of the paradoxical "recognized yet unrecognized subjects," to use the phrase P. L. Wagner and M. W. Mikesell applied to cultural geography.

Should geomorphic study of man-made land-forms prove useful, it may justify a distinctive name. Of currency, especially in Europe, is "anthropogene geomorphology," as used by Edwin Fels. A closer parallel to Ratzel's "anthropogeographie" is the polysyllabic "anthropogeomorphology." However, a name is simply a mnemonic tag, called for only if a delimiting or unifying device is needed. As indicated above, there is still no conceptual definition or methodological consensus. The bridge of nomenclature can be crossed in good time.

At a time when many of us are involved with hypothetical distributions and non-real spatial models, the study of man-made landforms has an earthy appeal. And certainly, if it is the aim of geographers to describe and explain features of the surface of the earth, man's geomorphic activity cannot be neglected.

Man in the ecology of tropical America

CARL O. SAUER

23

The writings of Carl Sauer are important enough to the development of cultural geography that they have already been collected in one anthology devoted solely to his work. However, this article from the Proceedings of the Ninth Pacific Science Congress, 1957, is like a minor anthology itself, for it deals with many of the themes Sauer developed in a life concerned with man's mark on the earth. Human migration and plant diffusion, the benign nature of the river margin environment, the use of plant poisons in piscicide, the dominant role of fire and man's responsibility for major savanna creation—all of these themes are developed in the article, distilled from more than 50

years of scholarship. Sauer's teaching is one of the primary founts for cultural geography in the United States today.

Tropical climate

For the present purpose, the Tropics are considered as the humid low latitudes, though not necessarily rainy at all seasons, or the classical Tropical Zone, if you will, flaring poleward on the eastern side of the continental masses, skewed equatorward on the western side. The concern here is not with any dispute as to where to run climatic boundary lines, those neat devices by which geographic realities are masked by the artifices of a numerical system, often compounded with an equal artifice of vegetation zones, but with the lower latitudes which have their weather determined by the equatorial low-pressure cells and their seasonal

Carl O. Sauer, "Man in the Ecology of Tropical America," in *Land and Life: A Selection from the Writings of Carl Ortwin Sauer*, ed John Leighly (Berkeley: University of California Press, 1965), 182–93.

shifts for parts of the Northern Hemisphere by monsoon effects. Short days, marked diurnal temperature range and low annual temperature range are implicit. Rainfall, with rare exceptions, has seasonal quality; "the rains follow the high sun." Poleward the air is stable, and there may be a good flow of trade wind or intruding continental air from high latitudes. The rains, which come in "summer," are mainly convectional; and hence, even in the heart of the tropics, the mornings, and an occasional series of days, have bright skies. Variability of weather from year to year is low. In Recent and Pleistocene time the low latitudes have been least affected by secular changes in climate; here if anywhere we may think of climatic stability.

Year-round raininess, humid air, and wet ground are restricted to minor parts of the tropics. Such is in the New World the *ceja de la montaña* of the Andes, especially on the Amazonian side, a very long strip of cloud forest that lies well above the tropical lowlands. On the lower slopes of the montaña there is the usual daily rhythm of sunshine and rain, and there are spells of bright, dry weather. Over most of the Amazonian drainage there occur rather well-marked dry periods, in which there may be partial defoliation of upland trees and a sort of period of maturing of fruits. Meteorologic totals and averages may be misleading as to sequence of weather. "Humid tropics" and "rain forest" are terms subject to oversimplification and distortion by statistics.

Ecologic systems

That various organisms share the same geographic space is the concern of ecology. This sharing includes so many kinds of living things that we hardly think of a total ecology, but have been prudently inclined to reduce complexity through setting up partial systems of recognition and relation. We know, for instance, almost nothing of the synecology underground of termites, earthworms, fungi, bacteria, and other soil organisms and their relation to life above ground. "Plant" and "animal" ecology largely have gone their separate ways. Vegetation complexes and "regions" are designated by habits of growth, abundance, and conspicuousness of constituent entities. In passing from such gross description to explanation, numbers, diversity, and variability of

forms and factors confound our understanding. Numerical counts and statistical correlations, experimental eliminations and controls are employed. Beyond the reach of such quantitative inspection and experimentation, however, are the greater events and processes of natural history and earth history, of the nonrecurrent and nonreversible actuality of time.

Plant ecologists have thought to reduce the difficulties of their problems by relating vegetation directly to physical environment, the geographic limits being thought of as set by qualities of the atmosphere and of the ground. The most comprehensive thesis is that a given site is populated by groups (associations) of plants, succeeding one another as stages, until a final assemblage (climax association) is constituted which is fully adapted to the site and is therefore stable. Such climax vegetation is considered as optimally adjusted or constituted with regard to its climate. Rather elegant models are thus constructed which, however, do not take into account the flux of earth, or natural and cultural history. How organisms have come to live together in any part of the world, together with their evolutionary changes, is an historical problem of large and actual time which may not be explained by schemes of successive stages and climatic climaxes.

Tropical origins, dispersals, and increase of man

In this discussion attention is directed to the place of man in the biota of the tropical world. In our present state of knowledge there is a dispute as to whether the cradle of mankind was tropical Asia or tropical Africa. It may also be suggested that Man as our acknowledged direct ancestor may have descended from sources both African and Asiatic and that he migrated to the New World repeatedly in late Pleistocene and Recent time. In the Old World tropics, his kind has been around from the beginning. He has inhabited the New World for tens, probably for scores, of thousands of years. (The time of his entry into New Guinea and Australia is still unclear but may also have been at similar times in the Pleistocene.) Whether his earliest homes lay in the tropical rain forest is uncertain; it has been thus argued from the finds in Java. At any rate, the lower latitudes of the Old World widely have yielded the hominid forms underlying the evolution of man. We are accustomed to think of the rainy tropics as having a vegetation so exhuberant that primitive man has found little to sustain him within their great forests; this is true. It is not true, however, that he has been unable to find early niches for himself there where he could live and increase in numbers and skills. I am able to agree, therefore, with Professor P. W. Richards in his informed ecological study[1] in which he says: "Until the most recent period in its history man has had little effect on the Tropical Rain forest; large areas of it have been altogether uninhabited or inhabited only by food-gathering peoples with no more influence on the vegetation than any of the other animal inhabitants." He makes no unusual restrictions in defining the tropical rain forest; his Indo-Malayan forest reaches from southern India across Malaya and Melanesia, the African one from the middle Congo through the Guinea coast, and the American one includes the Amazon basin, the Guianas, and the Central American and Antillean rim of the Caribbean.

Conditions at the time of discovery of the New World

The aboriginal presence and condition of man in the New World tropics bear little relation to rainfall and forest growth. The discoveries of Columbus, except for the pearl coast of Venezuela, were wholly in the rainier lands. The island of Haiti was praised by him in detail as an earthly paradise, with a teeming population of attractive culture. In his discovery of the Panamanian coast, Columbus spoke of the country about Porto Bello as "all like a painted garden" through which the houses were closely strewn. Eastern Panama to the Gulf of Darien and beyond to the Sinú River was well populated by agricultural folk, living in villages and larger towns. Because they possessed much worked gold, they were overrun quickly by the Spaniards from Darien, the first mainland town of Europeans in the New World. This original Spanish town was founded for convenience of access to the many Indian settlements in all directions. The native populations were soon

destroyed, and the Spaniards abandoned Darien for the town of Panama on the Pacific side. The site of Spanish Darien is now midway of what is today almost trackless and uninhabited forest that runs from Porto Bello well beyond the Gulf of Darien.

The party of Orellana that made the first descent of the Amazon found numerous agricultural tribes occupying large villages; now archeology is uncovering a chain of sites along the Amazon that may link the high ceramic art of the island of Marajó at the mouth of the Amazon to Andean cultures.

Our New World humid tropics had been well prospected for native settlement long before the coming of the Europeans, and held sedentary folk numbered in the millions. Except for the cloud forest on mountain flanks, climate was not at all the limiting factor. The environmental limitations were, as they are now, edaphic: waterlogged lowlands, the deeply-leached wide interfluve terraces of the upper Amazon basin, the sandstone cappings of the interior Brazilian and Guianan massifs, the clay pans of the Llanos, lateritic and bauxitic soils, especially on igneous and metamorphic bedrock of low relief.

Our tropical lands in large part have been exposed for geologic periods to tropical weathering, in many parts are of parent materials originally poor in nutritive minerals, and in part have lacked sufficient relief to limit the accumulation of leached residuum. Such infertile tracts were also thinly peopled; not so the more fertile parts.

Modern settlement of the American tropics is largely resettlement of aboriginally occupied areas, as is going on now in Venezuela, with extensions by the addition of drainage engineering. Archeology and soil surveys are in agreement as to ancient and current attractiveness of land.

Riparian habitat and habit at the primitive levels

However forbidding the unbroken tropical forest was to the most primitive folk, the water breaks in the forest invited his entry by the multitude of streams that keep their sunlit way open through the forest. Lake and seashore also offer open spaces. In large measure primitive man is a riparian creature anywhere; he moved

---

[1] The Tropical Rain Forest (1952); citation from p. 404.

into the tropical forest along the edges of the water, lived by the water, and there gathered everything needful. It made little difference how great or tall the forest, the sunny avenues of water provided a congenial environment; widely branching, they led far inland toward the watersheds. The riparian habitat, I wish to submit, has been favorable to progress, since its environment is diversified as to plant and animal life both of land and waters. Riparian folk are likely to live sociably in groups clustered at sites advantageous for getting a living and protected from flood hazard, and affording easy communication with other groups. The economic geography of such folk is to be read from the productivity of the kinds of stretches of water and their bordering lands, from what military jargon now calls "trafficability," and from the attractions of the sites selected for habitation. Here human ecology must begin with limnology as known and used by primitive man.

There are still remnants of very primitive collectors and hunters in the farthest parts of the Amazon basin, of the Guiana highlands, and perhaps elsewhere; people without any knowledge of agriculture, in some cases even of rafts or boats. Very little is known about them. Their survival may have been by retreat into the most offside and least attractive areas. Other tribes may know only archaic water skills, such as catching fish by hand ("graveling" in the American vernacular), spearing and shooting fish with bow and arrow, and especially the use of piscicidal plants, a widespread and well-developed ancient skill. Some such tribes use balsas (rafts) but make no boats. By the addition of boats, lines, and nets, the water economy is fully elaborated. The water's edge is especially rewarding to hunting. Here turtles come out to lay their eggs; rodents such as the great capybara live, and tapirs feed; and here are the greatest diversity and number of land animals, depending on the riparian vegetation. Of animal sources for the sustenance of man, there is no lack in quantity or diversity adjacent to and in the water bodies.

Man as a ground-living creature found his place at the edge of the tropical forest. The available and rewarding edges provided and maintained by nature along the water courses also afforded him an adequate plant economy. Interrupted forest canopy admits ample sunlight to ground level, where plants of lesser stature grow successfully. Shrubby and herbaceous plants, excluded from the forest, appear in diversity. Newly deposited alluvial materials, bars forming and shifting within the stream banks, trees toppled into the stream, all the accidents of rise and fall of water level maintain a zone of disturbance attractive to plants that are able to colonize with speed and to reproduce quickly. Such plants furnish for man not only food—fruits, fleshy stems, and starchy rhizomes—but also raw materials for other uses. In the New World *Guadua, Gynerium,* and other giant grasses provide man with most of the equivalents of the Old World bamboos. In addition to true palms, the *Carludovicas* are used for making baskets and matting. Aroids yield tubers and fruit (*Monstera*). Bihai (*Heliconia*) leaves supply wrapping for things to be stored or carried in, for cooking, and plates for serving food. These plants and many other bushes, climbers, or trees of low habit belong to the unstable forest edge.

As to artifacts, the primitive tropical forest folk may perhaps be said to have a wood culture, which also includes the canes and palms. Their weapons are of wood and cane, from shaft to points. Bast supplies cordage and clothing. The equivalent of ropes is provided by the woody vines called *bejucos* (lianas). Rafts and fishing floats are made from light wood such as *Ochroma*. Dugout canoes are shaped by artful charring of tree trunks of certain species such as *Ceiba, Cedrela,* and *Swietenia*. Since stone and pottery may not have been used at all, or but little, archeologic sites may be lost, unless recognized by an anomalous vegetation.

Alteration of the habitat

Not even the more primitive nonagricultural folk may be considered as merely passive occupants of particular niches in their forest environment. By their continued presence and activity, they enlarged such niches against the forest. In time, most of them added to fishing, hunting, and gathering agricultural occupation of their land. (I am not implying any spontaneous, independent development of agriculture and plant and animal domestication.) It is significant of the extent of culture replacement in our tropics that the historic survivals of nonagricultural peoples are so few and small and that they are found in edaphically adverse rather than climatically limiting areas, to soils too greatly leached or tough of structure to reward planting, or to swampy lands. A continued intervention of man in the ecology of the land has been the rule. The aquatic life was used, but hardly modified. Serious depletion of aquatic animals came with European arrivals; I know of none earlier. The inference is of normal predation, not of depredation of aquatic resource.

Man has been present in the continental tropics and their epicontinental islands from very remote times. Since climatic change here has been minimal, he has not been forced to abandon any part of his range other than lowlands submerged by postglacial rise of sea level. With every increment of skill that he gained, there was an increase in his numbers, for such skills were directed to the greater utilization of plants and animals. By his persistence, increase, and initiative, he has directed more and more selective pressure upon the rest of the biota. His acts have increased and perhaps introduced some organisms, and at the same time reduced and possibly eliminated others. An ecology without man, almost unchecked as he has been as to numbers and powers, is true only for an environment without man. I have grown more and more suspicious of any biogeography or ecology of the land from which man is thought of as eliminated as a factor of major importance.

Sedentary and social habit

Village dwelling of sorts is characteristic of water-side living. The site, if available, is chosen above high-water level. (In the New World tropics there was also an interesting habit of setting houses on high posts or piles, the distribution of which is in need of study. It may have originated where people lived in wide and flooded plains, but the style was carried into highland dwelling, as among the Chocó. Also, here and there people lived in clusters of tree houses, as in the Atrato flood plain.) The village required a landing place where boats could be beached. Stream junctions and rapids mark sites of permanent natural advantage for assembling supplies, for controlling the tributary economic area. A superior site for settlement continued to be so and normally con-

tinued to be occupied. Man is sedentary by preference, mobile by necessity; here the necessity was and is exceptional. The place that is called home acquires additional attachments, as traditions and ceremonials become rooted there. Persistence of place of habitation and cult observance is one of the major themes of cultural topography, and it extends into remote time. Nucleated and permanent settlement is the rule for most tropical habitation; the situation appears to be the same in the New World and the Old, in particular for Southeast Asia.

The village is a continuing and growing center of ecologic disturbance. Cleared spaces and refuse heaps acquire introduced plants, the two kinds of sites being edaphically in contrast. Outskirts experience the attrition common to woodlots. The knowledge that woody dicotyledons may die when the outer conductive tissue is interrupted is immemorial among woodland dwellers and perhaps common to all such people. Tropical-forest folk make little use of the ordinary fiber plants, but have many important uses for bast, both felted ("bark cloth") and twisted into lines and cords (as especially of numerous Moraceae) ; loss of inner bark may kill the tree. Also gums and resins are variously applied, in the tapping of which lesser damage is done to trees. The lessons of damage and destruction of the phloem were learned early. When agriculture was introduced, cutting or battering off a ring of phloem served to deaden the trees and admit the sunlight needed for planting. The dead trees provided dry wood for burning, the easiest way to meet fuel shortages as firewood grew scarce about the settlement. The "deadening" gradually becomes a "clearing" as storms break off the branches and finally topple the trunks. The mastery of the forest by man requires no axe; where tree trunks were desired as for canoes, or balsa, fire served to fell the tree, cut it to desired lengths, and to shape it to the finished craft.

Degrading the forest by fire

The most powerful tool by which man has altered his habitat and diversified his habits is fire, and this is true I think of all climes and all cultures. At the hearth fires, the processes of preparing food and the basic industrial techniques were worked out. Out of doors, man learned ways of setting fires so as to facilitate his appropriation of flora and fauna, thereby modifying both, by accident and also deliberately. It has been to his advantage to bring about what the ecologist calls secondary or deflected successions. A fully-grown forest, fully stocked with large trees, is a vegetation in its least useful condition for man. Except for lumber he has little benefit from the big trees. Together with other creatures that live on the ground his harvest is restricted to low-growing things, his interest is in a retarded or degraded "plant succession." He sets up and keeps up ecologic disturbance and drives the primary forest back. His unending attempt is to master and manage the living environment, and this he does by substituting lesser and short-lived plants for the great ones, by breaking down the forest margin into brush and herbs and widening more and more the zone of disturbance and diminution. This he has done most easily and most frequently by fire, to make easier the harvest of plants and animals and also to manage his land for greater productivity. The practices of Indian burning make clear that purpose and result were understood, be they agricultural, hunting, or collecting. Attrition and alteration in significant part have been deliberate.

The effectiveness of man as disturber of biota probably diminishes from the margins of the tropics to their equatorial regions. The domesticated plants of the New World mainly point to an origin in the outer parts of the tropics. The central tropical areas, it may be inferred, were agriculturally colonized from nearby lands of contrasted rainy and dry seasons. However, the tropical rain forests are not resistant to penetration and modification by agricultural folk. These often were its most effective attackers. "Winter" dry seasons characterize most of the Amazon and Orinoco basins, Central America, and the West Indies; at such times the surface of the ground and its litter dry out, and fires are effective and may spread until stopped by breaks in the topography. Even in the Amazonian montaña, where rainless days are few, litter is burned regularly before planting. The thin-barked and hence poorly-insulated trees of the humid tropics, particularly while young, are readily killed by burning. The continued persistence of natural vegetation unmodified by man is, I repeat, nearly limited to edaphic situations adverse to human interference, not to climate.

The question of the savannas

The shrinkage of rainy seasons away from the equator to give way to a great dry season in the outer tropics is often climatically described as the change from wet tropical to savanna climates. Vegetation in the latter is made up largely of more xeric plant forms, although trees characteristic of the rain forest may still be present. An objection may be entered here against identifying savanna climate and savanna vegetation. The climatic transition from precipitation in all seasons to a long and marked dry season is delimited conventionally by convenient but noncritical precipitation data. When the Spaniards picked up the term *savanna* from the island Arawaks of Haiti and Cuba, it had no climatic meaning, nor too clearly a vegetational one. Savannas were first of all plains, largely open and grassy, but not without groves of trees, and often studded with tall palms. The rainfall in the West Indian savanna lands ranges from a hundred to a hundred and fifty centimeters a year; in parts of the savannas of Venezuela and Central America, however, it may be twice as much, in other parts less than in the West Indies. The great savannas of the Orinoco lowlands include rain-poor to very rainy areas; it may be noted that they are called the *llanos* (plains).

The inference that savannas are climatically determined tropical grasslands is not justified. They extend across very different parent materials from which different soils are derived. In part, I think in minor part, they may be edaphically based; but if so they have been greatly extended beyond primevally grassy tracts. Their one common quality is that they are plains. Another equally old vegetation term out of the West Indies is *arcabuco,* thorny thicket (largely Leguminosae) and bearing also the connotation of broken terrain. Savanna and arcabuco are contrasted first by relief and then as to plant cover.

The only explanation for the great savannas that meets all conditions is fire; fire that has run often and far over plains in dry season. Except where man has continued to burn them to the present, as in the llanos, they have lost their grassy appearance. At the north, in Cuba, Haiti, and on the mainland south into Nicaragua, woodlands of Caribbean pine and related yellow pines form rather open grass-floored stands. These may extend to low elevations and into areas of heavy rainfall (as in the Mosquito coast). Fire resistance, as by corky insulating bark, germination in mineral soil that has been exposed by soil erosion, and full exposure to the sun have given opportunity to xeric woody forms, perhaps mainly of northern origin, to extend their range. The situation resembles somewhat that of the yellow-pine forests of the southern United States coastal plain, in which controlled burning is being applied to the maintenance and reproduction of pine stands.

Changes by the European conquest

The coming of Europeans had early and far-reaching effects. Great native populations of sedentary farming habits were decimated or died out in a generation or two. Mostly this collapse took place in the coastal lowlands, Yucatán being the principal exception. The Caribbean shores, the lowlands of Vera Cruz, and the Pacific lowlands from Panama to the northern limit of high culture in Sinaloa were nearly and quickly depopulated. European livestock, cattle, horses, and dogs ranged over former Indian fields, the New World becoming largely stocked from herds built up first on Haiti and Cuba. These animals contributed to the loss of their own range by disseminating seeds of woody plants through their excrement. The Spaniards complained, for example, of loss of range on Haiti to *guayabales,* thickets of guava (*Psidium*), within a generation of their arrival; these thickets are still extensive.

Various secondary vegetations may still help to identify prehistoric settlements. In the Mexican West I have thus noted colonies of mesquite (*Prosopis*) in Sonora, *Pithecollobium* and *Brosimum* farther south, and massive stands of coquito palms (*Attalca Orbignya*) as markers of once flourishing communities. Some of these archeologic dominants are not known in these parts except on old settlement sites. Chicle hunters have long been known as discoverers of Mayan archeology through the concentration of chicle trees (*Archras zapote*) about ruins. Mahogany (*Swietenia*) and tropical cedar (*Cedrela*), which are good colonizers, may also have maximum stands where old fields lay. The Cecropias come quickly into abandoned land and fade out soon, as may *Carludovica, Heli-*

conia, and more slowly such trees as *Ochroma, Guazma,* and various Malpighiaceae; but after four hundred years of abandonment of fields, certain trees (and palms) still identify the places of human habitation. Some of these are trees that had been valued by the natives and were introduced, as the coquito palms appear to have been, or protected, as the chicle trees. Others, such as perhaps mahogany and tropical cedar, may be colonists that hang on. Their persistence may underscore the extent of man's former activities. The Old War, insofar as I know, offers no parallel to this drastic elimination of human occupance.

Steepness of slope did little to reduce the exploitation by aboriginal inhabitants; even now *conucos* and *milpas* are laid out by preference on steep and broken terrain, not by any means only because there is shortage of land for planting, but often because of better drainage and aeration.

Conclusion

Lack of drainage and lack of relief, with which lack of fertility is associated, have been the main deterrents to aboriginal man in the New World. Here, and perhaps only here, may be asserted the survival of an extensive primary vegetation—of a vegetation that has been unaffected by man.

North of the American tropics we have radiocarbon dating of the presence of hunting man for more than thirty-eight thousand years (the present limit of age determination), of agricultural man for eight thousand years (Tamaulipas, by McNeish) with plants that were domesticated in the tropics at an unknown time earlier. During all his time, Man as collector, hunter, and fisherman, employed fire. As agriculturist, he was well and widely established at a time at least comparable to the western part of the Old World. As tropical planter and fisherman, his mode of life resembled that of Southeast Asia, except for lack of wet-land crops. At the time of European discovery, he was sedentary in strength in parts of the tropics that are now empty or are only now being colonized again. Under the supposed primeval forest lie the sites of quite advanced cultures. Something has been left out of the systems of synusiae and seres of ecology.

The organization of space

3

As we have seen, man has labored extensively to make the earth productive. As the primary tool-wielding animal, he has been governed by a second imperative as well—the need to make a mark of his own on the landscape where he is active and settled. This mark—this organization of the space about him—may be a minor clearing in the forest or it may be a massive conurbation spreading man's artifacts over thousands of miles. In both cases, and in the many instances between these two extremes, the elements of the cultural landscape may be seen as manifestations of the human decision to modify the earth. As in the case of man's husbandry, the examples available for consideration are varied, but they all represent a fundamental expression of man's need to arrange, to modify, and to organize the landscape.

One type of organization may be described as the architecture upon the landscape—that is, the actual morphology of the cultural landscape. Another type of organization is the process of regional perception, in which artificial lines are perceived to exist around areas of special quality. These areas may be described as regions, and they are a prime representative of the intellectual organization of the landscape by man in his attempt to make order out of his world. Both the explicit and the perceptual regions are considered in this section.

The geometry of the landscape

Spatial organization is kept relevant to cultural geography by primary concern with landscape morphology and its genesis rather than the social structure which influenced the landscape's creation. Though there are—and must be—open borders between the disciplines of anthropology, sociology, history, and geography, due to the close interaction of society and landscape, the cultural geographer's concern with man's husbandry of the earth delimits his realm of concern. Man's organizing of space in quest of subsistence, satisfaction, and a benign and productive niche, is a facet of his activity which is vital to the study of cultural geography. Two especially interesting aspects of spatial organization are the religious and the urban landscapes.

In any religious community there is a desire to make some mark upon the land in praise of the deity or deities to whom the group pays obeisance. In Western society, the most commonly cited instance of such a drive is the church. However, the church is only one of the visual manifestations of man's spiritual shaping of the landscape. Erich Isaac draws on some African examples in his article "The Act and the Covenant."

Isaac chronicles the ritual observances of the Budja, a Shona tribe of Southern Rhodesia, and the Dogon of the Upper Volta Republic in West Africa. The distinct ways in which they respond to their somewhat dissimilar landscapes are predicated upon religious belief. The Dogon, because of their genesis myth, have created a miniature cosmos within their village territory. "District, villages and homesteads all repeat the primeval pattern," Isaac points out. He posits a provocative dichotomy in his analysis of religious landscape by suggesting that the society which sees its origin as coincident with world creation—the Dogon for example—will more completely sculpt the landscape. The society which places its genesis at some point in time after the creation of the world—the Budja —tends to have a less overtly religious landscape.

This article and others exploring the role of religion in the development of landscapes indicate that there are many features of the landscape reflecting ritual.

It is in the urban realm that man has expressed his desire for organized space most explicitly. Although the spatial extent of orderly, cropped fields is far greater than the extent of urbanized land, it is the city which is the most dramatic product of man's manipulation of the landscape. From the city have come the demands which prompted the most radical modifications of the rural landscape. To the city have continually come the peoples who find the world of the rural hinterlands no longer adequate to their needs or interests.

Lewis Mumford in his classic The City in History offers a hypothesis on the genesis of the city. His view, as well as the whole problem of urban genesis, is of particular interest to cultural geographers because of the intricate combination of agricultural, social, and religious elements in the unique meeting of previously agricultural people that the city constitutes. With the formation of the city, there emerged for the first time a significant segment of the population which gained its living from some means other than cultivation or hunting and

gathering. Though Mumford's notion of the importance of the hunter is not shared by all, his general views on historical urban processes have been of major importance to the study of the city. While not a geographer in any strict sense, Mumford is frequently cited by cultural geographers, who generally find his analysis of the uses of space to be illuminating.

The ramifications of landscape ordering can be viewed in many ways. One of the most striking examples of social change generated by a change in the geometry of the countryside is seen in the European pattern of enclosure. This process of field boundary modification began in the Middle Ages and had effected a profound social and demographic change by the last decades of the eighteenth century. J. M. Houston, in the selection from A Social Geography of Europe, chronicles the village abandonment, population redistribution, and urban growth attendant upon governmental decisions to give a new system of order to the countryside. It is this interaction between man's organizing of space and his creation of social organization that gives real significance to the study of the cultural landscape.

John Hunter offers another illustration of the connection between geometric order and social order. In his article about the Nangodi of northern Ghana he traces the role of a cultural idiosyncrasy, the notion of dispersed settlement, in the creation of a well-defined settlement region. Despite administrative and economic pressures being exerted upon the Nangodi to further concentrate their villages, social mores calling for dispersed settlement are effectively maintaining traditional patterns. Hunter's research into the origin and growth of these patterns exemplifies a distinctive social perspective on the region, viewing this social convention as the dominant factor in the creation of a particular cultural landscape.

The most effective illustration in this section on the regularity of geometrical patterns upon the landscape is the excerpt from Norman Thrower's monograph, Original Survey and Land Subdivision. The survey pattern detailed by Thrower contains a rectangular skeleton which can be seen in the development of transportation lines, town placement, and internal structure, and even farmlot borders. The entire landscape of the Township and Range System implies order, regularity, and predictability.

Thrower's tandem consideration of such a landscape with a geographically homologous area lacking such order makes the impact of the ordered landscape even more striking. To the observer of the cultural landscape seeking the genetic relationship between initial settlement and subsequent landscape morphology, Thrower's monograph offers prime material.

J. B. Jackson in a Landscape *article, "A New Kind of Space," points out the different legal views of fencing, an entity fundamental to spatial organization. Showing how the New England farmers placed the burden of fence construction on stock owners while farmers had to carry the same burden themselves in the Great Plains states, Jackson makes evident basic relationships between legal system, landscape, and land tenure practices. Jackson also discusses the significance of gateways and walls and their relationship to fences to contain and fences to exclude. It is articles like this one, which make up some of the most provocative and stimulating approaches to cultural geography.*

Walls have other functions too. The high walls of the Mediterranean pleasure gardens were intended to minimize the dessicating effects of the dry winds of southern European summers. These gardens were the only spots kept moist and cool in this dry summer zone. The gardens, reflecting traffic with all corners of the world in their flora and architecture, were akin to religious landscapes; time and care were given to their intensive cultivation even though the gardens were not significant producers of foodstuffs. The criteria for their architecture and maintenance were exact and unchanging, once a particular motif had been established. These miniature landscapes often told the history of the lord of the house whose grounds they adorned. Orderly, well-favored, and distinctive in their visual impact, these pleasure gardens are an excellent example of highly organized space.

A final example of urban order comes in the discussion of the origin and development of the New England town commons. David Brodeur well documents the range of justification man has offered to keep open these lightly wooded tracts adjacent to the most valuable commercial land in New England towns and cities. Initially appended to the first town meeting houses, the lots later came to be town-owned greens, landscaped in honor of Civil War dead. The town

commons then emerged as an area by which to construct town buildings and churches. Though the lots have in many cases been diminished because of economic growth in the central business districts of these New England communities, an open, landscaped "town common" has often been retained amid the commercial centers. The three-century long tradition is a neat example of the longevity of man's initial decisions about the organization of space in a pre-urban center.

Husbandry and migration, too, affect the way man makes his mark on the land. This realization, in fact, is one of the primary goals of cultural geography; the recognition of man's penchant for landscape creation is the foundation for interpreting the cultural landscape.

This leads us to the second consideration of spatial organization, one which moves along perceptual rather than geometric lines. This section illustrates the persistence of the concept of region as evidence of man's attempt to organize his world.

Regional perception

The region is a container employed by all geographic analysis. It is intrinsic to geographic teaching, researching, and even to the comparison of systematic phenomena. While the region is in no way the unique creation of geographers, they have done more with its development and acceptance than any other writing and teaching group. This is the obvious result of the spatial and areal concern fundamental to geography. In order to deal with manageable segments of the earth's surface for the instruction of specifics, and for purposes of topical comparison, geographers have created units of the earth's surface. The region for the geographer is as the period is to the historian; both disciplines realize that borders are difficult to define, but in a broad sense, the respective containers of space and time yield more efficient scholarship and teaching.

In a professional approach, the abstractions which create a region can be generally translated into quantifiable and observable entities. A geographer decides on the criteria he can competently chart and creates a container around the space within which these criteria interact. Again, as a historian knows that movements do not absolutely begin or end on certain dates, the geographer realizes that even the most carefully chosen criteria often have expression beyond the arbitrary limits he sets for his region. The study, however, of this observable interrelationship is most easily dispatched if there is some limit to its spatial expression, some border which can confine the relevant phenomena.

This concept has grown and become increasingly sophisticated with man's attainment of encyclopaedic awareness of the physical and cultural elements on the full face of the earth. For our purpose of viewing the significance of regions to the cultural geographer, there are two perspectives which will afford adequate comprehension of man as a regionalizer.

The subjective view of the region

Few people are aware of the statistical criteria geographers utilize in their creation or delimiting of a region. Yet each individual contained within that region as well as the majority of those living adjacent to it has a "sense" of that region. This subjective view of region is what creates a regional consciousness and is frequently responsible for interregional mobility and migration. Since he is primarily concerned with systems of culture and their conception and development, the cultural geographer may find this subjective view of region as valuable as the more rigidly quantified one.

Khushwant Singh, in this selection from his powerful novel I Shall Not Hear the Nightingale, *creates a sense of region which is far stronger than one produced by analysis of climatic and meteorological data. The entire phenomenon of the summer monsoon takes on a vitality that makes it readily apparent why so much of the cultural pattern of India and the subcontinent is shaped by this season. For the reader who has never grasped any aspect of the monsoonal air flow and its precipitation patterns, the subjective comment of Singh will communicate something of the terrible, dry stillness which precedes the rains or the power of the rains. For the reader who understands the dynamics of the monsoon, the selection adds a new dimension to his perception.*

This subjective view is also expressed in Alan Beals' description of Hanumantha's village of Gopalpur. In this selection, Beals sets the stage

for his village and regional description by viewing the world through Hanumantha's eyes. Though this description is more academic than the rich prose of Singh, there is still a flavor of the subjective as the limits of Hanumantha's village world are established. The result is a fine combination of the subjective and the scholarly.

The social view of the region

The Chinese Communists have generated a significant urban migration through programs providing increased mobility for the Chinese populace and accelerated industrialization. The result, not really foreseen by the government, has been a serious social disaffection between urban and rural populations. Such a suspicion is common between these differently motivated groups, but the Communist revolution created a deceptive social homogeneity. As revolutionary fervor has waned under the problems of development and emergent factionalism, the Communists have sought to achieve again a union between these two segments of their population. The short article culled from the Communist press by Franz Schurmann and Orvell Schell testifies well to the social perspective on the region. It is felt that if the urban youth are made to see the rigor of life in rural and mountainous areas for several weeks or months, they will then treat the demands of these agrarian people with more respect. Implicit in this entire program is cognizance of the totally distinct demands rural life makes upon a person. And if the demands can be made upon the youthful segment of the population, perhaps respect for the nonurban life will be engendered for policy-making years to come. Though the article is short, it serves as an excellent example of the political utilization of the regional concept.

Richard Cooper, in another short selection, writes well of a region with a social cohesiveness scorning both economic and health concerns. In his article on an Appalachian mining community immediately following a disaster which claimed the lives of 78 miners, he chronicles the bonds which continue to make the community function. In this view of the region, we see physical and economic considerations blending to make a social tradition of mining.

The cultural composite of this region ties these people to it, despite knowledge of existing alternatives.

As an observer of the urban scene in mid-nineteenth century England, Charles Dickens effected some basic changes in the social reaction to the city. "Coketown," from Hard Times, *is an excellent example of Dickens' ability to portray an industrial scene. Even though his works can be criticized for exaggeration, his basic comments on the impersonality of this segment of urban life and industry stand as valid. To the geographer coming on the scene a century later, Dickens' works afford a harshly poetic view of those times. The cultural or historical geographer might add a comment on the social reform generated by Dickens' description of the city, showing again cultural geography's eclectic use of diverse sources.*

The social view of the region is man's view of a segment of earth surface which, because of a particular combination of economy, physical layout, and qualities of location, functions in a unique way to unite people with place. Since all regions share this quality of cohesion, the nuance is in the writer's perspective. To the student of the cultural landscape, who is particularly concerned with cultural configuration, this perspective is of special importance. And when realization of the close bond between landscape morphology and cultural configuration is added to this series of considerations, the diversity of man's spatial organization becomes apparent and significant.

maintenance of pleasure parks and gardens because the mild temperatures kept a succession of trees and plants in blossom all year round, brought winter blooms to the rose and almond tree, even in northern Italy, and renewed the freshness of the evergreen foliage during the winter rains; hence it rewarded the labor of the cultivator and preserved the beauty of the garden in the cold season. But gardens were the boon of summer. The long, hot, cloudless months made the shelter of vine-grown arbor and cypress avenue a welcome refuge. Eyes tired by a relentless sun and its reflection from the limestone roads rested gratefully upon the dark foliage of laurel or oleander. When the stifling afternoon passed and the people issued from their darkened houses, the garden paths invited to leisurely strolls between fragrant flower beds along murmurous irrigation conduits. In the Paradise legend, Adam and Eve heard "the voice of Jehovah God walking in the garden in the cool of the evening," after the custom of Palestine and other Mediterranean lands. Likewise Ammon Ra "walked abroad" in his temple garden at Thebes, where Queen Hatshepsut had planted myrrh trees imported from distant Punt.

Other factors, social and economic, contributed to the development of these ancient gardens: the early concentration of population in urban centers, the expansion of trade and accumulation of wealth, the stimulation of civilization by maritime intercourse between the various Mediterranean shores, the growth in every city of a cultured leisure class with its concern for the amenities and luxuries of life. A more potent factor still was the rapid advance of agriculture, till it attained the esthetic stage of development, crowning evidence of its intensive character.

The cultivation of land for the mere embellishment of life is a frequent concomitant of intensive tillage, even when scant arable area makes such use of the soil seem extravagant. It is conspicuous in warm countries where climatic conditions encourage an open-air life, but appears also in less exuberant form in colder countries with a long growing season like England. As a native growth it meets us in modern Japan, the Hawaiian Islands, in ancient Persia and Babylonia as in Kashmir and northern India under the Mogul rulers. All these countries developed intensive agriculture and all had to rely wholly or in part upon irrigation to secure an adequate food supply.

Elements of the garden

Ornamental gardening became a feature of ancient Mediterranean civilization. It began at the eastern end of the basin at an early period, and advanced westward in the wake of trade and colonization. Everywhere it took root, and became the fine efflorescence of that patient, tireless tillage which characterized Mediterranean lands. It grew out of the widespread fruit, flower, and herb culture, which in greater or less degree depended upon summer irrigation. The pleasure gardens originated in walled orchards and vineyards, in plantations of flowering pomegranates, quinces, plums, and apricots, in groves of stately date-palms, all with their irrigation pools and canals. The spaces between the rows of trees, for the more economic use of the precious soil, were often planted with flowers at once useful and beautiful, like the saffron-yielding crocus or the edible poppy, or "the henna flowers in the vineyards of Engeddi," or the violets, iris, and roses raised in Boeotia, Cyrenaica and other lands for the manufacture of perfumes and unguents.

The bloom and fragrance of the blossoming grape, the flowers of the pomegranate and nut tree were prized by the ancient Jews as were the fruits. "I went down into the garden of nuts to see the green plants of the valley, to see whether the vine budded and the pomegranates were in flower." Fig trees with their fresh spring foliage and grape vines trained up on trellis or pergola offered shade through the hot summer days. Orchards and vineyards, therefore, provided certain essential elements of the pleasure garden—blossoms, fragrance and especially shade. Hence the ancient Mediterranean gardens, in their long development, continued to employ vine-grown trellises, fruit trees, alleys of shade trees, and masses of dark-leaved shrubbery, and relied for their artistic effect only in part upon flower beds. Even then they preferred flowering shrubs, like myrtle, laurel, and oleander, which presented masses of green picked out with pink or white blooms. The esthetic value of the ripe fruit was never discounted.

In point of size the ancient gardens varied from the ample palace grounds and parks of kings,—which however reached only moderate proportions as a rule,—to the private home garden, whose size depended upon its location in town or country and upon the means of the owner. One seems to detect everywhere a certain restricting influence probably due to the high cost of irrigable land and heavy irrigation charges. Water theft from the public aqueducts was a common offence among Athenian citizens and the landed gentry of the Roman suburbs. The typical private garden was small, even diminutive. It lay near or behind the house to form an outdoor extension of the residence itself; and here much of the family life was led. The master could step from his drawing-room or dining-room to its flower-bordered terrace or shaded avenues. Resting on a marble bench or walking beneath a colonnade, he commanded a view of the whole. Its small size encouraged perfect cultivation and ample use of water, and did not necessarily lessen its beauty. A little garden dedicated to Eros is made to speak for itself in an anonymous Greek poem: "I am not great among gardens, but I am full of charm."

This small scale was yet further reduced in the exquisite miniature gardens planted in the peristyles of Greek and Roman houses in the last century before Christ, or perhaps earlier. The peristyle garden still survives in the patio of the modern Spanish dwelling, with its arcade, its central fountain, and its myrtles, pomegranates, jasmines, and palms growing in earthen jars. On the desert rim of the Mediterranean Orient, it survives also in the spacious court of the typical Damascus residence, whose tessellated floor is broken in the center by water basin and fountain, surrounded by flowering plants. Orange, lemon, and pomegranate trees furnish masses of dark green to rest the eyes. The fragrance of the jasmine fills the air and penetrates to the recessed colonnade or *liwan* whose cushioned couches look out upon this charming enclosure.

In contrast to the small private gardens, the sacred groves and temple grounds reveal a larger scale. These also, like the peasant's orchard, felt the transforming touch of the ancient Mediterranean gardener, and became beautiful parks for religious or secular use. The Temple of Jerusalem was an exception to the rule, because the Jews feared that trees in the courtyard might savor of the hill-top gardens or groves of Baal-worship.

The summer drought dictated the introduction of water as an unfailing feature of the garden. The air was cooled by the shower of a fountain; flower beds and shade trees had to be irrigated. Hence water was handled as an artistic *motif* in countless ways. It was conducted about the garden in stone, cement or tiled runlets; it emerged from some decorative opening in a terrace wall or issued in jets from a statue; it was collected in fish pond or lotus pool; it flowed from artificial grotto or leaped from a rocky ledge into a marble basin. Moreover, the irrigation canals with their secondary furrows necessitated a regular system, which tended to throw the garden plan into geometric forms. The modern oriental garden always seems dominated by the irrigation scheme on which its life depends. In the exquisite Indian gardens which one sees about Jaipur and Amritsar, the water conduits dictate the basic lines of flower beds, tree plots and pools, just as they do in the garden plans depicted on ancient Egyptian tombs.

The same thing is true of the Persian rose gardens which in Shiraz today reproduce the ancient garden pattern. An old description of a sixth century Persian rug shows the design of a pleasure garden, planted in fruit trees and flowers, crossed by straight paths and irrigation conduits, while the border represents long flower beds. Persian garden rugs of 1600 and later show the traditional design—a central water basin with fish and ducks, canals leading thence in formal arrangement, narrow paths following the canals, cypress alleys or slender flower beds in the border, trees and shrubs growing in jars, while the weave in the streams resembles "watered ribbon." The whole arrangement is rectilinear, reproducing the Persian garden plan as necessitated by irrigated horticulture in a semi-arid land.

Like their Persian prototypes, the Mediterranean gardens were for the most part formal and architectural in style. They were not an idealized landscape like the English park, or a miniature landscape like the Japanese garden. They had no place for winding paths or pools with the sinuous outlines of natural shores. Back of the ancient Mediterranean garden we see the engineer with his problems of hydraulic pressure, his traditions of durable and economical construction, even when pursuing aims of beauty, and his architectural skill in utilizing the small garden space at his command.

So much for the general conclusions. A survey of the ancient Mediterranean gardens according to countries will demonstrate the truth of these conclusions, and show the types that developed in various districts, owing to local differences of geographic, economic, and social conditions.

Oriental gardens

Paradise, that garden which "the Lord God planted eastward in Eden," was modeled upon the oriental gardens found in all the irrigated lands from Persia to Palestine; and it became in turn a prototype of those flowery retreats which attended Mediterranean civilization from Damascus, Jerusalem, and Antioch in the East to Roman Spain and Moorish Granada in the West. The river which watered Paradise was divided into several channels, after the manner of "the shorn and parcelled Oxus," the Nile and other irrigation streams. The garden contained "every tree that is pleasant to the sight and good for food." The tree of knowledge and the tree of life were rare exotics introduced by the early dramatist who staged here the first great tragedy of man.

The desert Arabs who skirted the high rim of the Mediterranean Basin from Moab to Mount Hermon, and looked down upon the irrigated gardens of Damascus and Ramoth-Gilead, pictured their Paradise as a pleasure garden, abounding in fountains of pure water and traversed by rivulets. There in the noonday heat the saints reclined on silken couches spread in deep shade, and enjoyed the fruits always ripe on the trees. It was the Garden of Resort in the Koran, the Garden of Eden, the Garden of the Most High. It contained everything to satisfy the taste and delight the eye of the blessed. "Close down upon them shall be its shadows and lowered over them its fruits to cull." Though this Arab Paradise waited for the pen of Mohammed, it belonged of old to the Semites of desert and grassland; it doubtless lived in Arab poetry sung in moonlit tents, ages before the seer of Mecca.

The oriental models found apt imitators in Palestine, Philistia, Phoenicia, and northern Syria, where geographic conditions encouraged their introduction and further development, and where the rich and powerful maintained large estates; but the Judean peasant enjoyed his leisure beneath his own vine and fig tree, or raised a few flowers in his herb garden. King Solomon had his pleasure park near Jerusalem, whither he was wont to go in the morning, Josephus tells us. It was laid out in fine gardens and abounded in rivulets of water. The author of *Canticles* described an ideal garden to which he compared his beloved. A high wall ensured its privacy, and a never failing spring or mountain stream watered its thirsty plants. Almond trees raised their crowns of pale pink blossoms. The scarlet fruit of the pomegranate trees punctured the dark foliage with points of light. There were beds of lilies or narcissi, of saffron-yielding crocuses, of sweet-scented henna, and all the aromatic plants which could be made to grow, while the blossoming grape vines gave forth their perfume. "Awake, O North wind, and come thou, South; blow upon my garden that the spices thereof may flow out." . . .

Egyptian gardens

Phoenicia and Palestine, through centuries of commercial and political affiliation with Egypt, drew suggestions for their horticulture also from the Nile valley. There all conditions encouraged the early development of pleasure gardens—the careful agriculture, the need of escape from the relentless sun, the great length and heat of the summer, the demand for flowers in the worship of nature gods like Isis and Osiris, and finally the presence of a rich and refined leisure class appreciative of this luxury. The Egyptian pleasure garden never lost the marks of its origin in orchard and vineyard, and of its conformity to the requirements of irrigation. The drawings in the tombs at Thebes and Tel-el-Amarna reveal formal gardens laid out with geometrical precision. Their marble pools pink with lotus blossoms, their walks spanned by vine-grown trellises, their avenues of fruit trees, their flower beds and summer houses show how readily Egyptian horticulture developed into a fine art.

Formal gardens existed in Egypt in the Fourth Dynasty (2800 B.C.). In the Eighteenth Dynasty garden technique was fully developed, and served to beautify the country estates of the wealthy or their city homes. Local plant resources no longer sufficed; incense trees and other exotics were imported. A garden of this period, depicted at Thebes, shows a walled enclosure laid out in eight sections. The middle section is occupied by a long grape arbor shading a path which leads to the dwelling. Nearby are two water basins with pavilions on their margins, lotus flowers floating on their surface, and ducks swimming about. Two other rectangular tanks, bordered by avenues of alternate palms and fig trees, occupy the front part of the garden. An artistic balance marks the composition of the whole.

A picture in a high priest's tomb at Tel-el-Amarna shows a complex of buildings comprising his residence and the storehouses of the temple, all surrounded by a garden. Trees set in depressions to hold water fill the spaces between the buildings. A palm garden has a square tank or pool in the center, around which other trees are planted in formal lines. Steps lead down to the water, while a summer house or kiosk overlooks the pool. This is a recurrent feature in the Egyptian gardens. A villa garden depicted on another Theban tomb has the usual combination of canal, water basin, shady avenues, and flower beds, but in addition shows an awning stretched over the entrance of the dwelling and projecting into the garden to form an outdoor room, where the mistress of the house is receiving guests.

Reading of these ancient Egyptian gardens,

one gets a vision of homes screened by plantations of fig and pomegranate trees from the outside world; one hears the ripple of water in the irrigation canal, the splash of ducks in the stone-lined pool. One catches vistas down shady walks beneath palm trees and acacias, where the fierce Egyptian sun can hardly penetrate; one smells the fragrance of flower beds when the slave moves about with his watering pot in the fading twilight. The Pharaohs themselves loved their trees and flowers. In his new capital in the Delta, Rameses III made "great vineyards: walks shaded by all kinds of sweet fruit trees with fruit; a sacred way splendid with flowers from all countries, with lotus and papyrus countless as the sands."

Flowers were used profusely in the social and religious life of the ancient Egyptians. At banquets they decked both table and guests. The latter wore lotus-buds in their hair, and held out the open blossom to cach other to smell. Garlands festooned the wine jars. Bouquets were offered to the gods; wreaths encircled the necks of sacrificial geese and bulls, and covered the mummy cases on their way to the tomb. Finally, according to a love song of the turin papyrus, a blooming garden is the trysting place of two lovers; and there beneath a wild fig tree they meet "on the festival of the garden." One is reminded inevitably of Japan, with its national flower festivals and its passion for gardens. . .

Evolution of the New England town common: 1630–1966

DAVID B. BRODEUR

31

The New England town common, the Mediterranean plaza, the Oriental open market lot in

David D. Brodeur, "Evolution of the New England Town Common: 1630–1966," *The Professional Geographer*, XIX, No. 6 (1967), pp. 313–318. Reproduced by permission of the Association of American Geographers.

front of significant temples—all three of these geometric landscape features have interesting roles in the continuing development of the urban areas which have grown up around them. In this article David Brodeur points out that these open spaces in the New England context were initially for the location of the town meet-

ing or parish houses. As the towns have grown, these open spaces have become islands of green and trees amid the prime commercial developments of the community. The commons have decreased in size, gained in landscaping as their functions have become more municipal, and even have similar land use patterns developing adjacent to them. Brodeur's ranging through county seats in quest of old town maps and notes on land use, as well as his researches in the local periodicals of these New England counties, reflects one process of landscape analysis.

The typical rural southern New England town common (or green) is an irregular grassy plot flanked by a tall, steepled church or two, and an aging Victorian-style town hall. Although many commons also have the usual park accoutrements (benches, bandstands, monuments, fountains and footpaths), it is certain that commons were not first conceived of as parks. Inquiry into the origins of these charming, informal open spaces reveals that, while a few of them do stem from the common grazing lands set aside by township proprietors in the early colonial period, the great majority actually derive from the original lot of the *first parish meetinghouse*. A few commons in the Connecticut valley are also remnants of broad survey

highways laid out to follow the longitudinal contours of the flood plain terrace settlements.

The tradition of having several unfenced pasturages for the common use of certain *freemen* or *free townsmen* was fast disappearing in its birthplace, England, when the first Pilgrims sailed from her shores, *via* Holland, in 1620. But the system of common pasturage had a special appeal in the first decades of the Massachusetts Bay Colony, because the Pilgrims soon learned that in order to survive in a hostile wilderness with severe winters they were compelled to share and cooperate in all undertakings. Later, however, land pressures created by the constant flow of new arrivals began to force a reduction in the generous size of tracts of common grazing land that were set aside by the township proprietors. By 1700, most outlying common lands in the coastal towns had been sold to new freeholders by towns hungry for revenue. In fact it was apparent at the very beginning that the growth of population made it impractical that so much land should remain in reserve for a few privileged *freemen* (or *free townsmen*) who enjoyed rights as *proprietors*. A few once marshy tracts of common grazing land have survived, among them the well known commons in Boston, and Salem, Massachusetts.

The survival of Boston Common (Fig. 1) was assured partly because of some lingering senti-

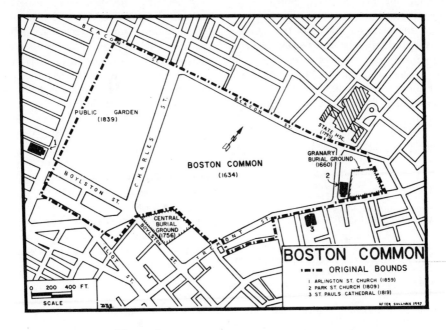

Figure 1.

ment for the ancient institution of common pasturage, but mostly because new functions were discovered for this inner pasturage as the town slowly grew around it. The Boston Common early served conveniently as a drill field for militia. It also attracted rope makers from the docks who needed a long open space for their work. It came to be appreciated, later, as a place for an evening stroll. Orators and evangelists flocked to Boston Common in the eighteenth century and on occasion can be heard there today. When, at various times, the town fathers made known plans to sell portions of the common for revenue, irate townsmen fell back on their right to tether a cow and the common was saved. This continued until 1830 when the city passed an ordinance forbidding grazing as an obstruction to traffic. In 1822, two years before Boston incorporated as a city, the last outlying common pastures on the neck were sold to make way for house lots. The city began to landscape her remaining forty-acre common on the flank of Beacon Hill after 1836.[1]

Most New England village greens derive not from common pasturage but from the meetinghouse lot. If they are sometimes also called commons it is because they served sporadically as night corrals for the domestic animals of the community. Also, a portion of the meetinghouse lot often was reserved as a training field for local militia and this may have contributed to the "common land" concept.[2]

Because the Puritans believed that no humanly conceived structure was worthy of being called a church, they referred to their place of worship as the *meetinghouse*. Provision for a large lot for the meetinghouse became a strict requirement of the General Court of the Massachusetts Bay Colony about 1650. For example, in 1667, the court provided that some fifty acres be set aside for the Worcester, Massachusetts, meeting-house (Fig. 2).[3] As historian Cushing

says, ". . . the transformation of the meetinghouse lot into a town common is part of the history of each community."[4] Such lots were successively encroached upon by abutting private property holders, rival church sects, and even taverns. This in part explains why so many commons are only three or four acres in area today. In the seventeenth century, all town business, religious and civil, was carried on in the meetinghouse by the ecclesiastical oligarchy, and the distinction between church and state in most of these communities was largely theoretical. Because the meetinghouse was not really a "church" in the traditional sense, there was rarely any objection to this arrangement.

More research needs to be done to determine just when the term "green" came to be applied to the inevitably reduced meetinghouse common lot. It probably followed the first attempts to beautify these commons in certain towns. While records show that the first tree plantings on the green at Canton, Massachusetts, were made in 1794 and those on New Haven's Public Square (Green), in 1799, Cushing claims that ". . . most commons were barren, unsightly plots from the early days until well after 1835. Brush, stumps, stones, rubbish, dead trees, and stagnant pools . . . typified a great many . . ."[5] The constant stream of settlers and other visitors from England in the nineteenth century, bringing with them vivid memories of the manicured English church green so often celebrated in verse, must have had its influence on the New England brethren. The landscaping of the commons or greens began in earnest, however, after the Civil War when communities were moved by patriotic sentiment to erect monuments to the fallen. With so much communal history already tied up in the site of the first parish meetinghouse, such monuments commonly were erected on the green which by then had often become separated from the meetinghouse by the formalization of old cow trails and wagon roads into town streets.[6] Although doubtless the New England town common or green has inspired some isolated imita-

---

[1] Brodeur, David D., *Geographic Consequences of the Location of Some New England Town Commons and Greens,* unpublished doctoral thesis, Clark University, Worcester, 1963, pp. 79–83.

[2] *Ibid.,* pp. 39–41. Famous Lexington Green, in Massachusetts, is also known as the Common. In Amherst, Massachusetts, the largest of three surviving commons was known in the nineteenth century as the "village green." Today it is called Amherst Common.

[3] *Records of the Proprietors,* Vol. III, Collections of the Worcester Society of Antiquity, p. 16.

[4] Cushing, J. D., "Town Commons of New England, 1640–1840," *Old-Time New England,* Vol. 50, No. 3, Jan.–March, 1961, p. 87.

[5] *Ibid.,* p. 92.

[6] Brodeur, *op. cit.,* pp. 43–47; see also Cushing, *op. cit.,* p. 90.

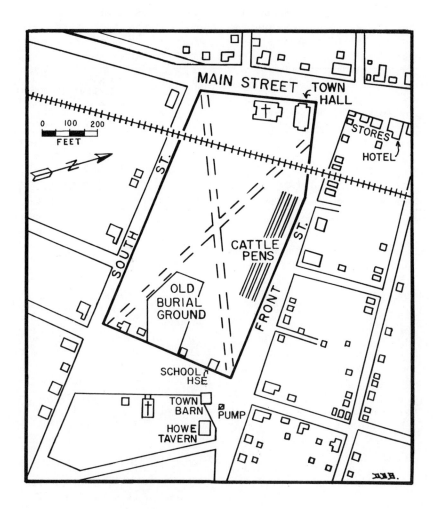

Figure 2.

tions in other parts of the United States, in particular some township squares in Ohio,[7] this phenomenon is limited not only to New England but, with few exceptions, to southern New England. The communities founded later in northern Maine, New Hampshire and Vermont were mostly the settlements of large, chartered land companies and their members were not of a Puritan cast of mind.

A survey of the communal land uses facing commons was performed by the author in 1962. As Table 1 shows, in half the 138 towns (with commons) on which land use data were collected, the town hall faced the common or

stood on a portion of it. In six out of ten communities, one or more churches faced the common or stood upon it. This phenomenon of church and town hall-on-common is the result of the legal formalization of the already realized separation of church and state in Massachusetts, Connecticut, New Hampshire and Maine in the second decade of the nineteenth century.[8] In Vermont and Rhode Island, where few Puritans settled, church and state had, in effect, never been united. The congregations of most towns continued to permit town business

7 Brodeur, *op. cit.*, pp. 26–27.

8 Sinnott, E. W., *Meetinghouse and Church in Early New England*, McGraw-Hill Book Co., New York, 1963, p. 73.

Table 1. Major land uses and land use combinations found on the central common of 138 towns*

	Town Hall	Library	Historical Society	Church(es)
No. of commons with cited use	69	58	30	81
Use as a % of all commons cited	50%	42%	21.7%	60%

	Res.	Business	Mixed R. and B.	Other Town Bldgs.
No. of commons with cited use(es)	47	18	64	36
Use(es) as a % of all commons cited	35%	13%	47%	27%

* Source: Brodeur, *Geographic Consequences . . .* p. 68.

to be conducted in the meetinghouse. It was not until the 1840's that most New England towns got around to building a hall for the purpose of town business.[9] When they did they usually chose, for the sake of tradition and convenience, a spot by the common. In like manner, such sects that evolved from the Puritan church, the Congregationalists and Unitarians, as well as Methodists, Baptists and others, also preempted a place on the common.

Commons and greens in New England have served for two centuries as the conspicuous setting for finely designed churches. They have also served to attract a number of private schools whose religiously motivated founders wanted to be close to the meetinghouse. Among such common-oriented secondary schools are Governor Dummer Academy on Byfield, Massachusetts, common; Northfield Academy on the common at Northfield, Massachusetts, and Deerfield Academy, which moved to its present location on the common at Deerfield from another location in that town in 1878.[10] Among the colleges that were founded on sites overlooking commons are Dartmouth, in Hanover, New Hampshire; Harvard, overlooking the common at Cambridge, Massachusetts, and Mount Holyoke on the small common at South Hadley, Massachusetts. Yale College, founded at Saybrook, Connecticut, removed to New Haven, overlooking the green, in 1717. The green was

the site of the first meetinghouse (1640) and, later, the State House.[11]

Towns and cities have long since acquired control of the common, the norm usually being outright ownership. An exception is found in the Public Square (or Green) at New Haven, Connecticut, which has been controlled since 1641 by an elected Proprietor's Committee. Another exception is the village green at Bedford, New York, a town that was founded as a part of Connecticut. In Bedford, the green is controlled by the descendants of the original proprietors.[12] In Newington, New Hampshire, the town owns both the common and its meetinghouse.[13]

In recent decades, historic district zoning and urban renewal have combined to contribute to the preservation or restoration of certain commons in Massachusetts and Connecticut. The recent transformation of Salem Square on the south fringe of the city common at Worcester, Massachusetts, illustrates what has been done for commons through urban renewal (Fig. 3). Until 1960, an ugly three-story brick loft, a relic of the bygone textile era, could be found facing the square. The loft was demolished and eventually replaced by the relocated city public library, while dilapidated bus terminals on the south side of the square were torn down, expos-

9 *Ibid.*, pp. 72–73.

10 Chamberlain, Samuel and Henry N. Flynt, *Historic Deerfield: Houses and Interiors*, Hastings House, New York, 1965, p. 17.

11 Reps, John W., *The Making of Urban America: A History of City Planning in the United States.* Princeton University Press, Princeton, 1965, p. 126; Brodeur, *op. cit.*, pp. 49–50.

12 Conversation with William J. Millmore, Town Clerk, Bedford, New York, in 1962.

13 Sinnott, *op. cit.*, p. 41.

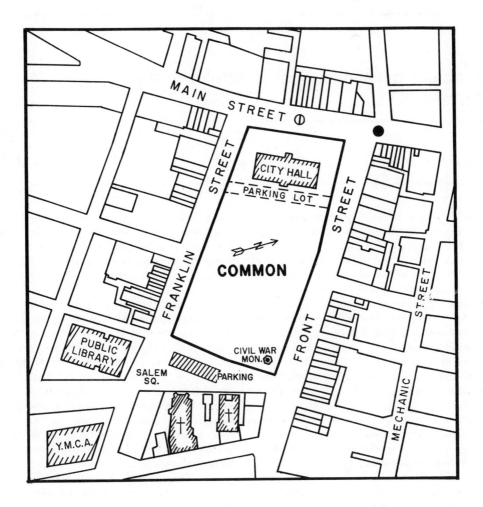

Figure 3.

ing again the nave of the Catholic church. A further contribution toward making the common a community center was in the construction of a well-designed YMCA facility beside the library. At the opposite or north end of Worcester Common stands the city hall on the site of the first parish church. A plaque there commemorates the fact of the first public reading in New England of the Declaration of Independence on July 14, 1776.[14]

---

[14] Paine, N., "Worcester's Old Common, with Some of its Neighbors and Incidents," *Worcester Magazine*, Vol. 1, Jan.–June, 1901, pp. 347–355.

Municipal quasi-exclaves: examples from Yonkers, N.Y.

ALEXANDER MELAMID

32

In his initial settlement of a given region, man is apt to establish some of his borders along the lines of the natural landscape. Then, as development of the settled area continues, he reshapes this natural landscape as he organizes it more efficiently for his uses. There are times when such a sequence creates situations which are neither natural nor efficient. One such development is described below by Alexander Melamid. In organizing urban space in this case, man was not far-sighted enough to see the potential confusion caused by not modifying municpal boundaries at the same time that he modified natural boundaries by filling in the margins of the Bronx River. The article notes the strange economic relationships which have sprung up because of this failure to coordinate these various landscape changes.

The boundaries of the city of Yonkers were determined before construction of railroads and modern streets and highways. Due to the nature of the terrain, north-south boundaries were made to follow rivers—the Hudson in the west, and the Bronx River in the east. East-west boundaries were drawn as straight lines between these rivers without considering relief. Subsequent construction of transportation facilities was easily coordinated with the location of the straight line boundaries; however, along the rivers, straight or nearly straight railroad lines and limited access highways frequently cross the previously determined curving river boundaries. This caused no problems along the wide navi-

Alexander Melamid, "Municipal Quasi-Exclaves: Examples from Yonkers, N.Y.," *The Professional Geographer*, XVIII, No. 2 (1966), 94–96. Reprinted by permission of the Association of American Geographers.

gable Hudson River where foreshore rights could be acquired easily. In the east the boundary, located in the center of the Bronx River, was a meandering brook, about ten feet wide flowing in a fairly straight swampy valley about 1,000 feet wide and between 50 to 100 feet lower than the surrounding land. This brook was relocated twice: first, in the 19th century to permit the railroad from New York to White Plains to be constructed on the eastern side of the valley, and in the 20th century for the building of the Bronx River Parkway west of the railroad. The river was straightened as the result of these relocations, and now flows mostly between the railroad and the parkway. Both transportation avenues are straight or gently curved and follow the general direction of the boundary; they can be crossed at only a few points. The railroad runs on a high embankment, and the area between the railroad and the eastern side of the valley was raised by means of dumping and filling. The swamps have disappeared altogether and most of the valley west of the railroad, if not used by the parkway or river, has become a public park.

Despite these significant changes in the valley, the boundary was never adjusted. It still follows the former river-bed criss-crossing the railroad, the parkway and the river. As a result quasi-exclaves of Yonkers lie to the east of the parkway, railroad and river, and are accessible only by long detours through the city of Mount Vernon, the Borough of the Bronx (part of New York City) and villages of Eastchester Township. Similarly, quasi-exclaves of these cities and villages are accessible only through Yonkers territory. As services, such as sewers and police and fire protection have to be provided for these quasi-exclaves, a number of problems arise. These problems are not important west of the railroad, and east of the railroad and north of quasi-exclave A, as these parcels of land are part of the Westchester County Park system and east of the railroad and north of quasi-exclave A most of the filled land to the eastern edge of the Bronx River valley is zoned for use by light industries, warehousing, and retailing in all municipalities. Here observations regarding the service problems of municipal quasi-exclaves can be made.

Quasi-exclave A contains a fuel depot which adjoins the railroad and a supermarket with its parking lot. The latter straddles the Yonkers–Mount Vernon boundary and its entrance is located entirely in Mount Vernon. The fuel oil depot pays taxes only to Yonkers, while the supermarket pays taxes to Yonkers and Mount Vernon according to the geographical division of the property. Services should be supplied by

the two cities according to the same division, but in fact easier access from Mount Vernon encourages use of Mount Vernon services. For example when a thief was observed in the Yonkers portion of the supermarket, Mount Vernon police were called in to make the arrest.

Quasi-exclave B contains a builder's warehouse which also straddles the boundaries of Yonkers, Mount Vernon and the Bronx. Direct road access is available only to Mount Vernon. Originally the office of this warehouse had been deliberately located in Mount Vernon territory in order to obtain all services from that city. Services are still supplied by this city although the new office straddles the Yonkers-Bronx boundary and taxes are equally divided between all three municipalities.

Quasi-exclave C contains a manufacturing plant two-thirds of which extends into the Bronx; a small portion is also located in Mount

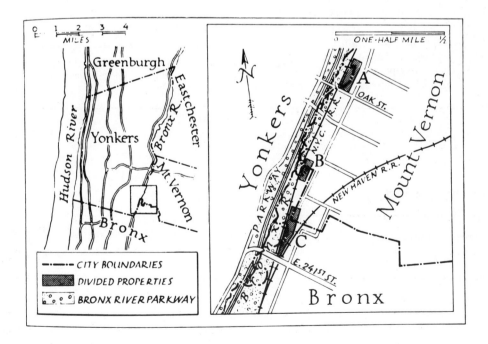

Figure 1.

Vernon. Another railroad and a high bridge (East 241st Street) crossing the valley make the Bronx area of the plant into a quasi-exclave of the Bronx which can be reached by road only through Mount Vernon. This quasi-exclave extends to area B, covers a total of eight acres and is about as large as all the quasi-exclaves of Yonkers together. Taxes are paid according to the geographical division of the land occupied by this plant, but building plans were filed only in the Bronx as the bulk of the building is located there. To avoid New York City sales taxes, truck loading bays were deliberately located in the Yonkers quasi-exclave, where the city of Yonkers paved about 40 yards of road-way to make it a Yonkers public street and to assert its rights. However, this Yonkers public street can be reached only by private roads of the plant through Mount Vernon and the Bronx. The mail address of the plant is also in Yonkers but no mail is delivered and the firm picks it up at a Yonkers post office. By special arrangement Mount Vernon sewers drain the whole area. Police and fire protection are expected from all three municipalities, but in fact are provided by the railroads which also use the remaining land of this quasi-exclave of the Bronx.

Despite the limited number of cases, the examples appear to demonstrate the difficulties in supplying municipal services to quasi-exclaves and the general preference of uses of exclaves for services by the most accessible municipalities. Adjustment of the boundary according to these criteria has been officially suggested by Yonkers and Mount Vernon but has not been carried out due to disagreement on compensation for assessed values. The straddling of the boundary by most establishments appears to be unimportant in the context of provision of services for quasi-exclaves. Provision of services by other parties, as by the railroads in the case of quasi-exclave C, although resembling some of the arrangements in neutral territories[1] appears to be a coincidence resulting from the geographical distribution of railroad land not related to the local agglomeration of quasi-exclaves. In none of the cases investigated was the location in a quasi-exclave a desideratum and all firms would have preferred locating in normal territories of municipalities. According to interviews, shortage of suitable land in the general area north but not too far from New York City made the firms accept location in quasi-exclaves. Additional observations on other municipal boundaries, particularly with reference to services for residents (schools, etc.) will be required to establish more thorough generalizations, and the writer would appreciate receiving references to such material.

---

[1] Alexander Melamid, "Economic Geography of Neutral Territories," *Geogr. Rev.*, Vol. 45, July, 1955, pp. 359–375.

The monsoon

KHUSHWANT SINGH

33

The creation of a regional identity is one of the most appealing aspects of Khushwant Singh's writing. In this selection from I Shall Not Hear

Khushwant Singh, *I Shall Not Hear the Nightingale* (New York: Grove Press, Inc., 1959), 101–105. Reprinted by permission of Grove Press, Inc. Copyright © 1959 by Khushwant Singh.

the Nightingale, *he describes the anticipation and arrival of the summer monsoon. This singular feature of the environment of South Asia is rightly seen as dominant in the creation of the culture patterns of that region. Though a description such as Singh's fails to illustrate the actual dynamics which produce this still enig-*

*matic pattern of precipitation, it does give life
to the rains much as they give life to the land.
To a cultural geographer, who is as much concerned with perception of environment as he
is with the environment itself, authors like
Singh play a vital role in making explicit man's
reaction to various elements of his landscape
and skyscape.*

To know India and her peoples, one has to
know the monsoon. It is not enough to read
about it in books, or see it on the cinema
screen, or hear someone talk about it. It has to
be a personal experience because nothing short
of living through it can fully convey all it
means to a people for whom it is not only the
source of life, but also their most exciting
impact with nature. What the four seasons of
the year mean to the European, the one season
of the monsoon means to the Indian. It is preceded by desolation; it brings with it the hopes
of Spring; it has the fullness of summer and the
fulfillment of autumn all in one.

Those who mean to experience it should
come to India some time in March or April.
The flowers are on their way out and the trees
begin to lose their foliage. The afternoon
breeze has occasional whiffs of hot air to warn
one of the days to come. For the next three
months the sky becomes a flat and colorless gray
without a wisp of a cloud anywhere. People
suffer great agony. Sweat comes out of every
pore and the clothes stick to the body. Prickly
heat erupts behind the neck and spreads over
the body till it bristles like a porcupine and one
is afraid to touch oneself. The thirst is un-
quenchable, no matter how much one drinks.
The nights are spent shadow-boxing in the dark
trying to catch mosquitoes and slapping oneself
in an attempt to squash those hummings near
one's ears. One scratches and curses when
bitten; knowing that the mosquitoes are strok-
ing their bloated bellies safely perched in the
farthest corners of the nets, that they have
gorged themselves on one's blood. When the
cool breeze of the morning starts blowing, one
dozes off and dreams of a paradise with ice cool
streams running through lush green valleys.
Just then the sun comes up strong and hot and
smacks one in the face. Another day begins with
its heat and its glare and its dust.

After living through all this for ninety days
or more, one's mind becomes barren and bereft
of hope. It is then that the monsoon makes its
spectacular entry. Dense masses of dark clouds
sweep across the heavens like a celestial army
with black banners. The deep roll of thunder
sounds like the beating of a billion drums.
Crooked shafts of silver zigzag in lightning
flashes against the black sky. Then comes the
rain itself. First it falls in fat drops; the earth
rises to meet them. She laps them up thirstily
and is filled with fragrance. Then it comes in
torrents which she receives with the supine
gratitude of a woman being ravished by her
lover. It impregnates her with life which bursts
forth in abundance within a few hours. Where
there was nothing, there is everything: green
grass, snakes, centipedes, worms, and millions of
insects.

It is not surprising that much of India's art,
music, and literature is concerned with the
monsoon. Innumerable paintings depict people
on roof tops looking eagerly at the dark clouds
billowing out from over the horizon with flocks
of herons flying in front. Of the many melodies
of Indian music, *Raga Malhar* is the most
popular because it brings to the mind distant
echoes of the sound of thunder and the pitter-
patter of raindrops. It brings the odor of the
earth and of green vegetation to the nostrils;
the cry of the peacock and the call of the koil to
the ear. There is also the *Raga Desha* which
invokes scenes of merry-making, of swings in
mango groves, and the singing and laughter of
girls. Most Indian palaces had specially designed balconies from where noblemen could
view the monsoon downpour. Here they sat
listening to court musicians improvising their
own versions of monsoon melodies, sipping
wine and making love to the ladies of their
harem. The commonest theme in Indian songs
is the longing of lovers for each other when the
rains are in full swing. There is no joy fuller
than union during monsoon time; there is no
sorrow deeper than separation during the season of the rains.

An Indian's attitude to clouds and rain remains fundamentally different from that of the
European. To the one, clouds are symbols of
hope; to the other, those of despair. The
Indian scans the heavens and if cumulus clouds
blot out the sun his heart fills with joy. The
European looks up and if there is no silver
lining edging the clouds his depression deepens.
The Indian talks of someone he respects and

looks up to as a great shadow; like the one cast by the clouds when they cover the sun. The European, on the other hand, looks on a shadow as something evil and refers to people of dubious character as people under a shadow. For him, his beloved is like the sunshine and her smile a sunny smile. He escapes clouds and rain whenever he can and seeks sunnier climes. An Indian, when the rains come, runs out into the streets shouting with joy and lets himself be soaked to the skin.

The fact that the monsoons come at about the same time every year gives expectation a sort of permanent place in the Indian's mental calendar. This does not happen with other people, e.g., the Arabs, who also thirst for water and bless its descent. (If the Arabs had the monsoon turning up with the same regularity, their calendar would have taken note of changes of seasons instead of being linked with the vagaries of the moon.) All the different calendars current in India are a dexterous combination of the lunar and the solar systems. As a result, the correspondence between the month and the season is much closer. On the official day heralding Spring, the chill winds of winter mysteriously vanish and a warm breeze begins to blow. Similarly, while the coming of the monsoon may be any day in June or July by the Roman calendar, more often than not the first of Sawan will see it in full force all along the Western ghats and well inland up to the plains of the Punjab.

Sawan is the month for lovers. Just as Spring turns a young man's fancy to thoughts of love, in Sawan an Indian girl longs to be in her lover's arms. If her lover is not there, she languishes away singing songs of sadness. That spirit is expressed by the Guru in his composi-tion on the monsoon, in which, following the literary tradition of the time, he describes God as the Great Lover and the devotee as His mistress yearning for union with Him.

> The season of rains is here
> My heart is full of joy
> My body and soul yearn for my Master.
> The Master is away and if He return not,
> I shall die pining for Him.
>
> The lightning strikes terror in my heart.
> I stand alone in my courtyard
> In solitude and in sorrow.
> O Mother of Mine, I stand on the brink of
>   death.
> Without the Lord I have no hunger
> Nor no sleep;
> I cannot bear the clothes on my body.
>
> Spake the Guru: She alone is a wife true
>   Who loseth herself in the Lord.

•   •   •

The monsoon had burst some time after midnight. The thunder and lightning was enough to wake the dead but people had just lain in bed pretending that they were asleep. It came as usual: first a few heavy drops and everyone announced to everyone else, "It is going to rain," then suddenly it began to pour. There was shouting on all the roof tops and much bustle and activity as servants ran from their quarters to help bring the *charpoys* and bedding down into the verandahs. It took some time to get back to sleep again—but not too long. Nerves which had been frayed by the heat were soothed. And the sound of water spouting down from the roof, the gurgle of the gutters and of the rain falling in torrents was like a lullaby. . . .

The village world

ALAN R. BEALS

34

The most ubiquitous expression of the agrarian man is the farming village. Obviously, village morphology and social configuration differ a good deal from one locale to another, but most villages display similar characteristics of village life. Anthropologist Alan Beals has done a masterful study of this village pattern in the short book, Gopalpur: A South Indian Village. *In this portion of the first chapter of that book, he takes clear inventory of the elements of the material and social environment which shape the lives of the village population. Having minimal knowledge of the village hinterland five miles distant, but efficiently familiar with the soils, plants, pests, and climate of the farming land immediately adjacent to the village, these south Indians stand well as spokesmen for hundreds of millions of peasant people.*

Hanumantha stands upright in the center of a clearing. At his feet is a round granite stone considerably larger than a basketball. Over his head the leaves of a *nim* tree shift and turn in the sunlight. Hanumantha has removed his shirt and wrapped his *dhoti* around his waist, tucking it tightly between his legs so that the five yards of flowing white cloth resemble a tightly fitting pair of shorts. Deliberately, Hanumantha squats beside the stone. Seizing it with his hands he raises it up to his knee. Straightening his legs, he carries it up to his waist and rolls it up to his shoulder. Suddenly he loses control. The stone splashes into the sand as the barefooted youth dodges to one side.

In a few minutes, Hanumantha gives the stone to Sabe and sits beside me on the stone platform under the nim tree. "Is it true," he asks, "that in America people eat children?" He continues without permitting an answer, "I have heard about your country, people there don't do any work, everything is done by machines. You people are not very strong. That is why you must depend on us for food. We must work hard every day under the hot sun and even in the rain. You people work whenever you feel like working, and you eat rice every day. My brother has been to Bombay and has told me all about the way you Americans live."

"Actually," I tell him, "my country is not Bombay, it is many miles from Bombay."

"Yes," he says, "I know, it is in London."

Although he is only twenty-six, scarcely old enough to marry, Hanumantha has seen much of the world surrounding Gopalpur. He has been several times to the market at Kandkur, four miles away, and he has attended fairs and festivals in villages up to ten or eleven miles distant. He has never been to the town of Yadgiri, fifteen miles away, and is a little afraid of what might happen to him if he goes there.

Hanumantha's business is the business of almost every other adult male in Gopalpur. It is to plow the fields, to dig the gardens, and to harvest the ripened crops. The most important thing in Hanumantha's life is to find his place in the village. He must find a wife; he must have male children; he must have many friends; he must accumulate enough wealth to be able to arrange proper marriages for his children; and he must have a number of mourners at his funeral. To achieve these things, "to make his name great," Hanumantha must operate within the set of rules appropriate to success within the village. Many of these rules are unwritten and are not discussed by Hanumantha's relatives and neighbors. When someone breaks such rules, there may be little more than an increasing awareness that someone in the village is out of his proper place. When this happens, Hanumantha's neighbors take action to restore the pattern that has been warped or broken.

At the moment, Hanumantha is following the course of action suitable to a young man. By developing his physical skills as a weight lifter and wrestler, he hopes to win a coconut at a local fair and offer it triumphantly to the village god. Later, Hanumantha will learn, as the older men in the village have learned, that deeds of strength and heroism bring only a passing reward, and he will then turn his attention to the making of alliances and coalitions designed to shield his growing family from the whims of Nature and the uncontrolled impulses of his fellow men. As he moves into middle age, Hanumantha will find that the basis of success in Gopalpur lies not in physical prowess, but in the number of cattle and the number of men that he can control.

Hanumantha considers himself to be a free agent. He decides what he is going to do and he does it. At the same time, Hanumantha's freedom is limited by the context within which he operates. That context includes the natural and material environment of the village of Gopalpur; it includes Hanumantha's childhood experiences; it includes the people who live in Gopalpur and the region surrounding Gopalpur; and it includes the rules and the ways of life which have developed in Gopalpur over many generations.

The material environment

Using tools and techniques available to them, the people of Gopalpur have interacted with their physical surroundings to produce a material environment that is a result of their way of life and at the same time a cause of it. The buildings and walls of Gopalpur, most of which were standing when Hanumantha was born and will be standing when he dies, channel the flow of traffic through the village, and so influence the frequency with which Hanumantha will encounter particular friends or neighbors.

Many other things—the distance to the nearest neighboring village, the extent to which Hanumantha's ancestors have maintained the fertility of the village fields, the kinds of things that will grow in the fields, the forces controlling wind and rain—set subtle limits upon the possible ways in which Hanumantha can behave.

Gopalpur is a mile from the nearest neighboring village. Unless he wishes to expend considerable effort, Hanumantha must find his friends and enemies within his own village. The buildings in Gopalpur are rectangular structures of stone and mud. A typical house is perhaps thirty feet wide and forty feet deep. At the front of the house, there is a raised veranda six to eight feet wide. In the center of the veranda is a large double door, set in a carved wooden frame with carved horses' heads projecting just above and on both sides of the door. There are no windows in the walls; light and air are admitted in limited quantities through holes cut in the flat clay roof. When it rains, these skylights are covered with plates and the householders sit inside in the darkness wondering when the water will find cracks in the roof and pour down into the interior.

Just inside the doorway, at ground level, stand cattle solemnly munching hay that has been removed from a platform above their heads and deposited at their feet. Further back, in the darkness of the interior, is a raised area. Here, the floor has been carefully smeared with a plaster of hard red mud brought from a nearby hillock. Into the floor has been set a mortar and millstones used for pounding or grinding grain so that it can be made into one of several varieties of mush, or into flat round pieces of unleavened bread. Behind a door leading off the platform is a kitchen. At the left of the kitchen door on the opposite side of the room, a flat stone is placed at floor level and surrounded by a rim of mud and stone. A small opening leads from the stone through the wall. Brass and clay jars full of water standing beside the stone indicate that it is a bathing place. On the other side of the room is a low platform, with two small fire places cut into it at one end. Round-bottomed pots, full of cooked food or of stored grain, line the remainder of the platform. Each pot is placed on a ring of rice straw so that it cannot tip. Smoke from the fireplace fills the kitchen and drifts into the main part of the house. Behind another door is a smaller room used for grain storage.

The house in Gopalpur is a fortress, used for cooking, the storage of valuables, and the keeping of cattle. The real business of living takes place outside, on the veranda or on the stone platform under the nim tree. People carry food outside to eat. Housewives have a second flour mill on the veranda, where they may grind grain and gossip with the neighbors. The old man spends his days sitting under the nim tree, meticulously twisting rope on his naked thigh. The baby lies on the platform, or in a cradle suspended on ropes from the ceiling of the veranda. Older children play in the dirt in front of the house, pretending to cook or plow, or enact parts in a drama or ceremony. At nightfall, the family's two cots are placed in the street or in a cleared space in front of the house. The wife sleeps in one cot with her mother-in-law and the baby. The husband sleeps in the other cot with his male children. The old man shuffles off to the fields where he sleeps on a platform overlooking the ripening crops.

In addition to the houses and stone platforms, the only structures of any importance within the village are small stone houses or shelters within which are placed the images of the various gods. The most important of these "god-houses" are those of the two village gods. One of these, dedicated to Hanumantha and his reincarnation, Bhima, is located at the southeastern edge of the village. It is surrounded by a cleared space and a low barrier. To this place come wedding parties from other villages and, on feast days, processions of people to make offerings. The other important godhouse, located outside the village, is the tomb of Shah Hussein. For generations, this god or saint has defended the village against hard times and misfortunes. Every year, when they feel happy, the young men of Gopalpur walk in procession, with drums beating, to the sacred Bhima River ten miles away. A Brahmin priest is paid ten rupees (ten days' wages) to carry a potful of water from the river to wash the tomb of Shah Hussein. Scattered throughout the village are smaller godhouses. There is a termite nest dedicated to Nagappa, the snake god, and there are temples to the often present meat-eating goddesses of cholera, of small pox, and of scabies.

The countryside

Outside the narrow compass of the village is a fence of thorns designed to protect the fields from roaming cattle. Here stand great stacks of hay used to feed the cattle during the hot dry months between March and June. Narrow passageways lead from the village down thorn-lined pathways into the fields. To the east runs a small stream, swollen with flood waters during the rainy summer season but reduced to a few stagnant pools in the hot season. At dawn and at twilight, the women of Gopalpur come to scoop out shallow pools in the sand and fill their brass water jars with the slowly gathering water. At other times, wrinkled old women wash their pet goats or water buffaloes, and small children wade in the lukewarm water and tumble in the sand. Men wrap their head-clothes around their waists, wash their bodies and then their dhoties (waist cloths) and shirts. Women wrap themselves in their husbands' worn dhoties and spread their saris (eight yards of colored cotton cloth) across the sand to dry.

Beyond the stream, looking toward the market town of Kandkur, lies the finest land in Gopalpur. During the fall and early winter, these fields bear great stalks of sorghum millet, eight to fourteen feet high. At the tip of each stalk is a heavy fistful of the grain that forms the basis for almost every meal. When the watchmen are not looking, passers-by stop to cut the ripening canes and then move on, chewing the sweet pith and spitting it out along the pathway. To own one of these fields is to be rich, for every acre yields three or four crops every two years.

North of the village, the land is higher and more sandy. Scattered through the fields are great mango trees whose acid, green fruit is the only fresh food available during the hot season. In a few places, ambitious farmers have scratched shallow wells and used them to irrigate patches of onions and chili and egg-plant. Closer to the village, wealthier men have built huge stone-lined wells resembling swimming pools. Older men enter these wells treading softly on slabs of granite thrust into the sides of the well to form a staircase. Younger men and children, when it is time for their weekly bath or when the weather justifies such sport, approach the well at a gallop and jump from the parapet into the water twenty feet below. The beginning swimmer's older brother attaches water wings of pithy wood to his shoulders and tosses him casually into the water.

South of the village the soil is quite sandy. In low-lying places, moisture has gathered and the land is barren and salty. Where water trickles through the salty soil, saltmakers come, collect the saltwater and pour it onto great flat stones rimmed with clay. The water evaporates, leaving behind it large crystals of off-white salt. Beyond this desert area, children six to twelve years old guide their sheep and cattle from shrub to forlorn shrub, or sit in a tree's scant shade and play forlorn melodies on their shepherd's pipes.

Beyond this pasture land, the terrain slopes gently upward toward the knife-edge of granite that marks the boundary of the village. Within the granite walls of this hill is said to be a secret cave where bandits once gathered to divide their loot. It is said that, even now a tiger lurks there. Young men sometimes come and search within the walls of the hill for bandits or tigers. In 1960, in a neighboring village, three young men found a *cheeta* (a leopard), attacked it with sickles and wood knives and, although they were seriously injured, gained a certain notoriety. Those who travel to the hill at dusk or dawn will surprise a herd of antelope and see them bound effortlessly away across stream beds and thickets.

From the top of the hill, the surrounding countryside is visible. To the north and east stretches a low range of rolling forested hills a thousand feet high. To the south and west, the plain stretches down to the gorge of the Bhima River. Fifteen miles west, hidden by hills, is the town of Yadgiri where there is a railway station and where the great officials of government have their offices. Fifteen miles east is the town of Narayanpet where people go to sell their surplus grain and to buy clothing for special occasions.

A view from the top of the hill suggests some of the limits and possibilities which result from the location of the village. Because Gopalpur is located in the center of the plain, it lacks extensive forests or grazing lands. Wild boars do not come out of the mountains to attack the growing crops, and cheetas rarely prey upon the calves or sheep. Because the streams are wider toward the center of the plain, the road from

Yadgiri to the distant city of Hyderabad by-passes Gopalpur and skirts the hill slopes where stream channels are narrower and more easily bridged. Because Gopalpur has a mixture of kinds of land, the village raises three separate major crops at different times of the year. This means that people in Gopalpur must work harder and more continuously than people in nearby hill villages, where rocky soil and good drainage make possible only one thin crop per year. Because the only road to Gopalpur is a three-mile-long cart track following the sand and mud of a creek bed, government officials and outsiders rarely visit.

In addition to that portion of the physical environment which can be viewed from a hill top, Gopalpur is deeply influenced by larger forces of geography and climate. Because the plain, or rather plateau, upon which Gopalpur is located is cut up by the deep gorges of such rivers as the Bhima and separated from other portions of the great central plateau of India by forested hills and mountain ranges, Gopalpur and the region around it has always been isolated from the main streams of history. Small kings and bandit chieftains have built great fortresses on the rocky monoliths of the plains and from them have raided each other's palaces and the surrounding villages. Even now, each village is a fortress and, hidden beneath grain sacks or in dark corners of his house, almost every man has a sword, a spear, and sometimes a breast plate and shield. When people in Gopalpur were told about another village where forest officials and other minor government servants took bribes and extorted money from the farmers, the response was immediate: "If anyone tried that here, we would kill him." Recently, thirty young men from a village near Gopalpur were arrested for making an armed attack on another village some fifty miles away. . . .

Food production

To deal with his environment, the farmer of Gopalpur has available to him a stock of techniques and ways of acting handed down to him from his forefathers. Tools are made in the village by the farmer himself, working with the carpenter and blacksmith. The plowshare consists of a curved, sharpened piece of wood with a flattened iron spike for a blade. A long pole runs from the top of the plowshare to a wooden yoke, which is placed on top of the necks of a pair of bullocks and held there by ropes and bars of wood tied beneath the bullocks' necks. Attached to the rear of the plowshare is a wooden handle, which the farmer grasps with one hand and tilts to the left or right in order to steer the plow. Except for the iron tip, the plow differs little from the earliest plows known to history. In addition to the plow, the farmer uses a harrow, a horizontal metal blade which is drawn through the soil, as well as an assortment of rakes, seed drills, and planks. All are of simple construction: planks and pegs made with an adze by the carpenter; metal tie bands and tips beaten out of soft iron by the blacksmith; parts tied together with rope twisted by the farmer. Carts have two solid wooden wheels attached by cotter pins to an iron rod running beneath the body of the cart.

A five-acre field must be plowed at least twice, requiring eight days of labor by one man and two bullocks. Cow manure and compost must be transported from the village to the fields before the crop is sown. This is done by two men working with short-handled hoelike shovels, two baskets, two bullocks, and a cart. The preparation of the soil may take as much as thirty days, depending upon the amount of manure available, the distance of the field from the village, and the amount of energy that can be mustered at times when the temperature in the shade exceeds 110 degrees Fahrenheit. Using a harrow to break up clods and to level the soil requires another eight days of labor by the farmer and a team of bullocks.

The field is then sown in one day, by three men using a seed drill and a pair of bullocks. Some crops, rice for example, are sown broadcast. Sowing marks the climax of one to two months of steady labor. After sowing, the farmer is free to rest, to care for one of his other fields, or to hire out as a laborer. After a month, the field must be weeded and the crop thinned. The work demanded by these two operations varies depending upon the amount of rainfall and the number of seeds that have germinated. Usually, ten to fifteen people must work for three or four days to complete the weeding, thinning, and transplanting necessary to bring order to a newly planted field. After thinning and weeding has been completed, one member of the family must remain in the field

at all times, day and night, to guard against theft by men, cattle, birds, and antelope. This watch must be maintained for two and a half to three months, until the crop is harvested. Harvesting, with locally made sickles, is done by ten men working for three or four days. The grain, still on the stalk, is carried to the threshing ground which has been plastered with mud and swept clean. The grain has been spread out to dry during the morning. In the afternoon, eight to ten bullocks, cows, and water buffaloes are driven around and around a stake in the center of the center of the threshing ground, until the grain is knocked off the stalks by their hooves. Hay must then be removed with a forked stick and the remaining grain and chaff swept up by the farmer's wife who fills her husband's winnowing basket and hands it up to him as he stands on a three-legged stool, shouting angrily at the coy gods who control the wind. When a gust of wind comes, he pours the contents of his basket out and the wind carries away the chaff, leaving a pile of grain directly under the basket. This is swept up by a third worker, perhaps a teen-age son, and placed in burlap sacks. While these operations vary with the kind of crop and the amount of the harvest, as a rule they require from four to seven days of labor. Later on, if beans, peas, or other legumes have been planted between the rows of grain, they too must be harvested, threshed, and winnowed.

A single five-acre field absorbs from four to six months of intermittent labor; rice fields are smaller but require more intensive cultivation, and constant attention. Most farmers in Gopalpur own a few acres of black soil land, a fraction of an acre of rice land, and a larger patch of sandy land. Each of these kinds of fields is planted at a different time of year to a different kind of crop. The farmer begins his agricultural year with *Ugadi*, the New Year festival, in March or April. During May and the early part of June, the hottest months of the year, he transports manure to those fields which are to be planted in June. Toward the end of June, the hot season ends and the monsoon rains begin. In July, the farmer plants millet and legume crops on his sandy fields. Sometimes, he lets his black soil fields lie fallow; sometimes, if he has plenty of manure, he plants a first crop on them. In August or September, if the rains have been good and the irrigation tank (reservoir) is filled with water, the farmer plants his patch of rice land. In September or October, the black soil fields are planted to "white sorghum," the major food crop of the village.

In addition to the basic millet and legume crops, there is a host of minor crops. Everyone tries to have a few mango and tamarind trees; everyone has a small vegetable garden devoted to chili, eggplant, onion, and leafy vegetables. For cash, people plant peanuts, tobacco, or cotton, or they may sell surpluses of any of the other crops. Virtually every family tries to have a female water buffalo for milk, two plow bullocks, and a few sheep, goats, and chickens for feasts and sacrifices. Except during the hot season from the end of February to the end of June, there is always more work than it is possible to do. A little more manure can be collected and added to the compost pit; a few more green branches can be cut for the goat; more time can be spent plowing and leveling the fields. If a man is really ambitious, he can plant trees or dig a well and start a garden.

Times and seasons

Men and women in Gopalpur rise with the first light of dawn. The woman stumbles into the black interior of the house and brings out cold food left over from the day before—perhaps a jar of liquified mush to be drunk hurriedly this early, perhaps a little rice. The farmer wolfs his light breakfast and hurries off to his field, carrying his plow over his shoulder and driving his cattle before him. When the sun becomes warm and the bullocks begin to tire (10:30–11:00 A.M.), the farmer returns to the village. If the day is very hot, he comes back early in order to swim and to rinse out his clothing before eating. Otherwise, he splashes water over his legs and arms and then sits on the kitchen floor, or outside on the veranda to eat.

While the farmer plows, his wife has brought several pots of water from the stream. She has swept the house and the yard in front of the house, and carried the rubbish and manure to the compost heap outside the village. She has dried grain on the roof and ground it, swinging the stone handmill with muscular arms and the weight of her body. She has started a fire in the kitchen using only a few small sticks of wood. Over the fire, she has placed an earthenware pot containing chili, beans, leafy vegetables, tamarind, salt to taste and water to cover. Each

day, this mixture is slightly different: the vegetables change, the beans may be fresh or dried, and of several different varieties. Whatever else the mixture may contain, it must always include an abundance of chili and a reasonable quantity of salt.

While the vegetables simmer, the housewife mixes water with sorghum flour, pats the dough into thin cakes of unleavened bread and toasts them over the fire. After pouring water over her husband's arms and legs, she serves his meal, spooning the vegetables onto the bread to make a kind of open-faced sandwich. With this basic meal, people may have a little rice, some mango pickles, or perhaps some yoghurt mixed with water. If the water buffalo is giving milk, *ghi* (clarified butter) is poured over everything that is to be eaten.

After the meal, from about twelve to three, people sit quietly in the shade and gossip. The farmer, if he is tired, sleeps. Younger men and children play games in the shade. At three in the afternoon, nine hours after dawn by the local reckoning, men return to the fields to work until dusk. Women, too, go to the fields during this part of the day to collect grass for the cattle, or to perform light chores connected with weeding or harvesting. At dusk, people return to the village to consume cold meals by the pale light given by cotton wicks placed in clay lamps. If the moon is full, people gather in the streets. Men laugh and gossip; women form groups and sing songs and dance. If there is no moon and the night is dark, people go early to bed, and by nine o'clock the village is silent.

During the rainy season and the cold season, when such activities as weeding and harvesting are at their peak, people spend the entire day in the fields. The men are joined at noon by the women who had remained home to cook. During the sowing and harvesting seasons in particular, men do not bathe or have haircuts; they live, eat, and often sleep in their fields, taking advantage of every moment of daylight. On some days, when there is not much work in the fields, the whole family will get up while it is still dark and go off noisily with their neighbors to the forest, four miles away. There, long before the forest rangers have risen from their comfortable cots, firewood is collected in great headloads, and carried back to the village. Sometimes in the forest, young people stray away from the group. It is here, that the young man whose marriage has been too long postponed, or whose wife is too young to provide appropriate companionship, meets the housewife whose husband is too old, too disagreeable, or too dark to please her.

If there is excessive dalliance in the forest, members of the group may delay their return to the village. When this happens, they are likely to be met at the road by the forest rangers. The forest rangers confiscate blankets or shirts or headcloths of the villagers, and send them on their way. Later, these items of clothing will be ransomed for a rupee (a day's wages) apiece. Anyone who is caught by the head forest ranger is required to pay five rupees for the privilege.

During the hot season, the pattern of life in Gopalpur changes. Every night, when the moon is shining, some communal activity takes place. Once it is the puberty ceremony of a young girl, to whom the women, sitting around the honored maiden, sing instructive songs. The next time, a group of older men from a neighboring village, dressed in the finery of borrowed clothing, arrive to discuss marriage arrangements with the father of one of the village girls. On other occasions, there is an all-night drama rehearsal, a visit to a wrestling match in another village, or a ceremony and feast in honor of one of the village gods. In the daytime, the village is quiet. Men sleep in the shade or in a cool corner of their house, or, for that matter, in someone else's house if it is cooler or quieter. Women hurry through their chores and, by afternoon, all are sleeping.

Mastery of the environment

Although, at times, people in Gopalpur are oppressed by the heat of the sun, by the darkness of the night, or by rain or cold, they feel themselves to be the masters of their natural environment. Anyone in Gopalpur who is ready and able to work can earn an adequate living, and enjoy the available luxuries. Almost everyone receives three meals or more per day. Every four months almost everyone receives a shirt, a dhoti, and a headcloth, or a sari and blouse. Everyone in Gopalpur has a place to sleep and cook. There is no one who cannot afford the price of a haircut. Almost everyone manages to obtain tobacco to smoke, and betel leaves and areca nut to chew. Everyone can afford to provide a coconut, or a banana, or some sandalwood for the worship of the village gods. Any

young man who needs cash for his marriage can find employment for a year as a landlord's servant. Every woman wears jewels given to her at the time of her marriage. The tax collector always receives the money due him. True, almost everyone in Gopalpur is in debt, but because the money lenders are astute and knowledgeable, the size of a man's debt is itself an index of his prosperity. Only a wealthy man can borrow large sums of money.

The fact that, at any given time, most people in Gopalpur are satisfied with their manner of earning a living and control over the physical environment, does not mean that this control is perfect. There are too many weeds, and every year the farmer sees ants and caterpillars and stem borers and antelope and rats carry off a major fraction of his crop. Although most people in Gopalpur are healthy, very few mothers can boast that all of their children are living. Malaria, cholera, small pox and bubonic plague are familiar visitors to the village. These failures in the control of the environment are not really sources of anxiety, for even in these instances, people in Gopalpur believe that they have control and understanding. Disease, for example, is considered to be a punishment for sin and a normal result of the neglect of one's responsibilities toward the supernatural world. Crop failure, flood, and disease are regarded as disasters to be dealt with when they appear in accordance with traditional techniques.

Although the material environment shapes and influences almost every aspect of life, people do not regard Gopalpur's pattern as something to be changed, improved, or fought. Things, both good and bad, are as they always have been and as they always will be. For Hanumantha, the problems of life stem; not from the material world, but from the human beings who occupy it. Hanumantha knows that his crops will sometimes fail; he knows that he will suffer from headaches and fever during the hot season. He is not concerned with increasing production so much as he is concerned with protecting his fields from thieves. He is not concerned with curing illness so much as he is concerned with preventing it by preventing sinful behavior in himself and in his neighbors. People in Gopalpur are more concerned about the mastery of human relationships, than they are about the mastery of things. . . .

Tragedy part of lives for mine-area families

RICHARD T. COOPER

35

It is not the discussion of a region which makes this selection by Richard Cooper a worthy representative of the literature of cultural geography. Though it does contain superficial note of the major characteristics of this region, Cooper's article is more important because of the human beings he depicts. These people are the foundation for any region. The academics who parade by noting the various quantifiable elements which can be used to abstract the region, seldom communicate the highly personal and complex pattern of thinking which induces a person to stay in a region which to the stranger seems so barren of reward. Of particular note in Cooper's article is the thought expressed by Mrs. Scott, who says "her husband will quit mining now, but she does not seem confident when she says it." Decisions for involvement in a region, like decisions for departure and migration, are very difficult to simplify; Cooper has admirably preserved their complexity.

Farmington, W. Va.—In the soft coal fields of the Allegheny Mountains, the people have learned to absorb tragedy in their daily lives, but there comes a moment each time when the protective mantle of custom is torn away.

That is beginning to happen to families of the 78 miners trapped below ground since last Wednesday, when explosions wracked Consolidation Coal Co.'s No. 9 mine and fires began to eat their way along the hundreds of narrow tunnels.

Earlier, the people appeared to be supported

The *Los Angeles Times,* November 24, 1968, Sec. A, p. 3. Copyright, 1968, by the *Los Angeles Times.* Reprinted by permission.

by their tradition of fatalistic, silent courage, by their elemental religion and by hope.

Increasingly now the agony is unrelieved.

Anthony Megna, 40, and his married sister, Betty Friend, 37, edged into the midst of a press briefing Saturday and demanded that company officials make greater efforts to contact possible survivors by drilling more holes down to the 800-foot working level.

Brother missing

Emilio Megna, 48, their brother, was a section boss on the midnight shift and was not among the 21 men who scrambled to safety after the first explosions.

"You've got to try!" Anthony Megna shouted at William Poundstone, executive vice president for operations. "Those men are down there. I've got a brother down there—we know he's alive. Someone's alive down there."

Their mother, Mary Megna, 69, cried out, "My son, he wants to come out!"

Poundstone, clearly shaken, answered softly, "I know he does," and dropped his eyes. He did not answer Anthony Megna's repeated requests for an explanation of why more drilling rigs were not being brought in from the surrounding area.

Air samples

At present, three rigs are boring down into sections of the mine, and a fourth hole has already been opened. The primary purpose of the drilling is to obtain air samples that give experts some insight into conditions underground.

In addition, if the drill pipe should come

down near survivors, it could be used for communication—as has happened in other mine accidents.

Poundstone said only that "it is not a matter of money," and left the makeshift press headquarters in the back of the company store that stands on a steep hillside overlooking the eastern portal of the mine.

What he found himself unable to explain apparently was that there were enormous technical problems connected with drilling and the odds were considered to be extremely long against making contact in this way in a mine of such mammoth size.

No. 9 is eight miles long and sprawls over about 30 square miles, but individual galleries are only about 16 feet wide. To drill into one, a surveyor must position a rig directly over it, despite the mountainous terrain, and the drill crew must avoid the natural tendency of a shaft to drift out of plumb.

In view of how bad conditions underground have been since Wednesday, and the odds against any number of drills happening on a spot in which a survivor remained, company officials think mass drilling is pointless.

Probably most dispassionate, reasonable men would agree, but they are not in the position of the Megna family. Even after Poundstone had gone, Mrs. Megna, a heavy-set woman in a gray wool coat, continued to plead.

"My son wants to come up. Take up my blood from the ground," she said with a heavy Italian accent.

"That's her oldest son. That's her first-born," a friend explained.

Waiting center

There will be other scenes like this in the days ahead, although efforts have been made to shield the families from view by converting James Fork United Methodist Church into a waiting center.

Since early Wednesday, fire has raged uncontrolled along a two-mile line from the Llewellyn portal, where the initial blast shattered the tipple and hurled the mine elevator up through the roof, to Mod's Run, a double air shaft that has been plugged with 1,000 tons of rough limestone in an attempt to cut the fire's oxygen supply.

Now, Poundstone believes, the fire is spreading eastward beyond Mod's Run and southward down a series of passageways leading to Mahan Portal, which had been designated as the best entry route for rescue specialists once conditions below were stabilized.

The Mahan section of the mine is almost certainly filled with smoke and fumes now. Black smoke pours from it in such volume that it has formed an ugly scarf across the mountaintops.

Air analyzed

Analysis of air samples continues to show little oxygen, much methane gas, and both carbon monoxide and carbon dioxide.

The only areas free of smoke are on the eastern end of the mine—the area from which the 21 survivors emerged four days ago.

When might rescue teams be permitted to go down? Not until experts are sure they will be in no danger, Poundstone said. He made it clear that officials are not close even to beginning a discussion on this point.

In fact, what is occupying the minds of some company officials is the question of how long they must wait before beginning to talk about sealing the mine—a step that would suffocate the fire and any surviving miners at the same time.

The problem, these officials feel, is that the families are psychologically unready to accept the end. The officials speculate privately that three or four more days must pass before the unthinkable can be openly thought about.

With developments so relentlessly negative, it is understandable that the waiting people are becoming more desperate. What is puzzling is why men keep working in these mines; tragedy and near-tragedy have dogged almost all of them for a long, long time.

Emilio Megna, who has three children and a new-born grandchild, worked in a dozen other mines before signing on at Consolidation No. 9 a year ago. He had been in many of what his brother calls "tight situations."

Their father, Peter, was saved only by chance from being one of those killed by an explosion at this mine in 1954. He had been part of a maintenance crew assigned to work overtime one Saturday, but decided to enjoy his day off instead. The other 16 died.

They always go

Immediately after an accident, miners often say they will go down no more, but their wives say ruefully that they always do.

Mrs. Mayme Scott, a pleasant-looking woman who serves food at one emergency center, recalled that her husband had once gone so far as to move out of the Farmington area.

"We moved up to Ohio on Lake Erie," she said. "It was pretty up there, but after a while, for some reason, he decided to come here. I don't know why."

Her husband, Galen, was not among those trapped Wednesday because the James Fork Boy Scout troop needed a new master recently and he was transferred off the midnight shift to take the assignment.

Men on the "cat-eye" shift often tend to be the younger, less experienced miners because they lack seniority, and Mrs. Scott has known most of them for a long time.

"I've seen a lot of those young ones grow up from rompers," she said.

Mrs. Scott believes that her husband will quit mining now, but she does not seem confident when she says it.

Coketown

CHARLES DICKENS

36

Passages of description from the belles lettres *of any period have relevance to the understanding of the cultural landscape for at least two reasons. They afford a view, though admittedly highly subjective, of the landscapes and cityscapes of the past. They may also occasionally have generated enough concern in an influential readership to initiate a change in social and cultural patterns. This selection from Charles Dickens'* Hard Times *(1854) has both of these qualities. The "blur of soot and smoke" by which Dickens characterized Coketown was the hallmark of mid-nineteenth century urban England, and the author's constant recall of that condition and, more importantly, the working conditions of the children who were confined within these "fairy palaces" provoked serious questioning of employment practices of the textile industry.*

No way out.

The Fairy palaces burst into illumination, before pale morning showed the monstrous

Charles Dickens, *The Old Curiosity Shop, Hard Times, and The Holly Tree Inn* (New York: John Wurtele Lovell, n.d.) , 599–600, 635–637.

serpents of smoke trailing themselves over Coketown. A clattering of clogs upon the pavement; a rapid ringing of bells; and all the melancholy mad elephants, polished and oiled up for the day's monotony, were at their heavy exercise again.

Stephen bent over his loom, quiet, watchful, and steady. A special contrast, as every man was in the forest of looms where Stephen worked, to the crashing, smashing, tearing piece of mechanism at which he labored. Never fear, good people of an anxious turn of mind, that Art will consign Nature to oblivion. Set anywhere, side by side, the work of God and the work of man; and the former, even though it be a troop of Hands of very small account, will gain in dignity from the comparison.

So many hundred Hands in this Mill; so many hundred horse Steam Power. It is known, to the force of a single pound weight, what the engine will do; but, not all the calculators of the National Debt can tell me the capacity for good or evil, for love of hatred, for patriotism or discontent, for the decomposition of virtue into vice, or the reverse, at any single moment in the soul of one of these its quiet servants, with the composed faces and the regulated actions. There is no mystery in it; there is an unfathomable mystery in the meanest of them, for ever. Supposing we were to reserve our arithmetic for material objects and to govern these awful unknown quantities by other means!

The day grew strong, and showed itself outside, even against the flaming lights within. The lights were turned out, and the work went on. The rain fell, and the Smoke-serpents, submissive to the curse of all that tribe, trailed themselves upon the earth. In the waste-yard outside, the steam from the escape pipe, the litter of barrels and old iron, the shining heaps of coals, the ashes everywhere, were shrouded in a veil of mist and rain.

The work went on, until the noon-bell rang. More chattering upon the pavements. The looms, and wheels, and Hands all out of gear for an hour. . . .

A sunny midsummer day. There was such a thing sometimes, even in Coketown.

Seen from a distance in such weather, Coketown lay shrouded in a haze of its own, which appeared impervious to the sun's rays. You only knew the town was there, because you knew there could have been no such sulky blotch upon the prospect without a town. A blur of soot and smoke, now confusedly tending this way, now that way, now aspiring to the vault of Heaven, now murkily creeping along the earth, as the wind rose and fell, or changed its quarter; a dense formless jumble, with sheets of cross light in it, that showed nothing but masses of darkness—Coketown in the distance was suggestive of itself, though not a brick of it could be seen.

The wonder was, it was there at all. It had been ruined so often, that it was amazing how it had borne so many shocks. Surely there never was such fragile china-ware as that of which the millers of Coketown were made. Handle them never so lightly, and they fell to pieces with such ease that you might suspect them of having been flawed before. They were ruined, when they were required to send laboring children to school; they were ruined when inspectors were appointed to look into their works; they were ruined, when such inspectors considered it doubtful whether they were quite justified in chopping people up with their machinery; they were utterly undone, when it was hinted that perhaps they need not always

make quite so much smoke. Besides Mr. Bounderby's gold spoon which was generally received in Coketown, another prevalent fiction was very popular there. It took the form of a threat. Whenever a Coketowner felt he was ill-used— that is to say, whenever he was not left entirely alone, and it was proposed to hold him accountable for the consequences of any of his acts—he was sure to come out with the awful menace, that he would "sooner pitch his property into the Atlantic." This had terrified the Home Secretary within an inch of his life, on several occasions.

However, the Coketowners were so patriotic after all, that they never had pitched their property into the Atlantic yet, but, on the contrary, had been kind enough to take mighty good care of it. So there it was, in the haze yonder; and it increased and multiplied.

The streets were hot and dusty on the summer day, and the sun was so bright that it even shone through the heavy vapor drooping over Coketown, and could not be looked at steadily. Stokers emerged from low underground doorways into factory yards, and sat on steps, and posts, and palings, wiping their swarthy visages, and contemplating coals. The whole town seemed to be frying in oil. There was a stifling smell of hot oil everywhere. The steam-engines shone with it, the dresses of the Hands were soiled with it, the mills throughout their many stories oozed and trickled it. The atmosphere of those Fairy palaces was like the breath of the simoon; and their inhabitants, wasting with heat, toiled languidly in the desert. But no temperature made the melancholy mad elephants more mad or more sane. Their wearisome heads went up and down at the same rate, in hot weather and cold, wet weather and dry, fair weather and foul. The measured motion of their shadows on the walls, was the substitute Coketown had to show for the shadows of rustling woods; while, for the summer hum of insects, it could offer, all the year round, from the dawn of Monday to the night of Saturday, the whirr of shafts and wheels.

Drowsily they whirred all through this sunny day, making the passenger more sleepy and more hot as he passed the humming walls of the mills. Sun-blinds, and sprinklings of water, a little cooled the main streets and the shops; but the mills, and the courts and alleys, baked at a fierce heat. Down upon the river that was black and thick with dye, some Coketown boys who were at large—a rare sight there—rowed a crazy boat, which made a spumous track upon the water as it jogged along, while every dip of an oar stirred up vile smells. But the sun itself, however beneficient, generally, was less kind to Coketown than hard frost, and rarely looked intently into any of its closer regions without engendering more death than life. So does the eye of Heaven itself become an evil eye, when incapable or sordid hands are interposed between it and the things it looks upon to bless. . . .

Educated youths who go to rural and mountainous areas have a great future

FRANZ SCHURMANN AND
ORVILLE SCHELL

37

The increased mobility of the Chinese people, particularly the youth, under the regime of the Chinese Communists has been one of the hallmarks of true revolution in that country. However, the consequent urban flow of youth has generated some serious shortages in agricultural labor in parts of the country. Still worse, in the eyes of the party leadership, the sudden divorce from the rigors of peasant rural life has created a less aggressive youthful population. As a result of this uneasiness, a number of campaigns and programs have been created to change the flow pattern of this young segment of the Chinese population in an attempt to acquaint or reacquaint them with the demands of peasant life. It is also intended to instill a sense of respect for the countryside population and its mode of life.

Notwithstanding the fact that this selection smacks of party propaganda, the concept of sending children raised in urban environments to the farm for a summer to "raise blisters on their hands and broaden their backs" has long been a part of urban man's approach to the rural region.

CHINA YOUTH DAILY.[1] Recently, large numbers of educated youths in many cities have rushed to the countryside, forming a new revolutionary current. This is an indication of prosperity of our nation, and a symbol of unceasing development in education in our country. Going to rural and mountainous areas, urban educated youths have embarked upon a glorious revolutionary road—a road on which they can join the masses of workers and peasants.

Some urban educated youths may ask: What can we do in rural and mountainous areas? Is there a bright future in plowing the soil? Our reply is: Educated youths will have an endless, bright and great future in rural and mountainous areas.

Why do we say so?

In the eyes of a proletarian, the future of a revolutionary is always closely linked with the future of the revolutionary cause. Our country's agriculture has extensive prospects, and our country's five hundred million peasants have a great future. . . .

Educated youths in some cities say: "Rural life is hard!" Yes, this is true. Though agricultural construction is now much better than that before the liberation, the laboring conditions are still poorer and life is harder in the countryside than in urban areas. Going suddenly to the countryside, we may not be accustomed to the environment physically and technically and in everyday life. Only if we make up our minds to temper ourselves, shall we be able, after a certain period of time, to get accustomed to the rural environment. If we think that what slight hardships we suffer today are for the sake of building a new, socialist countryside, creating

Franz Schurmann and Orville Schell, eds., *Communist China* (New York: Vintage Books, 1967), pp. 456–457.

[1] Translations nos. 34, 345, and 10,046 (Washington, D.C.: U.S. Joint Publications Research Service).

happiness for the younger generation, and rendering greater support to the revolutionary struggles undertaken by peoples of the world, we shall find happiness in rural life and shall not feel any suffering. It is good for youths to suffer some hardships during their time of growth. A revolutionary youth fears no hardships, does not wish to pass his days in quietness and comfort, but wishes to lead a life of fierce struggle. He is willing to create the world with his hands, instead of waiting to enjoy other people's achievements. The harder the conditions are, the more can he temper his revolutionary character and perserverance and learn the skills of overcoming difficulties. Many educated youths who have gone to the countryside have realized that it is impossible to carry out revolution and change the backward aspects of the countryside without first suffering some hardships and shedding blood and sweat. When they had just started to labor, blisters were formed on their hands, and their shoulders swelled as a result of carrying heavy loads. However, they were not scared by these difficulties. They said: "If we do not suffer hardships, we can never temper ourselves." "Suffering of hardships helps us get rid of arrogance and establish a revolutionary will." Imposing demands on themselves in this spirit, they will fear no hardships or tiring work, and can overcome all sorts of difficulties.

It can be easily understood that youths show concern for their future. The Party and the state also hope that the youths will have a beautiful and bright future. The purpose of carrying out the revolution and national reconstruction is to enable the people of the whole country and the younger generation to have a beautiful and bright future. Since we go to rural and mountainous areas for the purpose of carrying out revolution, we must, while considering problems concerning our future, combine our individual prospects with the great socialist cause. We must dedicate our wisdom and strength to the service of the motherland and the people and, by the effort of this generation, build a socialist new countryside. Educated-youth comrades, go bravely to the agricultural front, and let us press ahead bravely on the road of revolutionization! . . .

The contemporary cultural landscape

The articles in this section need less introduction than those making up the first three sections of The Cultural Landscape. The student may not be certain what the significance of Semple's Mediterranean pleasure garden or Parsons' starlings is, but he is certainly aware of the nature of the problems which beset our cities, our atmosphere, our water resources, and our human race. One can live his entire life and never ponder the significance of the introduction of maize from Middle America to Europe in the early 1500s, but it is very difficult to pass through a day and not be alarmed by environmental pollution.

The change in focus from the historic to the contemporary cultural landscape is a logical conclusion to this anthology. One of the two goals of the book has been to make the reader's eye more sensitive to the modifications man has wrought upon the earthscape. The major themes of mobility, husbandry, and spatial organization have been used to engender this sense of perception. Now, in consideration of the contemporary cultural landscape, one is able to see that the evidence of man's ability to shape his environment is not only universal but frightening.

The student of the cultural landscape may no longer be satisfied with scholarly analysis of the genesis, growth, and morphology of a given landscape; he must consider the wisdom of man's shaping it in such a fashion. This is both the burden and the opportunity of investigation of the contemporary scene.

Though such a role is not new to cultural geographers and other observers of man's landscape modification process, it has been only recently that people generally have become concerned over the scale of this activity. Recalling George Perkins Marsh and his disquietude a century ago over man's seemingly unbridled power to transform natural landscapes into useless, nonproductive vestiges, we find the same concern now preached from all sides. The key phrases are air pollution, population growth, resource depletion, wilderness preservation, urbanism, and so forth. They all conjure up the vision of man's powers of modification gone amuck.

Consider, for example, the themes included in this section on the contemporary scene. Ian Nairn takes America to task for not demanding more grace in the growth of her cities, particularly since the relative wealth of the United States should allow her population the most flexibility in shaping a city of order and good taste. The problem of wilderness land and its definition makes David Lowenthal ask who shall decide what land is to be "saved" from man's penchant for development. The question of taste takes on a new significance. No longer is man's technological ability to shape and sculpt the landscape questioned; the present concern is, should there be new criteria for shaping? Is it time to ask new questions as man continues in his spatial organization?

As Wayne Davis's article, "Overpopulated America," illustrates, the tone of the readings in this section is unlike that of the preceding three sections. Whereas observations were made and conclusions conservatively drawn as we viewed mobility, husbandry, and spatial organization, polemics predominate in this final section. Davis's diatribe against American patterns of resource abuse is a valid representative comment on the cultural landscape of the seventies. Though it may seem simplistic in laying the full burden of America's increasing pollution at the feet of the "affluent destroyers," it does enumerate the range of contemporary fears. And its focus on population and contraception is fully consonant with today's ecological awareness.

Eco-catastrophe is Paul Ehrlich's description of man's destruction of the environment. The processes we learned to perceive and, in part, respect in the first three-quarters of this anthology we now recognize as possibly leading to our undoing. Ehrlich's conclusion is disturbingly logical within the context of his scenario. However, the article must be viewed more as an attempt to open the apathetic reader's eyes than as a definitive monograph on ecological deterioration. Compare Ehrlich's treatment of worldwide ecological change with the article by Barry Commoner. Read in tandem, the articles show a common disquietude but very distinct elaboration of these pollution crises.

Apprehension—so evident in the works of Nairn, Davis, Ehrlich, Commoner, and others mentioned below—is evoked in the television, radio and publishing media and, hence, in ourselves. Davis and Ehrlich especially are capitalizing on the fact that perception of the landscape and the results of man's compulsion to modify it is at an all-time peak. Whether the focus of concern is urbanism, population, or pollution, the fact remains that man is now exceptionally aware of his uneasy dominion over the natural world.

Not all of the selections are general outcries against the alleged rape of the environment. J. Todd Snow's comment on the road is a very specific complaint. William Whyte's plan for renovation of American cities from within is equally pointed in its thrust, as in the Time essay on urbanism. But even these three tightly focused essays imply a larger uneasiness over population growth and runaway technology.

The final three articles move in a slightly different direction. Alfred Etter, arguing against the universal acceptance of quantification methods, represents a group of students who want to maintain a high degree of subjectivity and human focus in studies of landscape change. To require the quantification of most inputs to landscape analysis would be, in Etter's mind, tantamount to subordinating the human element in this process of change. Etter's articulate call for resistance against the reduction of all knowledge to numerical units deserves to be pondered by people concerned with the humanized landscape.

The entire focus of Section Four, and perhaps of the book itself, is implicit in Daniel Luten's "Empty Land, Full Land, Poor Folk, Rich Folk." He believes that geographers best comprehend the processes which have created the contemporary cultural landscape, and it should hence be geographers who help guide the direction of continued modification. Since one of the primary goals of The Cultural Landscape is to impart a sense of the pattern of the earth upon the reader, it seems logical that a person with such a sense would be in a prime position to aid in future change. Luten's contention is that if geographers, or others who share their preoccupation with the genesis, development, and morphology of the culture landscape, do not rise to this unique occasion, future development will continue to be directed by those unaware of the possibly dangerous ramifications of landscape alteration. Though it is apparent that an analogous situation has existed since the outset of cultural geography, Luten's point is that this is a singularly critical time.

The final question to be asked of the reader begs all of the preceding: Where is science *taking us? Technology, which has given man an unprecedented capability to modify nature, may not represent the optimum criterion for continued decisions for change. Raymond Fosberg asked this question of science in 1959, and it seems even more apt today. While population growth is the focus of Fosberg's article, the questions raised seem pertinent to all facets of man's tenure of earth.*

It is reasonable to end with a question. Section Four does not intend to solve anything. In fact, it raises a greater number of questions and generates more uncertainty than any of the preceding sections. This is intentional, however, for the students who deal with The Cultural Landscape *cannot escape making decisions. The burden of directing future landscape modification cannot fall on anyone but the people surrounded by the contemporary cultural landscape. The scale of change once suggested by Thoreau's bean field or a lone swidden farmer is obviously gone. Today's scale of change is massive, as are the decisions facing us in our continuing modification of the earth.*

The American landscape

IAN NAIRN

38

Perhaps the major success achieved by writers and disciples of cultural geography is the heightened cognizance man has of his power over the landscape. When George Perkins Marsh published the first edition of Man and Nature *in 1864, his suggestion that man had been a dominant factor in the modification of the face of the earth was skeptically received. Now, not much more than a century later, man has not only accepted the fact that he is an ecologic dominant, but frequently criticizes himself for not exercising this power toward the creation of a superior landscape. Ian Nairn is one of the most provocative of those who claim that man must accept the responsibility for landscape, or in this case townscape, sculpturing.*

In this selection from Nairn's The American Landscape *he establishes the fact, at least in his eyes, that Americans have failed completely to direct this power of creation toward any but an economic end. The burden upon man now, particularly upon the Americans who are most capable of modifying their habitat, is to create exciting and coherent townscapes in this urban age. He exhorts us to a considered organization of space.*

The only object of this book is to make the environment and hence life itself more exciting, humane and expressive. It is not a book about good design as such, it is not a book about preservation or tidy-mindedness, and it is certainly not a planner's textbook with figures and tables and standards. What it tries to show in

the simplest way is what happens to objects when they are set down together in the environment, the way in which they can be experienced by the people who use them, the way in which they have a potential for grandeur or mystery so often translated in fact into squalor or boredom. This is a book about the art of the environment, the art of placing objects together so that the result is something better than any of the original elements; the art of giving identity to places and hence to the people living in them. A new art needs a new name, and this one is called townscape.

In fact, of course, it is not new, only ignored or unrecognized. Men have always tried to make their towns expressive of the life inside them. In the Middle Ages the urge was as unconscious as the urge which made every church into an expression of religious feeling. In the Renaissance, men thought they had discovered the rules for this expression—simple, lucid and geometrical. What they had in fact discovered was the first few words of a language. By 1800, a few designers, such as John Nash in England, could speak it fluently. But then the Industrial Revolution came, and any thought of visual progress was swamped under more pressing needs—social, political, economic. Where expression or amenity was needed, the ideas of the Renaissance were used in ever broader and more grandiose forms.

And there we rest. We have an empirical modern architecture based (ostensibly, anyway) on specific needs, individual solutions, the creation of a humane and exciting environment, but we have no modern townscape to go with it, nothing to join up the individual masterpieces into a corporate place. On Park Avenue, New York, two undoubted masterpieces nod at one another across the street, each elegantly and humanely designed within its boundaries. But separating the Lever and Seagram buildings are a rush of cars, browbeaten shrubs, dumb pavements—a chaos of nonrelation. They remain architectural gems; but as attempts to be anything more, any part of the total city, they are stillborn.

This chaos of nonrelation is probably worse in America than anywhere else in the world. And this is odd, because most of the fifty states have created for most of their members the world's richest society. Nowhere else, ever, has the man in the street had so much money and so much leisure in which to spend it. Everywhere, interest in the arts is booming: yet the most continuous, most down to earth, most easily apprehended art of all—the art of making a pattern in the environment—is entirely neglected. It often exists inside a house, or up to the garden boundaries, but almost never beyond them. The job of this book is to take the eye over the garden boundaries out into the street, the parking lot, the gas station, and show how all these can be brought into relationship in purely twentieth-century terms. The whole land is waiting, to use or misuse as you will.

The intention is not, of course, to make each city into a pretty garden, with roses round the diner door. God forbid. Gardens where gardens are needed; industrial brutality, *terribilità*, canyon spaces and prairie spaces—each, too, where it is needed. This whole art of townscape is built on a fundamental principle—which can be a political and philosophical principle too—of the "is-ness" of parts: that each part of each city has its own specific character and that to give visible form and identity, this character must be expressed in its shape and pattern. The character may be anything you like, and the character may be sharply different from neighboring places—in fact, one of the keenest pleasures of townscape is the shock of contrast between two contiguous places with different patterns (the opposite of the endless drive through roadtown, when all places appear the same even though they aren't). Look at the glittering skyline of Detroit from across the river in humble Windsor, Ontario; look down from the decent quiet Duquesne Heights onto the roaring heart of Pittsburgh—if ever a city epitomized *terribilità*, in the sense of sheer Michelangelesque power, it is Pittsburgh; walk west from Lake Shore Drive in Chicago through

streets as wildly different as the variety of a global *smörgasbord*. The magic is beginning to work—the sense of the difference in places, however obscured or obstructed, will come through.

But surely all America is the same? Well, yes and no. On one level of course it is—the same paperbacks in the drugstores, the same kind of food in the Deep-Freeze, the same cars on the road. Yet in fact, this is largely a surface gloss of sameness, under which people and places are as different as ever: just as the roadtown of Gila Bend, Arizona, may look exactly like the roadtown of Trenton, New Jersey—yet New Jersey and Arizona are and always will be very different places. More than that, people will always want to feel different, to have individuality, just as at the same time they need to feel the same and part of the group. The problem is not to satisfy one or the other, but to satisfy both, simultaneously: the American environment satisfies the need for sameness completely, but does not begin to meet the urge to be individual. Even at the level already mentioned—the sameness of cars on the road—how else can you explain the need which drives the members of the proudest state in the Union to put on its indistinguishable Detroit-designed models, "Made in Texas by Texans"? This particular example is a kind of crux: because I am sure that a truly Texan car would neither look the same nor have the same performance or equipment as a car from Michigan or Ohio. The physical needs are different; it is really a monstrous cramping of life's potentiality that they have to be satisfied by one standard solution. We understand this very well in appreciating the natural environment—the Grand Canyon, the Ozark caves, Niagara Falls are all extreme cases of individuality in landscape. Townscape is an extension of this into the man-made environment. Just one example. Pittsburgh and Cleveland are only a hundred miles apart, yet they are completely different in almost every way: site, function, temperament. But almost nothing has been done in the man-made environment to express any of this (H. H. Richardson did it in his Allegheny County Jail at Pittsburgh, where he created a three-way masterpiece—splendid as a building, splendid for its function, splendid in a specifically Pittsburgh way). In most cases the basic materials are still around, ready at hand, waiting to be expressed: townscape would make Pittsburgh more Pittsburgh-like, intensify the Cleveland-ness of Cleveland.

And the aim, always, would be to improve and intensify the quality of life. America can do, quantitatively, almost anything it wants. It must transmute the endless quantity into quality or it will sink and die: 1984 will come on it from inside.

Townscape depends on two things: relationship and identity. Relationship means making the parts of the environment fit together—the supermarket, the gas station, the car lots; identity is the recognition and enhancement of the specific needs and qualities that make one place different from another. And here, right at the start, a big warning: that no identity is better than a false one. The needs and qualities must be real, not artificially tickled-up. It is natural, if most of the environment has no visual identity (and in America it hasn't), to swing the other way and attempt to be fiercely individual or to escape into a romanticized past. But that way lies the Nemesis of Old Sturbridge and the other reconstructed New England villages, of imagining yourself to be ante-bellum (with all the ante-bellum food in the post-bellum Deep-Freeze) or 1920's or any other time but the present. It is all very well, but only as a children's game.

One example. Albuquerque, for my money, is one of the stupidest wastes of human endeavor on this earth. It occupies a magnificent site between the Rio Grande and the Rockies, it pays no attention whatsoever to either, but simply goes on sprawling and spewing across the countryside to an endless repetitive pattern: without relationship, without identity. Yet, if it is a fearful mess, it is at least an honest mess. I would if I had to make the choice—but what a choice!—prefer it to the fearful mock-Spanish affectations of Santa Fe, where about six genuine Spanish buildings are lost in a welter of fake Baroque gables and commercialized Indian art. Albuquerque is the honest whore, Santa Fe is the wife who cheats. Making a pattern out of the environment has got to be conscious—the days when it would come naturally are long past for the U.S.A.—but not self-conscious.

But, with that proviso, the sky is the limit. The job is enormous, and it is a good thing that America has reached the point where almost any material advance and convenience can be had for the asking. All that ingenuity and abundance which up to now has merely resulted in gibberish must be given a change of direction to make the visible world—town, country, exurb—whole again.

Aw, what the hell. Why bother? There's always more land around the corner. Making places look nice is fine-art stuff. Anyway, my own subdivision has flowers in the gardens, my own living room is neat and tidy. Anyway, America is too young and too busy getting ahead.

A common enough reaction: an understandable one. But a reaction of a thrice-blind man. Blind literally, in that he cannot see the sheer excitement of making a place expressive. A walk in a town can be as refreshing and exhilarating as Scotch-on-the-rocks after a hot, tiring day: all that is needed is to open one's eyes to a new dimension of enjoyment.

At the other end of the spectrum, blind to the fact that whatever view one takes of the purpose of life, man is certainly not the only creature on this planet, but part of a natural order which is larger than he is and which he ignores at his peril. Heedless, reckless, large-scale tampering with the environment is one of the easiest ways to upset this natural order, an exact parallel to the heedless, reckless misuse of antibiotics on the human body, which is a microcosm of the natural order.

Man is not alone in the world and he cannot push the environment around as he will; it will turn back at him and hit him—at its simplest, this is the moral of the dust bowls in the Panhandle. But nature can also operate in more complicated and subtle ways. The correlation, unconfirmed but undoubted, between lung cancer and the various gases twentieth-century man inhales into his lungs is one example.

The third dimension of blindness is psychological, halfway between the simple reaction to the outside world and the cosmic relationship to every other thing in the planet. I am not setting up as a psychologist, but it seems a commonplace that almost everyone is born with the need for identification with his surroundings and a relationship to them—with the need to be in a recognizable place. So, sense of place is not a fine-art extra, it is something which man cannot afford to do without. However happy the family, however pretty the subdivision, unless it is part of a bigger community that can recognize itself as being specific, different (in the same way that you recognize your own children), something is missing. Where the hell *are* you if you live in, say, one of the fearful anonymities around Greater Boston, or on a subdivision ten miles from a Carolina town, five miles in the other direction from a school, two miles from a supermarket? The complete fragmentation of the whole man-made environment in this way is not a liberation of life but an explosion, and it will end in an equivalent fragmentation or disorientation inside the personalities of its inhabitants.

By an unhappy series of accidents, a lot of America has never really had any kind of man-made visual pattern and identity, in the sense in which English villages or German towns have. There is tremendous local feeling, but it is quite unexpressed in the shape of the place—or only expressed by functional accidents like the grain elevators and the water towers and the courthouse squares, grand though all these may be. With "the towns where the automobile got there first" there is not even that: around Van Horn in Texas, or in parts of the Deep South like Mobile, and of course in all the new settlements of the last twenty years. With exurbia it is a little more understandable: if you are way out on Long Island you do share, vicariously, a little of the identity of metropolitan New York. But more to the point are the brand-new settlements. I want to describe just one: Grants on US 66, between Albuquerque and Gallup. Now, Grants advertises itself stridently and repeatedly to the passer-by as "the uranium capital of the world," which is certainly something worth expressing and giving visible form to. And the site, where the desert runs into the San Mateo mountains, is superb too. Even if Grants is to be a short-lived mining camp, then it should be the most exciting, most expressive mining camp in the world. In the beat phrase, "get your kicks on 'sixty-six'" (and what a mockery that is—US 66 has more potential excitements deadened and made dull than any other road on earth), Grants ought to be one of the kicks. And in fact Grants is just the same old stuff as though it were New Grantville in Pennsylvania or El Granto in California. Everything is hung on the landscape—which in a mining camp is perhaps legitimate. My point is that it is no longer flung with panache or passion, with a sense of the

importance of the occasion. Virginia City, Nevada, is a real place, whether it has people in it or not. But at Grants this terrifying and exciting thing is reduced to a genteel drooling and dribbling on the landscape, a town gone visually 4F. In England I called this mindless mixing up of all man-made objects without any pattern of purpose or relationship by an invented word, subtopia: in America it seems simpler and more effective, more American, just to call it goop. Its archetype is man treating the landscape as a set of ruled squares and then filling them with low-intensity muck. . . . Put another way, almost everyone who acquires this book will have had to struggle through several miles of goop to get to bookshop or library. The problem is one that most people recognize. But the faults are not untidyness and brashness but universal propagation of lack of relationship and lack of identity. Hence the answer is not just a cleanup—that would merely give a genteel vacuum instead of a vulgar one—but a relearning of the physical laws of relationship and of the moral law that the same thing may not be valid everywhere: different places need different treatment. William Blake said it, as he said most things, in a very few words, and they might as well be the motto for the book:

One law for the Lion & Ox is Oppression

In other words, coexistence, recognition of departures from the norm, different environment for different types of people. Not an American Way of Life, second-rate, but a set of alternative American Ways of Life, all first-rate.

If some of these phrases, like coexistence, have become dirty words, I'm sorry. I didn't dirty them. And if readers cannot get behind the false faces put on words, they are unlikely to see in this book anything but what they expected to see anyway. If you go to the North End of Boston expecting to see slums, or to Pittsburgh expecting to see dirty industry, slums and dirty industry will be all you will get from them, and the best of luck to you: you may read town planning for a hundred years and never see the reality under the false faces of the "dirty words": that Boston's North End is one of the most human places in America, and that Pittsburgh is one of America's most exciting sites. The goal of this book could be described as giving each place, in its own terms and ways, the equivalent of the human excitement of the North End and the topographical excitement of Pittsburgh.

Excitement, kicks. If this begins to sound like a beat novel, it is no accident, and beatniks are in a way the proof of the proposition that everyone needs, and in America few have got, a sense of place. Why else the journeys, the fetish for travel, feverish search for places which *are* places, a search so often unsuccessful in America—why go to San Diego? Apart from the sunshine, man has made it indistinguishable from Detroit. Hence the desperate relief in finding personal symbols of topographical identity in default of general ones, and the pathetic seeking of universal value in the Greyhound waiting room or the corner of State and Main. Kerouac's Denver is in his own mind a glory of excitement, a mixture of Amsterdam, Chartres and Naples. But why does it have to be in his own mind? What are you doing in this twentieth century with its unlimited means, *not* to make Denver the equivalent in excitement of Amsterdam, Chartres and Naples?

Kerouac's *On the Road* is even more explicit: back and forward across the States until fulfillment, at last, in real places—across the Mexican border. The touching, wholehearted acceptance of this pattern and vitality is as unbeat as anything I have ever read.

The beats are the reaction againt placelessness in its purest form. But less extreme novelists show less overtly but more comprehensively the need and the lack of place. I am using novels here because American novels are as good as any in the world, and they work on purely American terms: what is wanted is that American towns should have the humanity, comprehensiveness, richness and excitement of the novels that are written about them. John O'Hara in *Ten North Frederick* and James Jones in *Some Came Running* describe and define places as well as people. Yet it had to be done purely in terms of people and the emotional change that they gave to those parts of the environment that are quite undifferentiated and indistinguishable in themselves—the Greyhound waiting room all over again. Gibbsville, Pennsylvania, and Parkman, Illinois, are places of tremendous identity and individuality, yet I am sure that they and their prototypes do not express any of this consciously. It is quite ob-

viously not a question of there being nothing to express.

That was *then,* you might say, even if the "then" was 1950. How about the *now* of universal mobility where 20 per cent of American families move every year, where Los Angeles is five and a half hours from New York by Boeing 707, where the same house designs are put up in every state? There are remarkable statistics, but they do not alter the basic human needs. The forms they take may change radically, but the need is still there. To give one more literary example, the four families in John McPartland's *No Down Payment* are about as typically exurban as anything in America, and their subdivision in San Mateo County needs no elaboration. Yet they created in spite of anonymous surroundings and divergence of jobs an almost feverish sense of place. So in every subdivision in the country. And as the subdivisions get bigger and the distances get longer and the frustrations earned by man's ingenuity multiply (i.e., you can't find any goddam place to park the goddam car any goddam where), the longings for some kind of reality in men's hearts will get deeper and stronger and more insistent. And, perhaps, more anti-social. A rape or a murder is real enough.

Mobility, also, is not really relevant. People put down roots and need to put down roots in a terribly short time: I myself take about forty-eight hours, and it is something that you can test for yourself every time you go on a two-week vacation. I would even argue, paradoxically, that mobility increases the sense of place: and that this rapid movement of people is something a town must have if it isn't to wither away. Ports are living definitions of mobility, yet it does not stop them from being among the most individual of places.

What all this adds up to is the proposition that twentieth-century America has basically the same needs as fourteenth-century France or eighteenth-century England or any other golden age of place-making: it is just that it has lost the know-how to build places. The "why" remains the same; the "how" has to be rediscovered. It is the job of this book to suggest the "how": and to suggest it with only American examples. This has been a hard job, harder than it would have been anywhere else in the world. I drove ten thousand miles through the States, and what I found could have been turned up, in analogy and equivalent, in any two-hundred-mile journey in England. This is not Limey superciliousness but a simple expression of facts. If I weren't convinced of the bottomless, unexpressed need for an environment which is not perennial low-grade chaos, I could not bear to write this. If there is no human need, all the know-how in the world might as well be put on the bonfire.

In fact, I think there may be more need in America than anywhere else. Examples pop up unsolicited: in this morning's (English) newspaper in an account of goings-on in Tell City, Indiana, on the Ohio river between Louisville and Owensboro. There they held their first Factory Steam Whistle Concert—"We think it's

the first time it's ever been done anywhere"—ending with a finale of "ten of the sweetest sounding whistles which could be found." America has a reputation for conformity, yet where else could such a splendidly nonconforming thing happen today? And what a terrific urban vitality that must premise—just the kind of directness that built Renaissance towns and Gothic churches: yet I am sure (I have not been there) that the surface appearance of Tell City, so different from the reality underneath, is like almost any other American river town—a brash gridiron half built up, turning its back on the river and greeting it, and the countryside at its edges, with all the junk it can muster.

Not every prospect pleases

39

DAVID LOWENTHAL

In his analysis, the cultural geographer is inclined to use subjectivity to a greater extent than colleagues committed to the more easily quantified economic and physical geography. There are few, however, who capitalize on this subjective license with the grace and style of David Lowenthal. In this short article, which Lowenthal subtitles "What Is Our Criterion for Scenic Beauty?", his discussion ranges from definitions of wilderness to a concluding truism that values of appreciation ultimately lie in the perception of each individual. The questions asked by Lowenthal concerning wilderness, litter, mountain land use, and appreciation of diverse environments in general are all pertinent to the education of anyone concerned with the cultural landscape.

I begin with a digression. Why do people feel as they do about particular landscapes?

David Lowenthal, "Not Every Prospect Pleases," *Landscape*, XII, No. 2 (Winter 1962–1963), 19–23.

My interest in this question was first aroused by a surfeit of sermons on the virtues of the wilderness. However, motions about wilderness serve me principally as points of departure for a broader inquiry: what is it that makes any landscape seem pleasant or repellent, fitting or unsuitable, to people of various backgrounds and inclinations?

The wilderness cult

Early man, according to some of his latter-day descendants, viewed his physical environment with awe and dread. To him, Nature was a tyrant; he survived only by strict obedience to her dictates. To us, it is not Nature but our own creations that are terrifying. Nature seldom threatens most urban Americans; indeed, she scarcely causes us discomfort.

Nevertheless, a new religion of nature is in the making. Worshipers of nature exhort us from the pulpits of countless conservation societies and Audubon clubs; the President's

Advisory Commission on Outdoor Recreation transmutes their dogma into national policy; *Life* magazine gives it a four-color imprimatur. Nature is wonderful, they tell us; pay homage to it in the Wilderness, and where there is no Wilderness, create Open Spaces.

The tone of Senator Wayne Morse's comment on the Wilderness Bill, in 1961, exemplifies the underlying rationale: "You cannot associate with the grandeur of this great heritage which God Almighty has given the American people and not come out of such a trip a better man or woman for having come that close to the spirit of the Creator." Americans are near a state of grace, runs this argument, thanks to their past and present intimacy with the wilderness. Our forefathers mastered a continent; today we celebrate the virtues of the vanquished foe: To love nature is regarded as uniquely American. "The outdoors lies deep in American tradition," chants *Outdoor Recreation for America*. "It has had immeasurable impact on the Nation's character and on those who made its history. This is a civilization painfully and only recently carved in conflict with the forces of nature . . . When an American looks for the meaning of his past, he seeks it not in ancient ruins, but more likely in mountains and forests, by a river, or at the edge of the sea."

But these are pious sentiments, not historical facts. Our civilization is mainly imported from Europe, and has had more to contend against in Main Street than in the forests and mountains; pioneer life was usually duller and safer than it is generally imagined; and Americans who seek the meaning of their past look for it in Europe, or in Bunker Hill, Gettysburg, Williamsburg, Freedomland, and the deserted mining towns of the Sierras, precisely because such places are humanized, not wild.

Converts to the wilderness cult, like conservationists generally, tend to feel that their preferences are not only more virtuous than those of others but also more enduring. "Conservation should preserve all the fine things in life. Our heritage must be preserved for those who come after us."—so runs a typical admonition. Long-term or eternal goals are considered ethically superior to immediate ones; and future generations are expected to accept present-day precepts about what is important. Yet our great-great-grandchildren may care little for our image of the wilderness. Moreover, a heritage cannot be preserved intact; if it were, it would have only antiquarian interest. Tomorrow's patrimony is bound to be different from today's. The wilderness was no 'heritage' to folk who had to cope with it; it became one only when it no longer had to be lived in. The same is true of pastoral landscapes, rural villages, even of 19th Century industrial centers; and landscapes now despised will some day be prized as a precious heritage.

The wilderness is not, in fact, a type of landscape at all, but a congeries of feelings about man and nature of varying import to different epochs, cultures and individuals. For Elizabethans, the wilderness was barren, chaotic, frightful, "howling"; for contemporary Europeans, it is often associated with primitive and romantic tribes in distant lands; for many Americans, it is an entity distinct from the workaday world, an oasis where the laws of nature still apply.

The cult of wilderness—its origins and history, its philosophies and programs, its impact on landscapes and its implications for mankind—should receive thorough scrutiny. The way Americans feel about wild nature is intimately bound up, as has been suggested, with this country's special history. But the wilderness is only a part of anybody's picture. And attitudes toward wilderness can hardly be understood except in the context of beliefs and assumptions concerning nature and landscape generally.

Elsewhere I have examined some causes and consequences of supposing nature to be good, wise, purposeful and balanced ("The American Image of Nature as Virtue," LANDSCAPE, Winter, 1959–60). Let me discuss some assumptions about the *appearance* of landscape—assumptions concerning its origins or antiquity, its cultural context or function, and its esthetic congruity. For judgments about the way things ought to look are conditioned by how things are thought to have come into being, how old they are, what they are used for, and how well they fit into their surroundings.

The genetic vision

Comfortably ensconced in a Pullman car moving through Pennsylvania, the book critic J. Donald Adams saw something from the window "which revolted me, and . . . made me boil with anger. We had been passing through hilly, forested country, still lovely, even in its second growth," writes Adams in his weekly *New York Times* column, "when suddenly I saw a mountain stream so discolored, so noxious as almost to turn one's stomach. It was easy to imagine how it had once looked, sparkling and clear, before the mines somewhere beyond had polluted its waters and made it a thing of blasphemy."

What seems ugly to Adams he condemns as evil; but which of these judgments determined the other? He cannot be certain that the stream is polluted—he is no hydrologist. Suppose he learned the water was discolored not by mining but by a sulfur vent upstream, or simply by turbid spring floods; would he still find it 'noxious'? If he knew nature were responsible for the color of the stream, would he "boil with anger"? Would he still conjure up an image of pristine purity? In short, Adams takes it for granted that landscapes he enjoys are natural, and that those he dislikes have been ruined by man. Nature beautifies; man deforms. To alter the natural order is inherently wicked and *hence* displeasing to the eye. The forest, like the stream, is judged by this dictum. "Still lovely, *even* in its second growth," the wooded hillside is more attractive than some denuded slope, but lacks the perfection of the primitive forest.

Where landscapes are not patently marred by man, it is all too easy to assume that they are primeval. To the city dweller, anything that is not geometrically arranged may seem in the realm of untouched nature. He seldom distinguishes the pastoral from the wild. Indeed, in a landscape seen for the first time every component—mountains, old houses, even billboards—is apt to strike the viewer as a durable fixture of the scene.

But no matter how natural or untouched they may look, most landscapes have been profoundly altered by man, directly or indirectly, over long periods of time. "A field of pasture grass looks as if it had been there forever," remarks Edward Hyams, "and it is hard to absorb the fact that, like any urban square, it has been imposed on the wild." One intuitively feels that if man had interfered with the lovely vista it would bear obvious marks of manufacture, alteration or decay. "Surely a

water-meadow, with its lush grass knee-high to the cows and its decoration of tall golden buttercups . . . is a gift of God, or nature." Not so; "we owe it all to the greed for gain of a speculating 17th Century nobleman and the engineering skill of some Dutch drainage expert." On the other hand, some aspects of nature seem artificial. Vegetation is apt to look more 'natural' than barren rock, because we perceive analogies between geological and architectural structures—many tourists, asserts Joseph Wood Krutch, assume the Grand Canyon is at least partly man-made.

Misconceptions about man's role in landscape formation are universal and probably inevitable. Appearances lead people in all cultures and eras to assume that some things are 'man-made,' others natural, when the truth would reveal the opposite, or more likely an intermingling of agencies. What is unusual—and, to my mind, destructive—is to combine wrong notions of landscape genesis with the moral judgment that men generally act for mean motives and with effects offensive to the sight.

The contemporary tendency to find beauty and good in the 'natural,' ugliness or squalor in what man dominates, is not only moralistic; it is an esthetic aberration in the history of landscape taste. The contrary view has usually prevailed. Thus to Daniel Defoe, Westmoreland was "the wildest, most barren and frightful" county in England; he liked nothing about it except "some pleasant manufacturing towns." In most canons of landscape beauty, man and his works occupy a prominent place. A century and a half ago, in a fairly representative view, Arthur Young described the clang and smoke and flames of the iron forges at Colebrook Dale as "altogether sublime." Russians today similarly admire Kochegarka mine, the "pride" of Gorlovka, with its magnificent slag heaps scattered over the steppe for miles around.

By and large, men find lived-in landscapes more attractive than wild ones. "We have in places made the Earth more beautiful than it was before we came," Sir Francis Younghusband maintained in his Royal Geographical Society address: "I can realize what the river-valleys of England must have been like before the arrival of man—beautiful, certainly; but not *so* beautiful as now. . . . Now the marshes are drained and turned into golden meadows. The woods are cleared in part and well-kept parks take their place. . . . And homes are built . . . which in the setting of trees and lawns and gardens add unquestionably to the natural beauty of the land."

Raw nature was condemned also by 19th Century Americans. The Rockies and the Sierras displeased early tourists. "The dreariness of the desolate peak itself scarcely dissipates the dismal spell," one traveler wrote of Pike's Peak, "for you stand in a hopeless confusion of dull stones piled upon each other in odious ugliness." Americans preferred the picturesque—caverns evocative of cathedrals, pillars resembling ruined castles. If they could not have real ruins, they wanted make-believe ones; they had had a plethora of wilderness. To admire, much less love, wild nature, as Daniel Beard advocated, initially seemed ludicrous to almost everyone. Indeed, the first forest reserves were called "primitive areas" because, according to Earl Pomeroy, the government feared "the public might find the word 'wilderness' repulsive."

All that is changed; for contemporary Americans, it is civilization that is hard to endure. A 'primitive area' is now a place, according to the Outdoor Recreation Resources Review Commission, in which one enjoys a 'wilderness experience'—"a sense of being so far removed from the sights and sounds of civilization that he is alone with nature." The implications of this statement underlie most of the issues I have raised. Are the "sights and sounds" of civilization more difficult to live with than those of nature? Is being alone with nature the only, or even the best, alternative to civilization? What about being alone in rural or pastoral countrysides, or in landscapes full of historic ruins but void of present day activity? And how much do these distinctions matter if one is not aware of them? Consider an urbanite walking in woods where human enterprise is apparent to any Indian or woodsman, but invisible to him; does he not feel as alone with nature as he would in a truly primeval landscape? Alternatively, if J. Donald Adams suspected the green on leaves came from manufactured chlorophyll, would he not find the forest ugly? Oranges look unnatural only when we are told their color is artificial.

Few Americans, however, are devotees exclusively of the aboriginal; many are fond of the merely old. Landscapes that cannot qualify as pure wilderness may still be acceptable if they are sufficiently ancient, uncontaminated by contemporary life, or relics of an epoch when (it is assumed) man lived in harmony with his surroundings. Americans tout no particular era as an acme of esthetic virtue; all they ask is certified antiquity, preferably numerically precise. It is the anachronistic appearance that is all-important. Critics of Malraux's clean-up program for the *monuments historiques* of Paris protest that rejuvenation "has robbed them of their weight of reality, that the Concorde palaces now look like Hollywood movie sets of the Concorde palaces." And the Hotel Crillon rejected cleaning outright because, noted Genêt in the *New Yorker,* "its clientele, especially the Americans, had faith in the dirt of the facade as a guarantee that they were living in a genuinely historic old place." Few people are really taken in by such a 'guarantee.' But this matters little; as LANDSCAPE suggests ("We Are Taken for a Ride," Spring, 1962) we are willing to be fooled even when we know we are being fooled.

At home, visual self-deception is unabashed. Dirt is all right on European facades; here, it is matter out of place. For every restored Williamsburg, there are countless generic prototypes like Old Sturbridge Village—sanitary facsimiles rather than actual places, which rely for verisimilitude on scholarly precision. Self-conscious and sentimental about the past, we fence it off in special landscapes of its own, as if history were a zoo. Repair jobs for Niagara Falls and other 'natural' scenic wonders are deemed proper because they preserve or restore nature's creations; artifice is the means, not the end. But even where entirely new effects are produced, as with floodlights in caves or music piped out of scenery, the landscape passes for 'natural' as long as the face of the earth is not grossly and visibly altered. In the classic phrase of a Long Island developer, "We don't tamper with nature . . . we improve upon it!"

The functional vision

What Americans see in landscapes, and how well they like them, depends also on how the landscapes are being used. Form is supposed to fit function; camouflage is arty and dishonest. We like to call a spade a spade: however ugly a factory, a city dump, a used-car lot may seem to the passerby, as long as it fulfills its function it is presumed to look all right. If the used-car dealer didn't like the way his lot looked, he'd do something about it—not for his own visual pleasure, to be sure, but to attract customers. To enjoy a landscape or to commune with nature, we go to the wilderness. We do not prettify the rugged face of workaday America.

The landscape, in short, is worthy of its hire. Its ultimate critics are its residents, not its visitors, however unappreciative the former, however learned or perceptive the latter. This is the burden of a passage in William James's "On a Certain Sense of Blindness in Human Beings":

Journeying in the mountains of North Carolina, I passed by a large number of "coves," . . . which had been newly cleared and planted. The impression on my mind was one of unmitigated squalor. The settler had in every case cut down the more manageable trees, and left their charred stumps standing. The larger trees he had girdled and killed . . . and had set up a tall zigzag rail fence around the scene of his havoc, to keep the pigs and cattle out. Finally, he had irregularly planted the intervals between the stumps and trees with Indian corn. . . . The forest had been destroyed; and what had "improved" it out of existence was hideous, a sort of ulcer, without a single element of artificial grace to make up for the loss of Nature's beauty. . . . Talk about going back to Nature! I said to myself, oppressed by the dreariness. . . . No modern person ought to be willing to live a day in such a state of rudimentariness and denudation.

Then a mountaineer told James, " 'Why, we ain't happy here, unless we are getting one of these coves under cultivation.' "

I instantly felt that I had been losing the whole inward significance of the situation. . . . To me the clearings spoke of naught but denudation. . . . But, when *they* looked on the hideous stumps, what they thought of was personal victory. The chips, the girdled trees, and the vile split rails spoke of honest sweat, persistent toil and final reward. . . . In short, the clearing, which to me was a mere ugly picture on the retina, was to them a symbol redolent with moral memories and sang a very paean of duty, struggle and success.

And he points the moral: "The spectator's judgment is sure to miss the root of the matter, and to possess no truth."

James considers the mountaineers' impression truer and nobler than his own, not because they see better, but because they have a better right to judge. Beauty is in the eye of the beholder, to be sure; but which beholder is right? Why, the man who is usually on the spot—presumably the shepherd on the Downs, the sexton at St. Paul's, the elevator operator in the Eiffel Tower. He may have no time, training, or inclination for an esthetic appreciation of landscape; no matter, he acquires it by osmosis.

The esthetic definition

Preoccupation with purpose is in fact no aid, but a deterrent to landscape appreciation. The man who has to consider what things are used for is least likely to note their shapes, colors and patterns. To exalt his judgment is to promote a complacent inattention to appearance, an abnegation of esthetic response. The visitor's view is discounted, but the resident is too preoccupied to have a view.

There are a few who care, or pretend to care, about the way things look where they live. But many homeowners are satisfied by linguistic landscaping. Through emotive names—even by such geographical fantasies as Hilldale Heights, Valmont Gardens, and Glencrest Homes—"an idealized landscape is imposed on an existing one by verbal *force majeure*," as Arthur Minton points out in *Names*. Maybe only God can make a tree, but any real-estate developer can create a veritable forest in the mind's eyes of his clients.

Few people really look at the places they live in, work in, or travel through. Anesthetized against their surroundings, they spare themselves pain. "Start by looking at things, and then one becomes aware how hideous they really are," writes F. F. C. Curtis in the *Journal of the Royal Society of Arts.* "Some towns are hideous from one end to the other. I think it is because people do not open their eyes and do not recognize them as hideous."

The concept of scenic beauty, formerly tied to specific attributes, has since the 18th Century lost all precise meaning; it now promiscuously denotes anything that gives pleasure. "We talk about a 'sublime' or 'lovely' landscape," as Fenichel says, "because we feel sublime or lovely when seeing a landscape of this kind." No longer captives of the picturesque, we do not require that scenery look like a painting; and we can enjoy landscapes that point no meaning or moral.

Nonetheless, certain landscapes look right, others wrong or unhappily composed. They may seem incongruous because we have a pictorial bias against certain combinations of form and color, or a teleological outlook that condemns assemblages unless they look planned. Some of us find landscapes deformed unless the visual assemblage is familiar. Various objects, shapes or colors may seem out of place in certain settings. The totally strange and new may be less unsettling than a combination of known with unknown elements, or of forms belonging to two or more disparate cultural contexts. Those used to Western European or North American landscapes find something absurd and dissonant in lands where mules coexist with motorcars, and temperate zone flowers compete with tropical vegetation. The commingling of familiar and exotic, or of past and present, can be bizarre and disturbing.

Whatever the reason, most people expect a measure of visual harmony in landscapes. But the measure is personal as well as cultural: variety pleasing to one individual may pass unnoticed by a second and seem a shocking mélange to a third. Take litter. Most Americans pile junk in town dumps and automobile graveyards or throw it in rivers and down railway embankments. But streets and the countryside generally are free of cans and paper— otherwise, someone complains.

Other cultures treat litter differently. From an apartment in one tropical land I recently looked out at a garden, a stretch of grass that passed as lawn, and pleasant buildings opposite. What made the scene seem so tawdry? Garden and lawn were strewn with paper and cans. Litter collected there, months on end, because *no one saw it;* to the residents, cans and paper did not seem out of place among grass and flowers. And to many folk, here as well as abroad, cans and paper are not litter at all, but valuable materials for construction and fuel.

The problem is made evident and vivid when litter is mistaken for something view-worthy.

Disillusioned by mistaking a piece of blue paper on a hillside for a flower, A. M. Sayers asks, in the *New Statesman, "Why* do we dislike litter? . . . Is the disgust rooted in fear of one's fellows as a whole? No. Ancient Roman or medieval 'litter' doesn't trouble us. . . . Is it to do with the Age of Paper? Why should amphorae be so much more respectable than old tin cans?" But some people see nothing disreputable in old tin cans. Everything depends on what is considered 'out of place,' on the rate of decay, on how rapidly artifacts cease to be junk and become part of the heritage. And these are matters of great complexity.

Consider the reactions of Reyner Banham on Tair Carn Isaf, in Wales. Fascinated by the spectral, other-worldly quality of the cairns, the rocks and the light, he stumbles against "a stumpy concrete obelisk"—an Ordnance Survey triangulation point.

> And it jarred. . . . The triangulation-point just seemed to dirty things up. It destroyed the landscape as surely as the sheep that were eating the grass cover off the peat-beds. . . . The thing was a mess in itself, rust-stained from its metal fitments. It was a mess functionally, weathered down to a drab grey-brown that made it invisible against the landscape, and thus useless as a sighting-point. . . . Failed on looks, failed on function, failed for cultural inertia, too, for what else could force the classical obelisk form, apt to stone and primitive technology, on a machine-age material whose nature enjoins no form in particular?

Man's other contributions to that landscape seemed to Banham quite inoffensive—the ancient castle across the valley, his own aluminum-stemmed pipe and butane-fueled lighter. These belonged, visually, because they were or had been functionally effective. "Success or failure by the norms of the time," Banham concludes, is "almost an absolute standard for evaluating buildings in the natural landscape. For the landscape . . . can never be anything but up to date. Against the ruthless standard of nature . . . only the most spit-hot artifacts can survive. The trivial pipe is competitive, so is the portentous castle, the dirty obelisk is not."

The principle Banham enunciates is debatable. But even if it is accepted, landscape judgments would differ from person to person.

Lacking his special knowledge of technology and architecture, most observers would probably not be bothered at all by the triangulation marker. The main point, however, is that all the considerations Banham mentions are pertinent. They do not merely justify esthetic judgment; they help to form it. What makes one landscape appear harmonious, another incongruous, is the entire experience of the viewer.

Overpopulated America

40

WAYNE H. DAVIS

The problem of overpopulation, like many of the topics of this section of The Cultural Landscape, *evokes strongly opinionated commentaries. Discussions tend to be characterized by fearful statistics and simplistic analyses. This is a direct result of the immediacy of environmental pollution, resource depletion, and population. Wayne Davis utilizes a unique statistical unit called the "Indian equivalent" to accentuate the destructive power of the contemporary American. Davis suggests that the American in his pursuit of his creature comforts is at least twenty-five times as destructive of environment and resources as the average Indian. An example which Davis uses to show the tight linkage between affluence and wastefulness is damage done to the Kentucky landscape because of the coal gained in the strip mines. This coal, utilized in thermoelectric power plants, generated the power to create cool air for urban America. While an article such as this may evoke a considerable variety of responses, it is a fair example of a genre of literature on landscape today. The highly polemic tone has become significant in the forming of present-day legislation and uneasiness over the cultural landscape.*

Wayne H. Davis, "Overpopulated America," *The New Republic*, Vol. 162, No. 2 (January 10, 1970), pp. 13–15. Reprinted by permission of *The New Republic*, © 1970, Harrison-Blaine of New Jersey, Inc.

I define as most seriously overpopulated that nation whose people by virtue of their numbers and activities are most rapidly decreasing the ability of the land to support human life. With our large population, our affluence and our technological monstrosities the United States wins first place by a substantial margin.

Let's compare the US to India, for example. We have 203 million people, whereas she has 540 million on much less land. But look at the impact of people on the land.

The average Indian eats his daily few cups of rice (or perhaps wheat, whose production on American farms contributed to our one percent per year drain in quality of our active farmland), draws his bucket of water from the communal well and sleeps in a mud hut. In his daily rounds to gather cow dung to burn to cook his rice and warm his feet, his footsteps, along with those of millions of his countrymen, help bring about a slow deterioration of the ability of the land to support people. His contribution to the destruction of the land is minimal.

An American, on the other hand, can be expected to destroy a piece of land on which he builds a home, garage and driveway. He will contribute his share to the 142 million tons of smoke and fumes, seven million junked cars, 20 million tons of paper, 48 billion cans, and 26 billion bottles the overburdened environment must absorb each year. To run his air conditioner we will strip-mine a Kentucky hillside, push the dirt and slate down into the stream, and burn coal in a power generator, whose smokestack contributes to a plume of smoke massive enough to cause cloud seeding and premature precipitation from Gulf winds which should be irrigating the wheat farms of Minnesota.

In his lifetime he will personally pollute three million gallons of water, and industry and agriculture will use ten times this much water in his behalf. To provide these needs the US Army Corps of Engineers will build dams and flood farmland. He will also use 21,000 gallons of leaded gasoline containing boron, drink 28,000 pounds of milk and eat 10,000 pounds of meat. The latter is produced and squandered in a life pattern unknown to Asians. A steer on a Western range eats plants containing minerals necessary for plant life. Some of these are incorporated into the body of the steer which is later shipped for slaughter. After being eaten by man these nutrients are flushed down the toilet into the ocean or buried in the cemetery, the surface of which is cluttered with boulders called tombstones and has been removed from productivity. The result is a continual drain on the productivity of range land. Add to this the erosion of overgrazed lands, and the effects of the falling water table as we mine Pleistocene deposits of groundwater to irrigate to produce food for more people, and we can see why our land is dying far more rapidly than did the great civilizations of the Middle East, which experienced the same cycle. The average Indian citizen, whose fecal material goes back to the land, has but a minute fraction of the destructive effect on the land that the affluent American does.

Thus I want to introduce a new term, which I suggest be used in future discussions of human population and ecology. We should speak of our numbers in "Indian equivalents". An Indian equivalent I define as the average number of Indian citizens required to have the same detrimental effect on the land's ability to support human life as would the average American. This value is difficult to determine, but let's take an extremely conservative working figure of 25. To see how conservative this is, imagine the addition of 1000 citizens to your town and 25,000 to an Indian village. Not only would the Americans destroy much more land for homes, highways and a shopping center, but they would contribute far more to environ-

mental deterioration in hundreds of other ways as well. For example, their demand for steel for new autos might increase the daily pollution equivalent of 130,000 junk autos which *Life* tells us that US Steel Corp. dumps into Lake Michigan. Their demand for textiles would help the cotton industry destroy the life in the Black Warrior River in Alabama with endrin. And they would contribute to the massive industrial pollution of our oceans (we provide one third to one half the world's share) which has caused the precipitous downward trend in our commercial fisheries landings during the past seven years.

The per capita gross national product of the United States is 38 times that of India. Most of our goods and services contribute to the decline in the ability of the environment to support life. Thus it is clear that a figure of 25 for an Indian equivalent is conservative. It has been suggested to me that a more realistic figure would be 500.

In Indian equivalents, therefore, the population of the United States is at least four billion. And the rate of growth is even more alarming. We are growing at one percent per year, a rate which would double our numbers in 70 years. India is growing at 2.5 percent. Using the Indian equivalent of 25, our population growth becomes 10 times as serious as that of India. According to the Reinows in their recent book *Moment in the Sun,* just one year's crop of American babies can be expected to use up 25 billion pounds of beef, 200 million pounds of steel and 9.1 billion gallons of gasoline during their collective lifetime. And the demands on water and land for our growing population are expected to be far greater than the supply available in the year 2000. We are destroying our land at a rate of over a million acres a year. We now have only 2.6 agricultural acres per person. By 1975 this will be cut to 2.2, the critical point for the maintenance of what we consider a decent diet, and by the year 2000 we might expect to have 1.2.

You might object that I am playing with statistics in using the Indian equivalent on the rate of growth. I am making the assumption that today's Indian child will live 35 years (the average Indian life span) at today's level of affluence. If he lives an American 70 years, our rate of population growth would be 20 times as serious as India's.

But the assumption of continued affluence at

today's level is unfounded. If our numbers continue to rise, our standard of living will fall so sharply that by the year 2000 any surviving Americans might consider today's average Asian to be well off. Our children's destructive effects on their environment will decline as they sink ever lower into poverty.

The United States is in serious economic trouble now. Nothing could be more misleading than today's affluence, which rests precariously on a crumbling foundation. Our productivity, which had been increasing steadily at about 3.2 percent a year since World War II, has been falling during 1969. Our export over import balance has been shrinking steadily from $7.1 billion in 1964 to $0.15 billion in the first half of 1969. Our balance of payments deficit for the second quarter was $3.7 billion, the largest in history. We are now importing iron ore, steel, oil, beef, textiles, cameras, radios and hundreds of other things.

Our economy is based upon the Keynesian concept of a continued growth in population and productivity. It worked in an underpopulated nation with excess resources. It could continue to work only if the earth and its resources were expanding at an annual rate of 4 to 5 percent. Yet neither the number of cars, the economy, the human population, nor anything else can expand indefinitely at an exponential rate in a finite world. We must face this fact *now*. The crisis is here. When Walter Heller says that our economy will expand by 4 percent annually through the latter 1970s he is dreaming. He is in a theoretical world totally unaware of the realities of human ecology. If the economists do not wake up and devise a new system for us now somebody else will have to do it for them.

A civilization is comparable to a living organism. Its longevity is a function of its metabolism. The higher the metabolism (affluence), the shorter the life. Keynesian economics has allowed us an affluent but shortened life span. We have now run our course.

The tragedy facing the United States is even greater and more imminent than that descending upon the hungry nations. The Paddock brothers in their book, *Famine 1975*, say that India "cannot be saved" no matter how much food we ship her. But India will be here after the United States is gone. Many millions will die in the most colossal famines India has ever known, but the land will survive and she will

come back as she always has before. The United States, on the other hand, will be a desolate tangle of concrete and ticky-tacky, of strip-mined moonscape and silt-choked reservoirs. The land and water will be so contaminated with pesticides, herbicides, mercury fungicides, lead, boron, nickel, arsenic and hundreds of other toxic substances, which have been approaching critical levels of concentration in our environment as a result of our numbers and affluence, that it may be unable to sustain human life.

Thus as the curtain gets ready to fall on man's civilization let it come as no surprise that it shall first fall on the United States. And let no one make the mistake of thinking we can save ourselves by "cleaning up the environment." Banning DDT is the equivalent of the physician's treating syphilis by putting a band-aid over the first chancre to appear. In either case you can be sure that more serious and widespread trouble will soon appear unless the disease itself is treated. We cannot survive by planning to treat the symptoms such as air pollution, water pollution, soil erosion, etc.

What can we do to slow the rate of destruction of the United States as a land capable of supporting human life? There are two approaches. First, we must reverse the population growth. We have far more people now than we can continue to support at anything near today's level of affluence. American women average slightly over three children each. According to the *Population Bulletin* if we reduced this number to 2.5 there would still be 330 million people in the nation at the end of the century. And even if we reduced this to 1.5 we would have 57 million more people in the year 2000 than we have now. With our present longevity patterns it would take more than 30 years for the population to peak even when reproducing at this rate, which would eventually give us a net decrease in numbers.

Do not make the mistake of thinking that technology will solve our population problem by producing a better contraceptive. Our problem now is that people want too many children. Surveys show the average number of children wanted by the American family is 3.3. There is little difference between the poor and the wealthy, black and white, Catholic and Protestant. Production of children at this rate during the next 30 years would be so catastrophic in effect on our resources and the viability of the nation as to be beyond my ability to contemplate. To prevent this trend we must not only make contraceptives and abortion readily available to everyone, but we must establish a system to put severe economic pressure on those who produce children and reward those who do not. This can be done within our system of taxes and welfare.

The other thing we must do is to pare down our Indian equivalents. Individuals in American society vary tremendously in Indian equivalents. If we plot Indian equivalents versus their reciprocal, the percentage of land surviving a generation, we obtain a linear regression. We can then place individuals and occupation types on this graph. At one end would be the starving blacks of Mississippi; they would approach unity in Indian equivalents, and would have the least destructive effect on the land. At the other end of the graph would be the politicians slicing pork for the barrel, the highway contractors, strip-mine operators, real estate developers, and public enemy number one—the US Army Corps of Engineers.

We must halt land destruction. We must abandon the view of land and minerals as private property to be exploited in any way economically feasible for private financial gain. Land and minerals are resources upon which the very survival of the nation depends, and their use must be planned in the best interests of the people.

Rising expectations for the poor is a cruel joke foisted upon them by the Establishment. As our new economy of use-it-once-and-throw-it-away produces more and more products for the affluent, the share of our resources available for the poor declines. Blessed be the starving blacks of Mississippi with their outdoor privies, for they are ecologically sound, and they shall inherit a nation. Although I hope that we will help these unfortunate people attain a decent standard of living by diverting war efforts to fertility control and job training, our most urgent task to assure this nation's survival during the next decade is to stop the affluent destroyers.

Eco-catastrophe!

PAUL EHRLICH

41

Especially in literature on environmental pollution, one is likely to find authors not merely describing a modification of the landscape but exhorting the reader to become concerned and take some sort of action, to do something about our air, water, and space resources. Satire, sarcasm, and polemics of all types have become acceptable. One reason for the attack is that the pace of environmental deterioration is increasing much more rapidly than even the greatest alarmists suggested a decade ago. Instead of

Paul Ehrlich, "Eco-Catastrophe!" *Ramparts*, Vol. 8, No. 3 (September 1969), 24–28. Copyright Ramparts Magazine, Inc. 1969. By permission of the Editors.

worrying about the twenty-first century, ecologists now are speaking of massive disasters in water and air pollution before the end of the 1970s.

One of the authors who has written powerfully about the impending crisis in environmental pollution is Dr. Paul Ehrlich. He is best known for his concern over population growth, but he has also written a significant article for Ramparts *dealing with the destruction of the oceans. This article, "Eco-Catastrophe!" effectively depicts the interaction between various seemingly dissociated facets of the cultural landscape.*

[I]

The end of the ocean came late in the summer of 1979, and it came even more rapidly than the biologists had expected. There had been signs for more than a decade, commencing with the discovery in 1968 that DDT slows down photosynthesis in marine plant life. It was announced in a short paper in the technical journal, Science, but to ecologists it smacked of doomsday. They knew that all life in the sea depends on photosynthesis, the chemical process by which green plants bind the sun's energy and make it available to living things. And they knew that DDT and similar chlorinated hydrocarbons had polluted the entire surface of the earth, including the sea.

But that was only the first of many signs. There had been the final gasp of the whaling industry in 1973, and the end of the Peruvian anchovy fishery in 1975. Indeed, a score of other fisheries had disappeared quietly from over-exploitation and various eco-catastrophes by 1977. The term "eco-catastrophe" was coined by a California ecologist in 1969 to describe the most spectacular of man's attacks on the systems which sustain his life. He drew his inspiration from the Santa Barbara offshore oil disaster of that year, and from the news which spread among naturalists that virtually all of the Golden State's seashore bird life was doomed because of chlorinated hydrocarbon interference with its reproduction. Eco-catastrophes in the sea became increasingly common in the early 1970's. Mysterious "blooms" of previously rare micro-organisms began to appear in off-shore waters. Red tides—killer outbreaks of a minute single-celled plant—returned to the Florida Gulf coast and were sometimes accompanied by tides of other exotic hues.

It was clear by 1975 that the entire ecology of the ocean was changing. A few types of phyto-plankton were becoming resistant to chlorinated hydrocarbons and were gaining the upper hand. Changes in the phytoplankton community led inevitably to changes in the community of zooplankton, the tiny animals which eat the phytoplankton. These changes were passed on up the chains of life in the ocean to the herring, plaice, cod and tuna. As the diversity of life in the ocean diminished, its stability also decreased.

Other changes had taken place by 1975. Most ocean fishes that returned to fresh water to breed, like the salmon, had become extinct, their breeding streams so dammed up and polluted that their powerful homing instinct only resulted in suicide. Many fishes and shell-fishes that bred in restricted areas along the coasts followed them as onshore pollution escalated.

By 1977 the annual yield of fish from the sea was down to 30 million metric tons, less than one-half the per capita catch of a decade earlier. This helped malnutrition to escalate sharply in a world where an estimated 50 million people per year were already dying of starvation. The United Nations attempted to get all chlorinated hydrocarbon insecticides banned on a world-wide basis, but the move was defeated by the United States. This opposition was generated primarily by the American petrochemical industry, operating hand in glove with its subsidiary, the United States Department of Agriculture. Together they persuaded the government to oppose the U.N. move—which was not difficult since most Americans believed that Russia and China were more in need of fish products than was the United States. The United Nations also attempted to get fishing nations to adopt strict and enforced catch limits to preserve dwindling stocks. This move was blocked by Russia, who, with the most modern electronic equipment, was in the best position to glean what was left in the sea. It was, curiously, on the very day in 1977 when the Soviet Union announced its refusal that another ominous article appeared in Science. It announced that incident solar radiation had been so reduced by worldwide air pollution that serious effects on the world's vegetation could be expected.

[II]

Apparently it was a combination of ecosystem destabilization, sunlight reduction, and a rapid escalation in chlorinated hydrocarbon pollution from massive Thanodrin applications which triggered the ultimate catastrophe. Seventeen huge Soviet-financed Thanodrin plants were operating in underdeveloped countries by 1978. They had been part of a massive Russian "aid offensive" designed to fill the gap caused by the collapse of America's ballyhooed "Green Revolution."

It became apparent in the early '70s that the "Green Revolution" was more talk than substance. Distribution of high yield "miracle" grain seeds had caused temporary local spurts in agricultural production. Simultaneously, excellent weather had produced record harvests. The combination permitted bureaucrats, especially in the United States Department of Agriculture and the Agency for International Development (AID), to reverse their previous pessimism and indulge in an outburst of optimistic propaganda about staving off famine. They raved about the approaching transformation of agriculture in the underdeveloped countries (UDCs). The reason for the propaganda reversal was never made clear. Most historians agree that a combination of utter ignorance of ecology, a desire to justify past errors, and pressure from agro-industry (which was eager to sell pesticides, fertilizers, and farm machinery to the UDCs and agencies helping the UDCs) was behind the campaign. Whatever the motivation, the results were clear. Many concerned people, lacking the expertise to see through the Green Revolution drivel, relaxed. The population-food crisis was "solved."

But reality was not long in showing itself. Local famine persisted in northern India even after good weather brought an end to the ghastly Bihar famine of the mid-'60s. East Pakistan was next, followed by a resurgence of general famine in northern India. Other foci of famine rapidly developed in Indonesia, the Philippines, Malawi, the Congo, Egypt, Colombia, Ecuador, Honduras, the Dominican Republic, and Mexico.

Everywhere hard realities destroyed the illusion of the Green Revolution. Yields dropped as the progressive farmers who had first accepted the new seeds found that their higher yields brought lower prices—effective demand (hunger plus cash) was not sufficient in poor countries to keep prices up. Less progressive farmers, observing this, refused to make the extra effort required to cultivate the "miracle" grains. Transport systems proved inadequate to bring the necessary fertilizer to the fields where the new and extremely fertilizer-sensitive grains were being grown. The same systems were also inadequate to move produce to markets. Fertilizer plants were not built fast enough, and most of the underdeveloped countries could not scrape together funds to purchase supplies, even

on concessional terms. Finally, the inevitable happened, and pests began to reduce yields in even the most carefully cultivated fields. Among the first were the famous "miracle rats" which invaded Philippine "miracle rice" fields early in 1969. They were quickly followed by many insects and viruses, thriving on the relatively pest-susceptible new grains, encouraged by the vast and dense plantings, and rapidly acquiring resistance to the chemicals used against them. As chaos spread until even the most obtuse agriculturists and economists realized that the Green Revolution had turned brown, the Russians stepped in.

In retrospect it seems incredible that the Russians, with the American mistakes known to them, could launch an even more incompetent program of aid to the underdeveloped world. Indeed, in the early 1970's there were cynics in the United States who claimed that outdoing the stupidity of American foreign aid would be physically impossible. Those critics were, however, obviously unaware that the Russians had been busily destroying their own environment for many years. The virtual disappearance of sturgeon from Russian rivers caused a great shortage of caviar by 1970. A standard joke among Russian scientists at that time was that they had created an artificial caviar which was indistinguishable from the real thing—except by taste. At any rate the Soviet Union, observing with interest the progressive deterioration of relations between the UDCs and the United States, came up with a solution. It had recently developed what it claimed was the ideal insecticide, a highly lethal chlorinated hydrocarbon complexed with a special agent for penetrating the external skeletal armor of insects. Announcing that the new pesticide, called Thanodrin, would truly produce a Green Revolution, the Soviets entered into negotiations with various UDCs for the construction of massive Thanodrin factories. The USSR would bear all the costs; all it wanted in return were certain trade and military concessions.

It is interesting now; with the perspective of years, to examine in some detail the reasons why the UDCs welcomed the Thanodrin plan with such open arms. Government officials in these countries ignored the protests of their own scientists that Thanodrin would not solve the problems which plagued them. The governments now knew that the basic cause of their problems was overpopulation, and that these problems had been exacerbated by the dullness, daydreaming, and cupidity endemic to all governments. They knew that only population control and limited development aimed primarily at agriculture could have spared them the horrors they now faced. They knew it, but they were not about to admit it. How much easier it was simply to accuse the Americans of failing to give them proper aid; how much simpler to accept the Russian panacea.

And then there was the general worsening of relations between the United States and the UDCs. Many things had contributed to this. The situation in America in the first half of the 1970's deserves our close scrutiny. Being more dependent on imports for raw materials than the Soviet Union, the United States had, in the early 1970's, adopted more and more heavy-handed policies in order to insure continuing supplies. Military adventures in Asia and Latin America had further lessened the international credibility of the United States as a great defender of freedom—an image which had begun to deteriorate rapidly during the pointless and fruitless Viet-Nam conflict. At home, acceptance of the carefully manufactured image lessened dramatically, as even the more romantic and chauvinistic citizens began to understand the role of the military and the industrial system in what John Kenneth Galbraith had aptly named "The New Industrial State."

At home in the USA the early '70s were traumatic times. Racial violence grew and the habitability of the cities diminished, as nothing substantial was done to ameliorate either racial inequities or urban blight. Welfare rolls grew as automation and general technological progress forced more and more people into the category of "unemployable." Simultaneously a taxpayers' revolt occurred. Although there was not enough money to build the schools, roads, water systems, sewage systems, jails, hospitals, urban transit lines, and all the other amenities needed to support a burgeoning population, Americans refused to tax themselves more heavily. Starting in Youngstown, Ohio in 1969 and followed closely by Richmond, California, community after community was forced to close its schools or curtail educational operations for lack of funds. Water supplies, already marginal in quality and quantity in many places by 1970,

deteriorated quickly. Water rationing occurred in 1723 municipalities in the summer of 1974, and hepatitis and epidemic dysentery rates climbed about 500 per cent between 1970–1974.

[III]

Air pollution continued to be the most obvious manifestation of environmental deterioration. It was, by 1972, quite literally in the eyes of all Americans. The year 1973 saw not only the New York and Los Angeles smog disasters, but also the publication of the Surgeon General's massive report on air pollution and health. The public had been partially prepared for the worst by the publicity given to the U.N. pollution conference held in 1972. Deaths in the late '60s caused by smog were well known to scientists, but the public had ignored them because they mostly involved the early demise of the old and sick rather than people dropping dead on the freeways. But suddenly our citizens were faced with nearly 200,000 corpses and massive documentation that they could be the next to die from respiratory disease. They were not ready for that scale of disaster. After all, the U.N. conference had not predicted that accumulated air pollution would make the planet uninhabitable until almost 1990. The population was terrorized as TV screens became filled with scenes of horror from the disaster areas. Especially vivid was NBC's coverage of hundreds of unattended people choking out their lives outside of New York's hospitals. Terms like nitrogen oxide, acute bronchitis and cardiac arrest began to have real meaning for most Americans.

The ultimate horror was the announcement that chlorinated hydrocarbons were now a major constituent of air pollution in all American cities. Autopsies of smog disaster victims revealed an average chlorinated hydrocarbon load in fatty tissue equivalent to 26 parts per million of DDT. In October, 1973, the Department of Health, Education and Welfare announced studies which showed unequivocally that increasing death rates from hypertension, cirrhosis of the liver, liver cancer and a series of other diseases had resulted from the chlorinated hydrocarbon load. They estimated that Americans born since 1946 (when DDT usage began) now had a life expectancy of only 49 years, and predicted that if current patterns continued, this expectancy would reach 42 years by 1980, when it might level out. Plunging insurance stocks triggered a stock market panic. The president of Velsicol, Inc., a major pesticide producer, went on television to "publicly eat a teaspoonful of DDT" (it was really powdered milk) and announce that HEW had been infiltrated by Communists. Other giants of the petrochemical industry, attempting to dispute the indisputable evidence, launched a massive pressure campaign on Congress to force HEW to "get out of agriculture's business." They were aided by the agro-chemical journals, which had decades of experience in misleading the public about the benefits and dangers of pesticides. But by now the public realized that it had been duped. The Nobel Prize for medicine and physiology was given to Drs. J. L. Radomski and W. B. Deichmann, who in the late 1960's had pioneered in the documentation of the long-term lethal effects of chlorinated hydrocarbons. A Presidential Commission with unimpeachable credentials directly accused the agrochemical complex of "condemning many millions of Americans to an early death." The year 1973 was the year in which Americans finally came to understand the direct threat to their existence posed by environmental deterioration.

And 1973 was also the year in which most people finally comprehended the indirect threat. Even the president of Union Oil Company and several other industrialists publicly stated their concern over the reduction of bird populations which had resulted from pollution by DDT and other chlorinated hydrocarbons. Insect populations boomed because they were resistant to most pesticides and had been freed, by the incompetent use of those pesticides, from most of their natural enemies. Rodents swarmed over crops, multiplying rapidly in the absence of predatory birds. The effect of pests on the wheat crop was especially disastrous in the summer of 1973, since that was also the year of the great drought. Most of us can remember the shock which greeted the announcement by atmospheric physicists that the shift of the jet stream which had caused the drought was probably permanent. It signalled the birth of the Midwestern desert. Man's air-polluting activities had by then caused gross changes in climatic patterns. The news, of course, played hell with commodity and stock markets. Food prices skyrocketed, as savings were poured into hoarded canned goods. Official assurances that food supplies would remain ample fell on deaf ears, and even the government showed signs of nervousness when California migrant field workers went out on strike again in protest against the continued use of pesticides by growers. The strike burgeoned into farm burning and riots. The workers, calling themselves "The Walking Dead," demanded immediate compensation for their shortened lives, and crash research programs to attempt to lengthen them.

It was in the same speech in which President Edward Kennedy, after much delay, finally declared a national emergency and called out the National Guard to harvest California's crops, that the first mention of population control was made. Kennedy pointed out that the United States would no longer be able to offer any food aid to other nations and was likely to suffer food shortages herself. He suggested that, in view of the manifest failure of the Green Revolution, the only hope of the UDCs lay in population control. His statement, you will recall, created an uproar in the underdeveloped countries. Newspaper editorials accused the United States of wishing to prevent small countries from becoming large nations and thus threatening American hegemony. Politicians asserted that President Kennedy was a "creature of the giant drug combine" that wished to shove its pills down every woman's throat.

Among Americans, religious opposition to population control was very slight. Industry in general also backed the idea. Increasing poverty in the UDCs was both destroying markets and threatening supplies of raw materials. The seriousness of the raw material situation had been brought home during the Congressional Hard Resources hearings in 1971. The exposure of the ignorance of the cornucopian economists had been quite a spectacle—a spectacle brought into virtually every Amrican's home in living color. Few would forget the distinguished geologist from the University of California who suggested that economists be legally required to learn at least the most elementary facts of geology. Fewer still would forget that an equally distinguished Harvard economist added that they might be required to learn some economics, too. The overall message was clear: America's resource situation was bad and bound to get worse. The hearings had led to a bill requiring the Departments of State, Interior, and Commerce to set up a joint resource procurement council with the express purpose of "insuring that proper consideration of American resource needs be an integral part of American foreign policy."

Suddenly the United States discovered that it had a national consensus: population control was the only possible salvation of the underdeveloped world. But that same consensus led to heated debate. How could the UDCs be persuaded to limit their populations, and should not the United States lead the way by limiting its own? Members of the intellectual community wanted America to set an example. They pointed out that the United States was in the midst of a new baby boom: her birth rate, well over 20 per thousand per year, and her growth rate of over one per cent per annum were among the very highest of the developed countries. They detailed the deterioration of the American physical and psychic environments, the growing health threats, the impending food shortages, and the insufficiency of funds for desperately needed public works. They contended that the nation was clearly unable or unwilling to properly care for the people it already had. What possible reason could there be, they queried, for adding any more? Besides, who would listen to requests by the United States for population control when that nation did not control her own profligate reproduction?

Those who opposed population controls for the U.S. were equally vociferous. The military-industrial complex, with its all-too-human mixture of ignorance and avarice, still saw strength and prosperity in numbers. Baby food magnates, already worried by the growing nitrate pollution of their products, saw their market disappearing. Steel manufacturers saw a decrease in aggregate demand and slippage for that holy of holies, the Gross National Product. And military men saw, in the growing population-food-environment crisis, a serious threat to their carefully nurtured Cold War. In the end, of course, economic arguments held sway, and the "inalienable right of every American couple to determine the size of its family," a freedom invented for the occasion in the early '70s, was not compromised.

The population control bill, which was passed by Congress early in 1974, was quite a

document, nevertheless. On the domestic front, it authorized an increase from 100 to 150 million dollars in funds for "family planning" activities. This was made possible by a general feeling in the country that the growing army on welfare needed family planning. But the gist of the bill was a series of measures designed to impress the need for population control on the UDCs. All American aid to countries with overpopulation problems was required by law to consist in part of population control assistance. In order to receive any assistance each nation was required not only to accept the population control aid, but also to match it according to a complex formula. "Overpopulation" itself was defined by a formula based on U.N. statistics, and the UDCs were required not only to accept aid, but also to show progress in reducing birth rates. Every five years the status of the aid program for each nation was to be re-evaluated.

The reaction to the announcement of this program dwarfed the response to President Kennedy's speech. A coalition of UDCs attempted to get the U.N. General Assembly to condemn the United States as a "genetic aggressor." Most damaging of all to the American cause was the famous "25 Indians and a dog" speech by Mr. Shankarnarayan, Indian Ambassador to the U.N. Shankarnarayan pointed out that for several decades the United States, with less than six per cent of the people of the world had consumed roughly 50 per cent of the raw materials used every year. He described vividly America's contribution to worldwide environmental deterioration, and he scathingly denounced the miserly record of United States foreign aid as "unworthy of a fourth-rate power, let alone the most powerful nation on earth."

It was the climax of his speech, however, which most historians claim once and for all destroyed the image of the United States. Shankarnarayan informed the assembly that the average American family dog was fed more animal protein per week than the average Indian got in a month. "How do you justify taking fish from protein-starved Peruvians and feeding them to your animals?" he asked. "I contend," he concluded, "that the birth of an American baby is a greater disaster for the world than that of 25 Indian babies." When the applause had died away, Mr. Sorensen, the

American representative, made a speech which said essentially that "other countries look after their own self-interest, too." When the vote came, the United States was condemned.

[IV]

This condemnation set the tone of U.S.-UDC relations at the time the Russian Thanodrim proposal was made. The proposal seemed to offer the masses in the UDCs an opportunity to save themselves and humiliate the United States at the same time; and in human affairs, as we all know, biological realities could never interfere with such an opportunity. The scientists were silenced, the politicians said yes, the Thanodrin plants were built, and the results were what any beginning ecology student could have predicted. At first Thanodrin seemed to offer excellent control of many pests. True, there was a rash of human fatalities from improper use of the lethal chemical but, as Russian technical advisors were prone to note, these were more than compensated for by increased yields. Thanodrin use skyrocketed throughout the underdeveloped world. The Mikoyan design group developed a dependable, cheap agricultural aircraft which the Soviets donated to the effort in large numbers. MIG sprayers became even more common in UDCs than MIG interceptors.

Then the troubles began. Insect strains with cuticles resistant to Thanodrin penetration began to appear. And as streams, rivers, fish culture ponds and onshore waters became rich in Thanodrin, more fisheries began to disappear. Bird populations were decimated. The sequence of events was standard for broadcast use of a synthetic pesticide: great success at first, followed by removal of natural enemies and development of resistance by the pest. Populations of crop-eating insects in areas treated with Thanodrin made steady comebacks and soon became more abundant than ever. Yields plunged, while farmers in their desperation increased the Thanodrin dose and shortened the time between treatments. Death from Thanodrin poisoning became common. The first violent incident occurred in the Canete Valley of Peru, where farmers had suffered a similar chlorinated hydrocarbon disaster in the mid-'50s. A Russian advisor serving as an agricultural pilot was assaulted and killed by a mob

of enraged farmers in January, 1978. Trouble spread rapidly during 1978, especially after the word got out that two years earlier Russia herself had banned the use of Thanodrin at home because of its serious effects on ecological systems. Suddenly Russia, and not the United States, was the *bête noir* in the UDCs. "Thanodrin parties" became epidemic, with farmers, in their ignorance, dumping carloads of Thanodrin concentrate into the sea. Russian advisors fled, and four of the Thanodrin plants were leveled to the ground. Destruction of the plants in Rio and Calcutta led to hundreds of thousands of gallons of Thanodrin concentrate being dumped directly into the sea.

Mr. Shankarnarayan again rose to address the U.N., but this time it was Mr. Potemkin, representative of the Soviet Union, who was on the hot seat. Mr. Potemkin heard his nation described as the greatest mass killer of all time as Shankarnarayan predicted at least 30 million deaths from crop failures due to overdependence on Thanodrin. Russia was accused of "chemical aggression," and the General Assembly, after a weak reply by Potemkin, passed a vote of censure.

It was in January, 1979, that huge blooms of a previously unknown variety of diatom were reported off the coast of Peru. The blooms were accompanied by a massive die-off of sea life and of the pathetic remainder of the birds which had once feasted on the anchovies of the area. Almost immediately another huge bloom was reported in the Indian ocean, centering around the Seychelles, and then a third in the South Atlantic off the African coast. Both of these were accompanied by spectacular die-offs of marine animals. Even more ominous were growing reports of fish and bird kills at oceanic points where there were no spectacular blooms. Biologists were soon able to explain the phenomena: the diatom had evolved an enzyme which broke down Thanodrin; that enzyme also produced a breakdown product which interfered with the transmission of nerve impulses, and was therefore lethal to animals. Unfortunately, the biologists could suggest no way of repressing the poisonous diatom bloom in time. By September, 1979, all important animal life in the sea was extinct. Large areas of coastline had to be evacuated, as windrows of dead fish created a monumental stench.

But stench was the least of man's problems.

Japan and China were faced with almost instant starvation from a total loss of the seafood on which they were so dependent. Both blamed Russia for their situation and demanded immediate mass shipments of food. Russia had none to send. On October 13, Chinese armies attacked Russia on a broad front. . . .

[V]

A pretty grim scenario. Unfortunately, we're a long way into it already. Everything mentioned as happening before 1970 has actually occurred; much of the rest is based on projections of trends already appearing. Evidence that pesticides have long-term lethal effects on human beings has started to accumulate, and recently Robert Finch, Secretary of the Department of Health, Education and Welfare expressed his extreme apprehension about the pesticide situation. Simultaneously the petrochemical industry continues its unconscionable poison-peddling. For instance, Shell Chemical has been carrying on a high-pressure campaign to sell the insecticide Azodrin to farmers as a killer of cotton pests. They continue their program even though they know that Azodrin is not only ineffective, but often *increases* the pest density. They've covered themselves nicely in an advertisement which states, "Even if an overpowering migration [sic] develops, the flexibility of Azodrin lets you regain control fast. Just increase the dosage according to label recommendations." It's a great game—get people to apply the poison and kill the natural enemies of the pests. Then blame the increased pests on "migration" and sell even more pesticide!

Right now fisheries are being wiped out by over-exploitation, made easy by modern electronic equipment. The companies producing the equipment know this. They even boast in advertising that only their equipment will keep fishermen in business until the final kill. Profits must obviously be maximized in the short run. Indeed, Western society is in the process of completing the rape and murder of the planet for economic gain. And, sadly, most of the rest of the world is eager for the opportunity to emulate our behavior. But the underdeveloped peoples will be denied that opportunity—the days of plunder are drawing inexorably to a close.

Most of the people who are going to die in the greatest cataclysm in the history of man have already been born. More than three and a half billion people already populate our moribund globe, and about half of them are hungry. Some 10 to 20 million will starve to death *this year*. In spite of this, the population of the earth will increase by 70 million souls in 1969. For mankind has artificially lowered the death rate of the human population, while in general birth rates have remained high. With the input side of the population system in high gear and the output side slowed down, our fragile planet has filled with people at an incredible rate. It took several million years for the population to reach a total of two billion people in 1930, while a *second two billion will have been added by 1975!* By that time some experts feel that food shortages will have escalated the present level of world hunger and starvation into famines of unbelievable proportions. Other experts, more optimistic, think the ultimate food-population collision will not occur until the decade of the 1980's. Of course more massive famine may be avoided if other events cause a prior rise in the human death rate.

Both worldwide plague and thermonuclear war are made more probable as population growth continues. These, along with famine, make up the trio of potential "death rate solutions" to the population problem—solutions in which the birth rate–death rate imbalance is redressed by a rise in the death rate rather than by a lowering of the birth rate. Make no mistake about it, *the imbalance will be redressed.* The shape of the population growth curve is one familiar to the biologist. It is the outbreak part of an outbreak-crash sequence. A population grows rapidly in the presence of abundant resources, finally runs out of food or some other necessity, and crashes to a low level or extinction. Man is not only running out of food, he is also destroying the life support systems of the Spaceship Earth. The situation was recently summarized very succinctly: "It is the top of the ninth inning. Man, always a threat at the plate, has been hitting Nature hard. It is important to remember, however, that NATURE BATS LAST."

The new road in the United States

J. TODD SNOW

42

One of the prime goals of contemporary transportation facilities is to insulate the traveler from the environment. Innovations occur in all phases of travel which minimize one's contact with the outdoors. Though the justification for this is generally given in terms of increased expediency and public desire, there are some who argue that transportation should be shaped so as to involve the traveler more immediately with the world through which he is moving. One author concerned with the barrier between traveler and terrain is J. Todd Snow. Snow offers a four-faceted history of the road with the New Road, the most recent one, receiving the greatest portion of his concern. This behavioral road (the New Road) ". . . starts everywhere and leads nowhere." This comment on changing transportation technologies and the consequent social changes is an excellent example of the cultural geographer's frequent suggestion that material progress is by no means wholly desirable.

What a road is has not been constant through history. Its physical form has varied, as has its cultural definition and meaning. At least four ideal types of roads have existed in historical sequence up to the present highways. The fourth type has only existed in the 20th Century; and it can either be seen as the sum of the previous three definitions, or as an unprecedented phenomenon which, because of its apparent similarities to previous roads, has not been widely appreciated for what it is and implies. It would be well, therefore, to consider some of the features and implications, espe-

J. Todd Snow, "The New Road in the United States," *Landscape*, XVII, No. 1 (Autumn 1967), 13–16.

cially to the landscape, of the road of the fourth definition, the New Road.

The personal road. The first road was defined solely in terms of behavior: The path of the person defined the road. Perhaps the person tended to follow paths laid down by animals; perhaps ridge lines or valleys. In any case, the person decided what to follow, where to turn, when to stop, where to go. Thus this was not a spatial but a behavioral road. It was not a particular place, nor was it tied to any particular place.

The legal road. The King's Highway was defined in terms of morality and legality. A person, subject or sovereign, had a right to travel between certain places, although a strip of land did not necessarily exist or exist in a usable condition. The termini demarcated the road, the person defined its detailed route. This again was a *nonspatial* road, although it was directly related to specific places.

The spatial road. This road, the one typically thought of as the road, was defined primarily in terms of geography: It was a definite place, a strip of land which went between other places. That is, it was a space and an extension of other spaces. When I use the term "old road" I refer to any and all of these first three definitions of the road, although primarily to this strip-of-land definition, since it is the most salient feature of the roads which directly preceded the New Road.

The behavioral road—the New Road. Like the earliest definition, simple passage, this road is defined largely in terms of behavior; in terms of what a person does, is able to do or wants to do. Like the third definition, the strip of land, this is defined in terms of space. Also a large part of this still emerging definition has to do with the rights of the person en route to enjoy freedom from interference. It is not only the possibility of passage through this space which is important, but the *experience* of passage. And this space does not connect points. It is not an extension of any place, but instead is an extension of man and his vehicle. This New Road is different from all previous roads in its origin, use, form and effect.

The New Road in the United States began to come into existence around the turn of the century. This was half a century after the old road had begun declining in relative importance and passability, if not in absolute use. The old road was near death for several reasons. First, one of the main historic uses of the road, communication, had ceased to be exclusively identified with transportation or travel and had left the road for the telegraph wires and telephone. Second, the cheapest means of transportation in the 19th Century—the waterway and the railway—both existed prior to major settlement in much of the United States west of the Mississippi, so that when settlement *did* occur, it was usually located along one or both of these channels and was not dependent on roads. Also, in the latter half of the 19th Century there were no persistent military threats which might have stimulated the creation of a more extensive network of roads or even the maintenance of existing roads. Therefore the old road was essential neither for the transportation of information nor of freight or troops. Never in the transcontinental United States did the road provide the predominant form of transportation.

Then, toward the end of the 19th Century, roads came into much greater demand. This demand, however, was of an unprecedented sort. Hitherto the greatest single reason for the establishment of all roads was for political (including military) purposes. The old roads were built and used to conquer, to defend, to rule and to maintain political contact. Roads also tended to occur wherever there was trade potential and passable terrain. Both of these reasons, however, played a very minor role in the initial development of the New Road. Instead, the reasons behind the development of the New Road can best be described as recreation. The

19th Century technology produced two toys, the bicycle and the automobile. Both sorts of equipment required durable, smooth and continuous roadways. Both provided groups to agitate for the roads they needed. And the required roads began to be built. There were other reasons, to be sure, for the creation of the roads, but the main reason behind the roads was that people enjoyed riding bicycles and driving gas buggies. The road was reestablished by recreation.

Even after good roads began to become prevalent, recreation remained the major stimulator of new mileage. Just as the new road was not initially motivated by military or economic needs, it was not soon put to much military or economic use. The reasons for this were partly based on the same mushrooming technology which had produced the bicycle and automobile: More suitable (roadless) automotive vehicles for military purposes were simultaneously being developed—track-laying vehicles, airplanes and amphibious vehicles; more suitable methods of transportation were being developed—faster ships and railway trains, pipelines and airplanes; and better communication devices were stealing from the road that communications traffic of political and economic importance which the telegraph had not already taken. Also, of course, the railways and waterways still held the advantage of the status quo, with trade and settlement established on their framework; until the heavy duty, low pressure pneumatic tire was developed in the thirties; and the military could not depend on having developed roads where fighting was likely to occur and hence hesitated for some time to switch over to road vehicles at all.

The political and economic sectors of the country did become somewhat dependent on the road after it was well on its way to being reestablished. But even this use of the road was different from the traditional one.

Thus the road from the early part of this century was of novel origin. It was essentially the outgrowth of what—in previous eras, at least—would have been considered unnecessary activities, activities which were carried on in what then were relatively useless but distinctly different vehicles. The activities, which ranged from sports to convenience traveling, were largely the result of the availability of certain kinds of vehicles, the bicycle and the automobile; the existence of the activities, in turn, called for more of these kinds of machines, and the combination of activity and particular kinds of vehicles led to a particular kind of road.

The activities of exercise, sports and travel are, compared to the activities of transportation and communication, relatively aimless. And they inspire an aimless road. True, the New Road generally seems to go between cities, but the primary requirement is that it start from where people are and go on indefinitely; not that it go between places or lead to places. The old road started from and led to the city. *The New Road starts everywhere and leads nowhere.*

Since recreational activities are manifestly indulged in for self edification or enjoyment rather than out of necessity, the road itself is expected to further, or at least not to frustrate, this enjoyment. Therefore the road becomes less important geographically and more important behaviorally: The right of passage becomes the right of *pleasurable* passage. This, combined with characteristics peculiar to the new vehicles, dictates the behavioral basis for the new road. Bicycles and automobiles require more attention of the driver than did the horse or the railroad engine, for these new vehicles have neither the nimbleness and self-control of the horse nor the inertia and precisely predetermined path of the train. They greatly amplify the driver's physical size and his responsibility. Also, since a broad segment of the population uses these vehicles, keeping them under control is dependent upon common skill and knowledge rather than on the specialized skills of a particular group. Hence the road has to be built so that it is more than merely navigable by a carefully piloted craft. It has to be passable and safe for the masses to use, thus accentuating the behavior-determined form. What is important about the road used by these new vehicles, then, can be described in terms of behavior rather than in terms of law and geography. The people expect or welcome a particular sort of experience from the use of the road, and the man-vehicle combination has a particular sort of behavior which has to be considered in designing the road.

Both the activities and the vehicles of the New Road influence the road so that it becomes extraordinarily public and extensive. Individuals from practically every sector of society engage in the new wheeled-recreation activities. The participants are virtually as abundant and as broadly based as the population of the country. The bicycle is in the tradition of the horse; the automobile, of the carriage: Both are in a tradition of private ownership and use. They are potentially directly proportional to the population in growth. As a result of the widespread actual and potential involvement of the society with the road there is relatively uniform and widespread public demand for and support of the road. Consequently the road, already the longest ever to exist, grows to ever greater size.

Finally, the vehicles by themselves are distinctively different from those of the old road in two main ways: Traction is by wheel and speed is high. These two characteristics, which influence the surface and configuration of the road, have a great effect on the New Road. Long curves, low gradients, smooth pavement, multiple lanes and elaborate patterns of controlling access result from these characteristics.

The New Road, then, has little more in common with the old road than a name. Genetically, functionally and morphologically it is different. Its impact on the landscape also is different. Directly, the form of the new road is such as to require considerable reworking of the landscape. Where the old road had "followed" or "scarred" the land, the new road changes it. Valleys are raised, mountains lowered, forests rooted out, streams bridged, properties divided. Also, the very pervasiveness of the New Road, the fact that it starts from every community in the country, makes it a dominant feature of the landscape. The settlement pattern gradually shifts to the road, overlaying the existing rail and water networks with a new network.

But perhaps the least apparent and most telling effects of the New Road on the landscape are indirect. The New Road brings changes to the political, economic and social patterns as well as to the total man-nature relationship.

Where the old road had tied people to a political center, the New Road frees people from connection with any particular center. The political system of the country had been based on a geographically static populace. The New Road, which does not lead to a political center but to everywhere, reduces the validity, if not the vitality, of the political system. Nevertheless the road fosters concern with the politics of the nation as a whole. At the same time that the voter is losing his interest and his power in local affairs he becomes more aware of the land—*his* land—and more likely to be interested in its overall condition and the political body associated with it. The New Road focuses on the state and nation and becomes a state and national concern.

The old road had a political value, and it also had a social value. Not only did it enable people to come together to enact public policy: it tended to bring people into contact with one another for pure socializing; that is, the road served both public necessity and private pleasure. The old road encouraged social contact largely, of course, because of its political function: the road led to a point of congregation, to some definite city. Also, travel by the old road was slow because of the nature of the vehicles as well as of the road surface. Hence the users of the road were brought close enough together for social intercourse. Since there were relatively few travelers on the old road there was more community between the travelers: they together faced a difficult and uncertain task in a place far from the help of other men. Use of the old road was a social effort. Finally, the distance each person traveled was likely to be restricted by the low speed of vehicles. Thus a person using the road tended to be exposed to a limited number of people and could develop a web of acquaintance over a period of time.

The New Road, on the contrary, does not foster social contact. The surface and configuration of the road necessary for safe passage by the new vehicles and their drivers, and the speed of the vehicles, precludes ordinary social interaction on the road. The high density of use of the popular road, as well as the fact that the user travels fast and far, causes him to be exposed to many people—so many, indeed, that the individual user rarely sees a face or even a particular vehicle often enough to recognize it, much less to feel familiar with it. And, to repeat, the road does not inevitably lead to a point of congregation, but goes on forever. The New Road and its vehicles make such an anti-social situation that if people meet on the road, it is accidental.

The result is that the New Road, although intensely public, is not part of the social community. Rather it is of approximately the same order as the city sewer system: if it ceases

to be usable the public as a body is soon aware of it, but as long as it is operative it is, in effect, part of the private sector of the life of the community. People—private citizens—are the ones to use it, and they are not really aware of the others who use it; in fact they have less social contact with them precisely because of the existence of the New Road.

The pattern of economic use of the roads is different, too. As I have pointed out, commercial interests played a very minor role in the initiation and development of the New Road. It was not until well after the new road had come into existence that real use was made of it. It was as a result of the need for greater transportation during the World Wars, the greater capacity resulting from the wars for producing vehicles, the modern tire and the fact that the road existed and that the settlement pattern was beginning to be based on the road, that the road began to be used in a major way by the economic sector of society. An increasingly greater percentage of transportation shifted from rails and water to the road. The New Road, however, with this new function of transporting goods and materials in the tradition of the old road, had a much more important, and novel, part to play in the economy, reflecting its genesis and primary function: The New Road was important first as a device for the consumption of goods. The economic function of transportation of goods to market did not begin to approach the economic function of expenditure brought about by the recreational use of the road. The transportation of goods to the junkyard, of fuel to the cylinder, and of people to places where they have to buy services, probably far surpasses in dollar value the worth of goods sent to market by trucks.

The New Road creates new conditions. The landscape feels them. And perhaps no place are they so readily apparent as in that part of the landscape known as the "roadside."

The old road was related not only to terminal places but also to contiguous places in a way quite different from that of the New Road. Since the old road was basically an extension of a place it partook of the nature of all places and was related to the geography beside the road as well as that of and at the end of the road. The New Road, however, is an extension of behavior and, as such, has nothing to do with beginning or end or margin. These things are no longer related to the road, and the new road is built without them. Phenomena nevertheless still occur near the road which are related to the traffic itself. These phenomena, while generically the same, are specifically different from those of the old road.

The old road, the road with an end, had an abundant, usually continuous roadside. The roadside of the new road is made scarce and occasional by the control of access (by means of laws, fences, speed, directionality, multiple lanes). With both the old and the New road the roadside was the location for supplementing and complementing the functions of the road itself. In the case of the old road, which led to a community or which created sociality, the roadside provided privacy. With the New Road, on the other hand, which leads nowhere and which precludes community, the occasional roadside installation provides a surrogate goal and temporary terminal, a community, and for those persons who wish to prolong their privacy or are unable to do anything else, facilities to reinforce privacy. On the endless road to everywhere, the bits of new roadside—which might appropriately be called "antiroads" and which sometimes are called "oases" but which most frequently are encountered in the form of "strips"—are *somewhere*. And here are to be found two sorts of establishments: those which accentuate and continue the nature of the road, which service the private role of the vehicle (the drive-ins of all sorts) and those which provide an antithesis to the road, which provide sympathetic people and pathetic things (the walk-ins).

The New Road, though publicly financed and used, does not promote publicity or social intercourse; this was left for the (generally privately financed) roadside. The old road was an extension of community through privacy; the New, an extension of privacy through community.

Not only does the coming of the New Road bring change to the humanized roadside, but also it has far reaching implications for the natural roadside and for the man-nature relationship. The users of the old road were in contact with the natural environment—they confronted it, and could not avoid it. They were aware of distance, climate, configuration, sounds. They were in a relative place which was part of a greater place—the land. Their activity was but one of the many activities which went on in this place. They could not ignore the area they were passing through nor the activities of the other users of that area—whether highway men or snakes or cows or birds. Their every sense was subject to intensive involvement with the environment. The relatively slow speeds of the vehicles accentuated this involvement. And just as the environment left its mark on them, so they left theirs on it. The road, and that constant refuge, the roadside, felt the impact of use, of constant confrontation.

The user of the New Road has a quite different experience and effect, resulting basically from the fact that vehicle and road are both extensions of his person. Instead of being totally and intensively involved with the immediate landscape, he is visually and extensively involved with the greater landscape. His thoughts can just as easily be concerned with exotic things as with the present surroundings. He is more likely to be impressed with the diversity of the environment, which he experiences at high speed, than with local qualities: the depths of the forest or the steepness of the mountain. And probably since he faces a preconfronted and largely conquered nature, he feels, if anything, a sort of good will toward it, a feeling he would not have been so likely to know had his relationship involved more of a struggle. But whatever the effect on the user, the user has little permanent effect on the landscape. With the old road he had been *in* the landscape; with the New he is in a pattern of behavior so specific that it is insulated from practically all surroundings.

The contemporary call for more recreational facilities as well as the tendency to justify the road on grounds of defense or for commercial traffic suggests a general lack of awareness of the recreational basis of the modern road and awareness of the fact that the whole country has been virtually rebuilt around this recreational framework. Perhaps the American people, still imbued with Puritanism, have thus rationalized the New Road because they do not wish to recognize its real nature. To think of the road in terms of transportation, as is usual, is to see but a fragment of reality and to be oblivious to the Road's potential. If the road were openly defined as recreational, as an end instead of a means, might it serve more satisfactorily as recreational? Or might it cause an increase in expenditure for some less patently recreational public effort, such as the space program? It is possible that the New Road has not been recognized as a recreational facility because it is not really a very satisfactory one in spite of a long history of beautification efforts. Only one sense—the visual—is operative while using the New Road and this one sense generally cannot provide the total involvement necessary to produce the kind of sensation associated with recreation. Perhaps its recreational shortcomings stem from the intensely individual nature of its use: if the road promoted sociability it might have a much different effect on its users.

Evaluating the biosphere

BARRY COMMONER

43

The specter of diminishing returns on man's modification of the environment can be shown graphically in one fact extracted from this article by Barry Commoner in the British Science Journal. "In the Texas cotton fields, for example, it took 50 times as much DDT to control insect pests in 1963 as it did in 1961." This phenomenon of decreasing value and increasing cost of man's tinkering with the nature of things is well exemplified in this article. The conclusions, not surprisingly, are blunt and frightening. The hidden costs of modern technology are shown to be enormous. For example, the lead and nitrate levels present in our atmosphere and surface waters due to automobiles and inorganic nitrogen fertilizers are high enough to seriously threaten the survival of our lakes and even atmosphere. And the emission of potentially critical quantities of iodine-131 from nuclear power plants is an almost assured feature of the remainder of the twentieth century, unless major modifications are made.

Obviously the automobile, power plants, and chemical fertilizers are very stable features of the cultural landscape in the contemporary scene. Yet these same implements of modern technology and landscape modification are massive contributors to environmental pollution. Commoner, seeing the inevitable incompatibility of this relationship, offers little in the way of solution, but presents the problem soberly and substantially.

The biosphere—the Earth's thin skin of air, water and soil—is the habitat of man, as it is of all other living things. Like every other living organism, man depends for his life on what the biosphere provides: water, oxygen, food and shelter. Unless the biosphere continues to provide these necessities of life, man and all his works cannot survive. This much is true of man, seen only as an animal.

But man is much more than an animal that requires water, breathes air, gathers food and seeks shelter. His intelligence has given him the power to acquire resources from the biosphere which are far in excess of those involved in bodily maintenance. For example, human beings expend in bodily energy roughly 1000 kilowatt-hours per year; in a highly developed country such as the United States, the actual expenditure of energy per capita is between 10,000 and 15,000 kilowatt-hours per year. This extension of the impact of human beings on the biosphere is, of course, the consequence of technology.

Barry Commoner, "Evaluating the Biosphere," *Science Journal* (October 1969), pp. 67–72.

Technology, therefore, powerfully amplifies the effect of human beings on the biosphere. Prehistoric man withdrew from the atmosphere only the oxygen required for respiration; technological man consumes a far greater amount of oxygen to support fires, power plants and chemical processes. The carbon dioxide produced by technological processes has measurably altered the carbon dioxide concentration of the atmosphere.

Apart from the amplification of such natural processes in the biosphere, technology has introduced into the biosphere substances wholly new to it: man made radioisotopes and a wide array of synthetic materials, such as plastics, insecticides, herbicides and numerous industrial materials. These, too, alter the biosphere.

We speak of the collective changes in the nature of the biosphere which has been produced by human activity as environmental pollution. In recent years this has become a matter of great public concern. Although the issue has become most intense in highly developed nations, it is now world-wide. The United Nations has recently undertaken to hold an international conference on the problem in 1972.

Public interest in recent changes in the environment has largely been motivated by concern with the resultant assault on the senses, on bodily functions and to a lesser degree on certain economic values. More fundamental, however, is the question of how the deterioration of the environment affects the resources in the biosphere on which human beings and human society depend for their very survival.

In this article I shall try to show from an evaluation of some of the effects of modern technology on the biosphere, that our technology as it is currently construed forms an intrinsically unstable relationship with the biosphere. Since the stability and integrity of the biosphere are essential for the continued operation of technology, the present situation represents a threat to the survival of our present system of technology—and, indeed, of man himself.

We are all aware that there is something very wrong with the relationship between technology and the environment—that there is an urgent lesson to be learned from the growing intensity of air pollution, from the continued deterioration of our surface waters, from the proliferating problems of the urban environment. What is less clear is what that lesson is.

A prevalent view is that environmental deterioration is a consequence of relatively minor faults in our technology—the lack of adequate scrubbers on smokestacks, of insufficient treatment of sewage, of the absence of proper fume traps on motor car exhausts. However, there is strong evidence which shows that the environmental deterioration that we are now experiencing is not due to minor faults in our technology, but to major ones.

One example is the fact that much of our present water pollution problem is not due to inadequate utilization of the present technology of sewage disposal, but rather to the very success of that technology. Present sewage treatment procedures were designed to relieve the burden of organic wastes on the self-purifying biological system of surface waters, by converting these wastes to supposedly innocuous inorganic products. This sewage treatment system is quite successful in achieving its aim. The system is failing, however, because its inorganic products are themselves reconverted to organic materials by the green plants that participate in the aquatic biological system, thereby frustrating the initial aim of the treatment process.

Another example is provided by modern agricultural technology, which is largely based on replacing the dwindling natural supply of plant nutrients in the soil by the massive use of inorganic fertilizers, especially nitrogen. These fertilizers do greatly increase the immediate crop yields; but, at the same time, the impoverishment of soil organic matter, by altering the physical character of the soil (especially its porosity to oxygen), sharply reduces the efficiency with which the added fertilizer is taken up by the crop. As a result, unused nitrogen fertilizer drains out of the soil into rivers and lakes, where it joins with the nitrate imposed on the water by the effluent of sewage treatment plants—causing overgrowths of green plants and the resultant organic pollution. The drainage of nitrogen from fertilizer has already destroyed the self-purifying capability of nearly every river in Illinois. In the Midwest and California fertilizer drainage has raised the nitrate level of drinking water supplies above the safe limit recommended by public health authorities.

A third example which is—surprisingly—

closely related to the previous ones is the matter of air pollution due to motor car exhaust fumes. This problem originates with the production of nitrogen oxides by gasoline engines; released to the air these oxides, upon absorption of sunlight, react with waste hydrocarbon fuel to produce the noxious constituents of smog. This problem is the direct outcome of the technological improvement of petrol engines; the development of the modern high compression engine. Such engines operate at higher temperatures than older ones; at these elevated temperatures the oxygen and nitrogen of the air taken into the engine tend to combine rapidly, with the resultant production of nitrogen oxides.

In the air nitrogen oxides are readily converted to nitrates, which are then brought down by rain and snow to the land and surface waters. There they add to the growing burden of nitrogen fertilizer, which, as shown in the previous examples, is an important aspect of water pollution. What is surprising is the amount of nitrogen oxides that are generated by our motor traffic: it now amounts to more than one third of the nitrogen contained in the fertilizer currently employed on United States farms. One calculation shows that farms in New Jersey receive about 10 kg of nitrogen fertilizer per year (a significant amount in agricultural practice) from the trucks and cars that travel the New Jersey highways. Another recent study shows that in the heavily populated eastern section of the United States, the nitrate content of local rainfall is proportional to the local rate of petrol consumption. Thus, the emergence of a new technology—the modern petrol engine—is itself responsible for most of the smog problem and for an appreciable part of the pollution of surface waters with nitrate.

As a final example of the intrinsic failure of a technology which bears a considerable responsibility for the present pollution of the environment, we may look at the current status of the insecticide problem. Recent reports from Asia, Africa and Latin America show that the massive use of synthetic insecticides to control pests of cotton, cocoa and other crops has been characterized by serious ecological hazards. With awesome regularity, major outbreaks of insect pests have been induced by the use of modern contact killing insecticides, because such insecticides kill the natural predator and parasitic insects which ordinarily keep the spread of insect pests under control. At the same time there is now increasing evidence that synthetic insecticides are responsible for declining populations of birds and fish. Because of such hazards, and the still poorly understood danger to man, DDT has just been banned in Sweden, and its official registry is being withdrawn in Michigan and other states in the US.

I have cited these examples in order to illustrate the point that major problems of environmental pollution arise, not out of some minor inadequacies in our new technologies, but because of the very success of these technologies in accomplishing their designed aims. A modern sewage treatment plant causes algal overgrowths and resultant pollution *because* it produces, as it is designed to do, so much plant nutrient in its effluent. Modern, highly concentrated, nitrogen fertilizers result in the drainage of nitrate pollutants into streams and lakes just *because* they succeed in the aim of raising the nutrient level of the soil. The modern high compression petrol engine contributes to smog and nitrate pollution *because* it successfully meets its design criterion—the development of a high level of power. Modern synthetic insecticides kill birds, fish and useful insects just *because* they are successful in being absorbed by insects, and killing them, as they are intended to do.

Other pollution problems arise as the result of a kind of chain reaction from the initial choice of the aim of a new technology. Thus, once the technology of the petrol engine became dominated by the aim of achieving high power, tetraethyl lead was introduced to smooth out the knock in the high powered cylinder explosions—with the resultant spread of near toxic levels of lead into the environment. Another concomitant of the choice of the internal combustion engine over less powerful external combustion techniques for automotive transport is the massive production of carbon monoxide—an increasingly dangerous pollutant of air.

In a sense these results are testimony to the often praised single minded thrust of modern technological development—the progress towards ever more powerful engines or increasingly concentrated fertilizers. This same concentration on the immediate purpose of a technology often leads to blind spots which generate further pollution problems. Thus, in the development of synthetic detergents 30 years ago, the research effort was concerned with cleansing power, economy and other features attractive to the consumer who was to buy them. What the research neglected was the ultimate consumer of anything that goes down the drain—the bacteria in sewage treatment plants and surface waters that must break down the new detergents. As a result, detergents accumulated in water supplies to the point that they had to be taken off the market in 1965.

Clearly we have compiled a record of serious failures in recent technological encounters with the environment. In each case the new technology was brought into use *before* the ultimate hazards were known. We have been quick to reap the benefits and slow to comprehend the costs.

An important question about new technology is: "Does it pay?" Whether we ask this question in the direct language of profit and loss or in the more abstract language of social welfare, the question is crucial. For, sooner or later, every human endeavour—if it is to continue—must pass this simple test: "Is it worth what it costs?"

It might appear that this question has already been answered. After all, power companies are eager to build plants for nuclear fuels rather than fossil ones; farmers rapidly adopt new insecticides, fertilizers and machines. Apparently their cost accounting tells them that the new technologies yield the best available margin between income and costs. I should like to suggest, however, that these calculations are not complete—that certain costs have not yet been taken into account.

For example, what are the true costs of operating a coal fired power plant in an urban area? The obvious costs—capital outlay, maintenance, operating costs, taxes—are of course well known. These costs are always less than the income derived from selling the power, given the requirements of our system of investment. But we have recently discovered that there are other costs and have even begun to put a value upon them.

We now know that a coal burning power plant produces not only electricity but also a number of less desirable things: smoke and

soot, oxides of sulphur and nitrogen, carbon dioxide, a variety of organic compounds and heat. Each of these is a *non*-good and costs someone something. Smoke and soot increase the householder's laundry and cleaning bills; oxides of sulphur increase the cost of building maintenance; for organic pollutants we pay the price—not only in dollars or pounds but in human anguish—of some number of cases of lung cancer.

Some of these costs can be converted to economic values. The US Public Health Service estimates the overall cost of air pollution at about $60 per person per year. A reasonable assessment of the overall costs of air pollution to power production from fossil fuels is about one third. This means that we must add to the cost of such power production, for each urban family of four, about $80 per year—an appreciable sum relative to the annual bill for electricity.

What are the costs of pollution from nuclear power plants? Although nuclear power plants are free of chemical pollutants, radioisotopes may be released by these plants and their associated fuel processing installations. Investigators at the University of Nevada, who studied the iodine-131 content of cattle thyroids during the period 1959–61 (in which there were only rare environmental intrusions of iodine-131 from nuclear tests), found that cattle thyroids always contained some iodine-131—about one picocurie per gramme of thyroid. They concluded: "This constant level in the absence of testing indicates that all the iodine-131 in the biosphere is not from nuclear explosions. Some other process (es) must be producing iodine-131 at a reasonably constant rate and in copious quantities. The principal known source of iodine-131 that could contribute to this level is exhaust gases from nuclear reactors and associated fuel processing plants".

Recent results, reported by the US Public Health Service for the period January–March 1968, are even more striking. During this period of time, in which there were no nuclear explosions capable of nationwide dispersal of radioactive iodine, such radioactivity was found in cattle thyroids in Georgia, Iowa, Kansas, Louisiana, North Carolina, Oklahoma, South Carolina, South Dakota, Tennessee and Texas. Average concentrations ranged from 1–68 picocuries of radio-iodine per gramme in the thyroid gland. From comparative studies of the uptake of environmental iodine-131 by cattle and human thyroids it can be estimated that in the foregoing areas human thyroids would be exposed to 0.2–13.6 rads of radiation on a lifetime basis (assuming a constant exposure to the indicated levels) .

For iodine-131 the most recent Federal Radiation Council (FRC) guideline states that the average lifetime exposure to the thyroid should not exceed 10 rads. In 1967 the US Atomic Energy Commission (AEC) projected for 1980 a national level of nuclear power production more than 100 times greater than the 1960–61 output; for the year 2000, the AEC projects more than a 1000-fold increase over the 1960–61 level. In simple economic terms this means that, if we are to stay within the present FRC radiation protection guide, the nuclear power industry will need to include in its projected costs of future power development at least a 20-fold improvement in the technique for restricting the release of iodine-131 into the environment. Obviously this will add to present projections of the cost of producing nuclear power, if indeed such an improvement is technically feasible.

The FRC also tells us that there is a human cost associated with the acceptance of its guideline—10 rads of radioactive exposure to the thyroid. It states that *"any* radiation exposure involves some risk". There is indeed some risk associated with a 10 rad exposure. One calculation suggests that a 10 rad dose to the thyroid would increase the national incidence of thyroid cancer about tenfold; another estimate suggests only a 50 per cent increase. In any case, if we accept as the price of nuclear power that citizens of the United States shall accumulate a radiation exposure of 10 rads to their thyroids for however long that industry endures, we must reckon with the knowledge that some people, at some time, will pay that price with their health.

Another example which illustrates the huge economic problem resulting from the environmental failure of modern technology is given by the paper pulp industry. It has been calculated that if the US paper industry were required to meet present water pollution standards, it would need to spend $100 million for each of

10 years. The total profit in the paper industry is $300 million per year, so that, as a minimum, the bill represented by the pollution caused by the paper industry, if paid, would reduce the industry's profit by one third for 10 years.

The total cost of bringing water pollution control up to present standards has been calculated at $100,000 million over the next 10–20 years. The total economic loss from air pollution has been estimated at $11,000 million annually. These sums loom large, even against the US total gross national product. More important, in certain industries they may represent amounts which are so large relative to the profits as to constitute a serious threat to the industry's viability—if it were required to pay the full bill for the hidden costs of operation.

The foregoing evidence shows that the faults in our new technologies which are revealed by environmental pollution are fundamental, in the sense that they arise from the very success of the new techniques themselves. It is also apparent that technology induced pollution considerably reduces the total economic value of a number of technological processes. Far more serious, however, is evidence which indicates that the environmental failures of our major technological innovations constitute a threat to the continued availability of essential resources provided by the biosphere, and therefore to the survival of our entire system of productivity.

All living things including man, and all human activities on the surface of the Earth, including all of our technology, industry and agriculture, are dependent on the great interwoven cyclical processes followed by the four elements that make up the major portion of living things and the environment: carbon, oxygen, hydrogen and nitrogen. All of these cycles are driven by the action of living things: green plants convert carbon dioxide into food, fibre and fuel; at the same time they produce oxygen so that the total oxygen supply in our atmosphere is the product of the plant activity. Plants also convert inorganic nitrogen into protein, a critical foodstuff. Animals, basically, live on plant produced food; in turn, they regenerate the inorganic materials—carbon dioxide, nitrates and phosphates—which must support plant life. Also involved are myriads of microorganisms in the soil and water. Altogether this vast web of biological interactions generates the very physical system in which we live: the soil and the air; they maintain the purity of surface waters and, by governing the movement of water in the soil and its evaporation into the air, they regulate the weather.

This makes up a huge, enormously complex living machine—the biosphere—and on the integrity and proper functioning of that machine depends every human activity, including technology. Without the photosynthetic activity of green plants there would be no oxygen for our smelters and furnaces, let alone to support human and animal life. Without the action of plants and animals in aquatic systems, we can have no pure water in our lakes and rivers. Without the biological processes that have gone on in the soil for thousands of years, we would have neither food crops, oil nor coal. This machine is our biological capital, the basic apparatus on which our total productivity depends. If we destroy it, our most advanced technology will come to naught and any economic and political system which depends on it will founder. Yet, the major threat to the integrity of this biological capital is technology itself.

Again, it is the effect on the environment which reveals the self-destructive nature of much of modern technology. For instance our reliance on an agricultural technology which is so heavily based on the massive use of inorganic nitrogen fertilizer grossly disrupts the natural nitrogen cycle and threatens to break it down completely. Relying on inorganic nitrogen for crop productivity, we no longer return enough organic matter to the soil. Organic nitrogen in the crops, used as food, appears ultimately in the sewage which waste technology imposes on surface waters—with the disastrous results that have already been described. Moreover, many modern agricultural systems have increasingly cut down on the use of legumes (such as clover) which with their associated bacteria, are capable of restoring the organic nitrogen content of the soil through fixation of nitrogen taken from the air. Recent studies, especially of tropical areas, suggest strongly that microbial nitrogen fixation is far more important in maintaining the nitrogen cycle than believed previously. There appear to be numerous bacteria, not only in legumes, but widely associated with many different species of plants that are capable of rapid conversion of air nitrogen into

useful soil materials. When this subject has been more fully investigated, it is likely to be found, I believe, that such widespread bacterial nitrogen fixation has been a major factor in maintaining the natural fertility of soil not only in the tropics but in temperate zones too.

What is particularly alarming is that this natural process of nitrogen fixation is seriously disrupted by inorganic nitrogen fertilizers. It has been known for some time, from laboratory experiments, that when nitrogen fixing bacteria are exposed to excessive amounts of nitrate, the process of nitrogen fixation stops, and certain of these bacteria may even be unable to survive in such conditions. Some recent experiments indicate that this same inhibitory effect of inorganic fertilizer on nitrogen fixation also occurs in the soil. Thus in one experiment, the investigators were able to achieve a 55 per cent increase in the yield of a rice crop by developing a special strain of nitrogen fixing bacteria that were adapted to a close association with the roots of the rice plant. However, when nitrate fertilizer was added to the system, the crop yield *declined,* apparently because of the inhibitory effect of nitrate on nitrogen fixation.

By depriving the soil of organic forms of nitrogen, from animal wastes, and by suppressing through choice of crops and the excessive use of nitrogen fertilizer the natural processes of nitrogen fixation which sustain the soil's organic nitrogen store, agricultural productivity becomes increasingly *dependent* on heavy use of inorganic nitrogen fertilizer. Under these circumstances we inevitably pollute the surface waters. But worse than that, this process itself makes recovery from the present disrupted state of the nitrogen cycle increasingly difficult.

As the organic nitrogen store of the soil is depleted its ability to support crops *without* excessive use of inorganic fertilizer deteriorates, and any effort to use the soil effectively for crop growth must await an increasingly longer period of restoration. It is probable, as well, that the widespread use of inorganic nitrogen fertilizer is depleting the natural population of microbial nitrogen fixers, upon which we would have to rely in any program to restore the natural efficiency of the soil. This may be a particularly crucial factor, because current research shows that the effectiveness of these organisms depends on the association of a particular species of plant with a very special variety of bacteria. Therefore in any future effort to restore the natural fertility of the soil we shall need to rely on the availability, in the soil, of a wide variety of nitrogen fixing bacteria for successful association with different plant crops. As we continue to use excessive nitrogen fertilizer, we run the risk of wiping out varieties of nitrogen fixing bacteria, upon which any effort at recovery will depend. Thus we are not merely using up the resource represented by the biological system of the soil, we are destroying its capability to recover.

A similar self-destructive course is evident in the consequences of modern insecticide technology. What has happened in attempts to control cotton pests—where the great bulk of synthetic insecticide is used—shows how we have broken down these natural relations and allowed the normal pest regulating machinery to get out of hand. Here the massive use of the new insecticides has killed off some of the pests that once attacked cotton. But now the cotton plants are being attacked instead by new insects that were never previously known as pests of cotton. Moreover, the new pests are becoming increasingly resistant to insecticide, through the natural biological process of selection, in the course of inheritance, of resistant types. In the Texas cotton fields, for example, it took 50 times as much DDT to control insect pests in 1963 as it did in 1961. The tobacco budworm, which now attacks cotton, has been found to be nearly immune to methylparathion, the most powerful of the widely used modern insecticides.

In certain important cotton growing areas, the insecticides kill off insect predators and parasites, which are often more sensitive to the insecticide than the pest itself. The result: insecticide induced outbreaks of pests. Finally, birds and fish which take up insecticide residues turn out to be sensitive to insecticides, and their populations are reduced.

The technology of insect control by means of synthetic insecticides appears to be nearing the end of the line. If we continue to rely on it, recovery of the natural forms of control will become increasingly difficult. Where restoration of natural biological control has been successful, it has depended on a natural reservoir of insects which are predatory or parasitic towards the pests; if, through widespread dissemination of insecticides, species that make up this natural reservoir are lost, biological control may be difficult to re-establish.

No optimistic assurances, no government guidelines, can give us release from a profound fact of modern life—that the environment exacts a price for the technological intrusions upon it.

The powerful illusion that we can avoid payment of this price is fostered by the enormous accomplishments of technology. Technology is widely credited with many of the good things in modern life: rising agricultural productivity, new sources of power, automated industries, enormously accelerated travel, a vast increase in the volume and speed of communication, spectacular improvements in medicine and surgery. Technology has greatly magnified the wealth that is produced by human labour; it has lengthened our lives and sweetened the fruits of living. All this encourages a faith that technology is an undiluted good.

In a sense, this faith is justified. The modern motor car or the nuclear reactor is indeed a technological triumph. In each is embodied the enormous insights of modern physics and chemistry and the exquisite skills of metallurgy, electronics and engineering. Our success is in the construction of these machines; our failure is in their operation. For once the motor car is allowed out of the factory and into the environment it is transformed. It then reveals itself as an agent which has rendered urban air carcinogenic, burdened human bodies with nearly toxic levels of carbon monoxide and lead, embedded pathogenic particles of asbestos in human lungs, and contributed significantly to the nitrate pollution of surface waters. Similarly, the design and construction of a nuclear reactor epitomizes all the skills of modern science and technology. However, once it begins to operate, it threatens rivers and lakes with its heated waters and human bodies with its radiation.

We have already paid a large price for our illusions. For the advantages of motor transport, we pay a price in smog induced deterioration and disease. For the powerful effects of new insecticides, we pay a price in dwindling wildlife and unstable ecological systems. For nuclear power, we risk the biological hazards of radiation. By increasing agricultural production with fertilizers, we worsen water pollution.

If we are to succeed as inhabitants of a world increasingly transformed by technology, we need to reassess our attitudes towards the natural world on which our technology intrudes. For in the eager search for the benefits of modern science and technology, we have become enticed into a nearly fatal illusion: that we have at last escaped from the dependence of man on the rest of nature.

The truth is tragically different. We have become, not less dependent on the balance of nature, but more dependent on it. Modern technology has so stressed the web of processes in the living environment at its most vulnerable

points that there is little leeway left in the system. Time is short. We must begin, now, to learn how to make our technological power conform to the more powerful constraints of the living environment.

Further reading

Science and Survival *by Barry Commoner (Viking Press, New York, 1966; Victor Gollancz, London, 1966)*.

Restoring the Quality of Our Environment *President's Science Advisory Committee (Government Printing Office, Washington, D.C., 1965)*.

The Killing of a Great Lake *by Barry Commoner (in Year Book—World Book Encyclopedia, 1968)*.

Lake Erie, Aging or Ill? *by Barry Commoner (in Scientist and Citizen 10, 10)*.

The tightened city

WILLIAM H. WHYTE

44

Most articles dealing with the various ills of the cities suggest large-scale, federally underwritten renewal projects. Though such solutions are currently being attempted, their magnitude creates many bottlenecks in implementation. In this article, William Whyte views the same problems of urban space and recreation and suggests alternatives to the macro-solutions of renewal.

The tightened landscape he speaks of is one which utilizes to the fullest lands already open and basically unused in the cities. These lands— ranging from vacant lots to unused right-of-ways—could be profitably turned into islands and paths of green and recreation. Such vest-pocket parks would dress up areas of the

central city while affording critically needed recreational space for urban populations now hemmed in by concrete and glass.

The metropolis, it would seem, is running out of space. There are too many people living on too little land, goes the diagnosis, and what land is left is so hacked up that the only sane planning policy is to look to the hinterland and start all over again. Lately experts have been drawing up Year 2000 plans for decentralizing the whole mess, pushing people outward beyond suburbia and putting them up in brand-new model cities. These are to come in all shapes and sizes—megacities, bubble cities, modular cities, platform cities, stilt cities—but the one thing they all have in common is space. There will be space within them for their controlled, optimum populations, and surrounding them will be vast greenbelts, which in the customary air-brush renderings are shown

Whyte, William H. "The Tightened Landscape," *Horizon*, Vol. 11, No. 3 (Summer 1969), pp. 66–72. © copyright 1969 American Heritage Publishing Co., Inc.

stretching out to infinity, with not a trace of the grubby old cities and suburbs.

There is a good chance, however, that the trend may be in the opposite direction. The edge of suburbia will undoubtedly ooze farther outward, but there are indications that most of our industry and most of our people are going to be working out the future within the metropolitan areas that we have now; that we are going to be more jammed together than ever. And it may not be such a bad thing if we are.

A prescription for disaster, some would say; there would be no breathing space left, no parks, no countryside. But there is plenty of land, right under our noses. The cost is high, to be sure, but there is one good thing about high land prices: they force ingenuity. When there seemed to be more land, we squandered it with impunity. We still do, but thanks to the very fierceness of the competition for land, we are beginning to seek a more effective and intensive use of it. If we succeed, the more crowded landscape of tomorrow may be more amenable, more open in feeling, than the less dense one of today.

Developers, of all people, have been helping to show the way. Until recently, they splattered their houses all over the countryside and used five acres to do the work of one. They had to. Suburban zoning boards laid down the ground rules, and they were gripped with the notion that the best way to save open space and the "character" of their area was to specify rigid lot sizes, usually set as high as local pride and income could enforce.

As a consequence developers were forced to chew up an enormous amount of land to house a given number of people and to lay down an overblown network of streets and utilities to tie all this together. The countryside had to be homogenized. If woods were in the way, down they went. If streams cut up the tract, they were buried in pipes. For a good clue as to what was to go next, one had only to check the titles of proposed subdivisions (Maple Grove, River View, Rolling Hills), characteristically, they are named after that which they are about to destroy.

This sprawling pattern not only looked like hell, it was uneconomical. It cost a great deal of money to level a landscape. As long as land prices were relatively cheap, developers could absorb the cost, but by the mid 1950's the price of land was rising faster than the price people were willing to pay for the finished house and lot. By the 1960's developers were in a bind. If they were not to go broke, they were going to have to find a better approach.

For years planners have been arguing that there was indeed a better approach. Cluster the houses, they said. Instead of spreading the houses all over a tract, developers could group the houses on the most buildable parts and leave the bulk of the land as open space. This way they would provide the residents with some really usable open space, spare the woods and streams, and save themselves the cost of improving these away. They would also have to lay down far less concrete for roads and fewer utility lines per house.

There was nothing particularly new about the idea—essentially, it was the principle of the New England town—but to developers chastened by soaring land costs, it now seemed a revolutionary concept, and with belated enthusiasm they began to promote it. Local zoning boards were suspicious; if cluster was so good for developers, they figured, there must be something wrong with it. But here and there a few cluster developments went up. They worked. Contrary to the widely held assumption that all Americans hankered for a home set in as large a lot as possible, people liked the cluster arrangement. Most of the early cluster developments sold as well or better than conventional developments in the same price range. Today there is still plenty of resistance in many a suburb, but the cluster approach is well on its way to becoming the dominant trend.

The homeowner's private open space, often in the form of a patio or walled garden, may be small—sometimes no more than twenty by twenty feet. Despite the snugness, however, or more likely because of it, people have found these enclaves more useful than triple the acreage in side yards and back yards. And there is no lawn to mow. The common greens and surrounding open spaces provide a full range of recreational facilities—swimming pools, golf courses, bridle trails, and sometimes, as at Reston and Columbia, man-made lakes for boating.

One of the most promising things about cluster development is the opportunity it provides for tying the separate spaces together into some sort of a network. Philadelphia provides an excellent example. When its Far Northeast section was on the brink of development, the city planners decided that they were not going to let it be hacked up by a miscellany of separate plans. They would lay down the developers' open space for them and a good bit else besides. The houses would be grouped in clusters and the acreage along the wooded creeks that ran through the area would have to be deeded by the developers as community space.

Developers took to the idea. A host of them were involved, but because of the preplanning bestowed on them by the city, *in toto* they have provided a magnificent open-space network that cost the city nothing and will one day be priceless. The neighborhood is no showcase—the houses are stock builders' houses and quite ordinary. But this is why it is so significant. If this kind of amenity can be built into tract housing in a city, surely the potential elsewhere must be tremendous.

However, we cannot expect developers to save the land we need the most. For the core of any open-space network the public is going to have to spend its own money buying land, and a very great deal of money. At the moment the prospects would not seem too good, since the supply of land appears to be diminishing. Most of the big open spaces have already been bought, or lost, and there are few to be had in urban areas at any price.

There are lots of small spaces, however. Total them up and you will find that they account for more than one half of the land in most metropolitan areas. It is true that they are scattered in bits and pieces and odd shapes and do not provide the form and structure that many regional planners think is necessary. But their potential is great just the same, and with ingenuity many of them can be linked in such a way as to make them more effective for people than huge greenbelts or wedges would be.

We are dealing with two kinds of reality. One is open space as it appears on a map. This is the big picture, or macroview, highly satisfying to planners. The other reality is open space as people perceive it. There is quite a difference. If you were to chart the impressions people have of open space, you would get a highly skewed picture, much like the joke maps of a New Yorker's eye view of the United States.

But this subjective reality is extremely important. As different as people's impressions might be, any composite would show that most people are aware of only a fraction of the open land, that small areas stand out the most, and that people grossly exaggerate the size of such areas.

Big spaces are certainly valuable, and we ought to have more of them. But it is the edge of the space that counts most. This is what people see, and though they should venture beyond them, they rarely do. Close to many of our big cities are large forests, but their interiors, for most people, simply do not exist. Use tends to be concentrated in a few accessible spots along the roadsides. For most of the people most of the time the edge of the open space *is* the open space.

This is one of the reasons why small spaces can be so efficient. Proportionately, they provide more edge, especially when they are linear. To oversimplify a bit, let us take an area of four square miles. If it were all in one space and roughly square, there would be eight miles of edge.

If we were to take the same amount of land and lay it out in a strip a half a mile wide, we would have eighteen miles of edge.

If we pursue the edge concept too far, of course, we will end up with all edge and nothing else. It should be obvious, however, that per acre, linear strips are probably the most important kind of open space that we can lay our hands on. They are not only worthwhile in their own right, they are also useful in tying other kinds of open space together.

There are all sorts of connective strips to be had. Our metropolitan areas are crisscrossed with them. The same changes in transportation that have made it so difficult for people to find a place to walk or cycle have made obsolete many old rights-of-way—aqueducts, canals, railroads, interurban trolley lines. Some have been obliterated, but a tremendous amount of mileage lies unused and weedy that with not too much expense could be rehabilitated into a system of trails and walkways. Along the Hudson River corridor, for example, there are 350 miles of abandoned railroad lines, 190 miles of abandoned canals, and 60 miles of aqueduct rights-of-way through which water has long since ceased to flow.

The Croton Aqueduct is a good example of the riches to be found. Back in 1837 the City of

New York bought a 66-foot-wide strip and buried a pipe in it to carry water from a reservoir in Westchester County to the city. By the 1930's it had become almost obsolete. Some parts of the right-of-way were made available as little parks, but the city also began giving permits to abutting landowners, and the right-of-way became interrupted with parking lots, dump heaps, and link fences. By 1955 it had been more or less abandoned as an aqueduct, but because of legal complications it continued to lie in limbo.

In 1965 the Hudson River Valley Commission held up the aqueduct as a classic example of access and urged that the whole length be transformed into a linear park. The exciting thing about a project like this is that it can be made ready in fairly short order. It will take time to clear out some of the encroachments, but the bulk of it will soon be available to the public, and in several years it will provide a reasonably continuous walkway all the way from the Bronx to northern Westchester County.

Railroad rights-of-way are another great asset. The railroads have been abandoning service on them at a rapid clip—some 10,000 miles in the past decade. These rights-of-way, which range from 50 to 150 feet in width, make excellent bridle trails and walkways. One such project is the "Illinois Prairie Path," a stretch running from Chicago to its western suburbs along the route of the old Chicago, Aurora and Elgin trolley line. Under the leadership of the Chicago Open Lands Project, private groups and public agencies are trying to acquire the right-of-way and make it the spine of a walkway and bridle trail system.

Many canals await rediscovery. The most celebrated, thanks to the itinerant Justice Douglas and his annual hikes, is the Chesapeake and Ohio, bordering the Potomac. This is a particularly entrancing stretch and one of the longest—about 185 miles between Washington, D.C., and Cumberland, Maryland. But there are others across the country that have almost as great a potential, and the cost of rehabilitating them as walks need not be prohibitive.

Stream valleys are the best connectors of all; they are usually good-looking to begin with, but a humdrum watercourse, even one that is dry most of the time, can be the makings of an excellent facility. Ordinarily engineers don't

like such streams and put them into concrete troughs whenever they can. Stream beds that run through metropolitan areas in the West and Southwest are thus tamed, and people are not supposed to trespass. But water flows in them only a few days a year, and a number of communities have begun to use them as cycling paths. A next step would be to deconcrete some streams and plant their banks with thirsty trees, like sycamores or willows.

Small arroyos that the engineers have not gotten around to can also be useful. Ordinarily these dry creeks are thought of as nuisances: they make steep ravines and are often choked with thickets of brush. But there is much that can be done with them. In Santa Barbara, California, for example, the arroyos provide a natural framework by which the open spaces of new developments can be linked together. The county has been allowing developers to reduce lot sizes somewhat if they will dedicate the ravine portions as permanent open space.

Utility rights-of-way are another overlooked asset. These swaths are usually regarded as eyesores, but with a little work they can be transformed into walkways and cycle paths. One county that has made the attempt is Santa Clara, in California. Its flat valley floor has been so splattered with subdivisions that it is the classic case of urban sprawl, and one would think any kind of open-space network out of the question. But blight has been the mother of invention; the county is weaving rights-of-way for aqueducts and high-tension lines, creekside strips and school sites, into a fine system of "greenways."

The surest way to save such open spaces is to acquire full ownership. But there is neither the money to buy up all the land to be saved nor the money to maintain it afterward. If the landscape is to be kept alive, furthermore, it is often better to have the most comely open space kept up by landowners. The question is how to make sure the spaces stay open. Up to a point, zoning can help. This is especially true of flood plains and land along the creeks, which usually happen to be the most attractive land; it is such land that ought to be kept open to protect the public from flood damage.

But zoning is highly vulnerable to local pressures. A more permanent measure is the acquisition of an easement. Through this ancient device the public buys away the landowner's right to louse up his own property. He keeps title to it and can do to it what he always did. The easement specifies that on the portion covered—the land 300 feet on each side of the stream—he will not put up houses or billboards, cut down trees, or dig pits.

Easements work best when they are applied along key natural features, such as streams and riversides, or along roads. They would cost too much if they were used to interdict development of large areas, but when they are closely tailored to the topography, the cost can be quite reasonable. Wisconsin has been buying scenic easements from farms along the Great River Road bordering the Mississippi for about twenty to twenty-two dollars an acre.

An easement program benefits landowners; it protects their flanks, and they know they won't wake up one day and see bulldozers felling the woods on their neighbors' property. In some areas it has been the landowners themselves who have initiated easements. A group of landowners on the Maryland side of the Potomac across from Mount Vernon pledged that they would give scenic easements on their property if Congress would appropriate sufficient money to buy parkland in fee simple as an anchor.

Within the cities connective links are harder to come by. Most of what open land remains is in small and scattered pieces, and old-line park officials look down their noses at such spaces: they like to work with big spaces and charge that small, odd-sized parks are difficult to maintain and are a prey to vandalism. But these pieces are what we have to work with, and with imagination they can be fashioned into tremendous assets. The fact that they are surrounded by development not only makes them accessible to people, but their enclosure by surrounding buildings often makes them seem much bigger than they are.

Lately there has been a move to "vestpocket" parks, and despite the warnings of some park officials, the initial programs have been encouraging. The lesson seems to be that there has to be a sort of critical mass; the parks have to be well distributed throughout the neighborhoods, and the people of the neighborhoods have to be heavily involved in the plan. Where these conditions have been met, as in Philadelphia's excellent program, they have proved very popular.

Another thing to be encouraged about is the revolution that appears to be under way in park design. It is long overdue. Most of our urban parks and playgrounds look as if they were designed by administrators—administrators who dislike children. There is the inevitable expanse of asphalt, the standardized swings, and the signs and fences that are clearly meant to keep the little beggars at bay. Children like trees, especially the kind with branches low enough to climb—but trees are supposed to be a hazard and require additional maintenance. So there are no trees.

The Europeans with their "adventure" playgrounds have demonstrated that the children have a whale of a time with dirt, trees, old crates, and rubble and that they bang themselves up less in the presence of such hazards than they do in standardized playgrounds. We are just beginning to experiment with the same approach, though in a much less permissive way. The best of our new adventure playgrounds are highly designed by adults, but they are very well designed. A few have been a bit too chic for their clientele, but most of them, such as Riis Plaza on New York's Lower East Side, have been extremely popular. Instead of conventional equipment, the new playgrounds provide a maze of forms: igloos made of stone, tunnels and pipes to crawl through, tree houses to climb on. They also do wonderful things with water—it jets out of pipes and fountains, runs down walls, and streams through labyrinthian sluiceways.

The most striking thing about these playgrounds is their jam-packedness. Per square foot they handle an extraordinary number of children. Nearby, a conventional playground may be almost empty, but the new ones will be jammed with enough children to suggest that the sheer density is one of the reasons they find them so attractive. Psychologists and ecologists who worry about rats' reactions to high-density living ought to look into such phenomena.

Another kind of small space we should have more of is the small midtown park for office workers and shoppers. The outstanding example is the tiny park donated by William S. Paley in midtown Manhattan—fashioned, appropriately enough, on a site once owned by a night club. It is only 42 feet wide and 100 feet deep, but it is an utter delight. The landscape architect Robert L. Zion, who had long been plumping for such an experiment, has used the surrounding buildings to create an outdoor room that is wonderfully snug and attractive. This experiment is not easily reproduced—it cost more than a million dollars—but the basic idea has great universality. In the heart of almost every city there is a wealth of suitable sites. Look down from a plane. Our downtowns are a checkerboard of small spaces—parking lots—and in some cities more land is covered with cars than with buildings. Surely a few of these spaces could be reclaimed for people; the overall economics of downtown would be better if they were.

Rooftops ought to be used more. Many low structures provide a ready-made base for park and recreation areas, and if new buildings were planned with such double use in mind, the results could be felicitous. This should be especially true of municipal structures, usually the dreariest example of single-purpose design. Sewage disposal plants are a case in point. Horizontally they take up considerable space; vertically, very little—and they look terrible. Cities would get a lot more for their money if they laid parks over the tops of them, or as New York City has thought of doing, put fountains on top of them.

There is tremendous potential in the use of air rights. Railroads have been selling the rights to build over their tracks for all sorts of projects—many of midtown Chicago's new buildings have been going up over tracks. Soon the highway people will be doing the same The New York Thruway Authority has been soliciting developers to put up projects over various urban sections of its rights-of-way. ("Fashion Your Future Out of Thin Air," the promotional brochure is titled.) Why not parks, too? Parks would fit in with any development scheme and would help convert some of the most divisive urban strips into community assets. Subway and railroad freight yards, which account for a large part of city land, could also be decked over to good effect.

Many other techniques could be cited: purchase of scenic easements from landowners along streams and ridges, the landscaping of our growing supply of rubbish to provide parks and hills, the reclamation of sand and gravel pits and quarries. Individually, no one approach can accomplish much, but together they open up exciting opportunities.

Many experts criticize such attention to detail as palliative, a microview that obscures the need for a bold restructuring of the metropolis. Others damn such measures with the epithets "cosmetic" and "prettification"; and there is never a conference on the subject but some hero doesn't stand up and say we have to get down to basics and, gentlemen, planting trees and creating small parks won't solve the root problems of poverty.

And indeed it won't. Let us just say that trees are nice to have. Such measures do not add up to the grand-sweep approach to urban design, but they have the advantage of practicality. The opportunities can be seized now, and have to be if they are to be seized at all. Let us, in sum, plan for today. As for the landscape of the year 2000, our grandchildren can take it from there.

What makes a city great?

TIME *MAGAZINE*

45

This short essay from Time *illustrates the difficulties one has in evaluating the most conspicuous of all features of the cultural landscape—the city. Just as the* Time *author is unable to articulate the qualities which make a city great, many urban dwellers lack the ability to say exactly why they choose to continue to live in these centers of crime, pollution, and high expenses. The entire city phenomenon takes on qualities of irrationality when one considers in depth the nature of urban versus nonurban life. There is no more impressive or more compelling example of the earth's modified landscape, however, than man's creation of the urban scene.*

"It is difficult to speak adequately or justly of London," wrote Henry James in 1881. "It is not a pleasant place; it is not agreeable, or cheerful, or easy, or exempt from reproach. It is only magnificent." Were he alive today, James, a connoisseur of cities, might easily say the same thing about New York or Paris or Tokyo, for the great city is one of the paradoxes of history. In countless different ways, it has almost always been an unpleasant, disagreeable, cheerless, uneasy and reproachful place; in the end, it can only be described as magnificent.

Babylon, for example, was the first great city of the ancient world; according to the Bible, it was "the mother of harlots and abominations of the earth." Ancient Athens, for all its architectural and intellectual glory, was scarcely more than an overgrown slum; the grandeur of Rome was overshadowed by its ramshackle ghettos, crime rate and traffic jams. Sanitation

"What Makes a City Great?", *Time*, November 14, 1969, 47–48. Reprinted by permission from *Time*, The Weekly Newsmagazine; Copyright Time Inc., 1969.

was so bad in the Paris of Louis XIV that two miles from the city's gates a traveler's nose would tell him that he was drawing near. Scarcely anyone today needs to be told about how awful life is in nerve-jangling New York City, which resembles a mismanaged ant heap rather than a community fit for human habitation.

Indeed, the poet Juvenal's complaint about ancient Rome might be made against almost any modern city:

> *No matter how I hurry, I'm hampered by the crowds*
> *Who almost crush my ribs from front and back; this one*
> *Strikes me with his arm, another with a heavy board;*
> *My head is brushed by a beam, then I have an encounter*
> *With an oil-barrel. Mud clings to my legs in heavy clods,*
> *Large feet step on mine, and my toes get painfully*
> *Acquainted with a soldier's nailed boots.*

Yet despite everything, including itself, the truly great city is the stuff of legends and stories and a place with an ineradicable fascination. After cataloguing the horrors of life in imperial Rome, Urban Historian Lewis Mumford adds, almost reluctantly, that "when the worst has been said about urban Rome, one further word must be added: to the end, men loved her."

Uncomfortable and unbeautiful

What inspires such love and pulls people to the great cities? What indeed is a great city? It is almost easier to say what it is not. Except for its wealthy elites, great cities do not always provide easy or gracious living: lesser communities are almost always more comfortable. Juvenal could have walked peacefully in any number of attractive provincial cities. The average resident of one of Britain's planned new towns lives better than his counterpart in London. Yet London, notes Robert Ardrey, author of *The Territorial Imperative,* was a great city "even when the food was terrible, and you couldn't get a hot bath." Stockholm, Geneva and Johannesburg, by contrast, are three of the most comfortable cities in the world, but not one of them has even a shadowy claim to greatness.

The great city is not necessarily beautiful or well-planned. Venice and Florence are delights to the eye; yet neither has been a great city since the Renaissance. Brasília, one of the most elaborately designed of modern cities, is also one of the deadliest. An impressive physical setting is essential to city's greatness, but by itself that is not enough. Take Pittsburgh: its natural setting, at the junction of two rivers, is magnificent. Man botched the job of doing anything with it. Grand avenues and impressive architecture, though necessary to a great city, do not satisfy the equation. If the Third Reich had lasted another ten years, Berlin, which Hitler planned to rename Germania, would have become the world's most monumental city. It also would have been the most monumentally dull. In fact, it became second-rate on Jan. 30, 1933, when Hitler took power. A city cannot be both great and regimented. Blessed with culture, history and size, Moscow, Shanghai and Peking ought to be great cities, but they are not. They all lack the most important element: spontaneity of free human exchange. Without that, a city is as sterile as Aristophanes' Nephelococcygia, which was to be suspended between heaven and earth—and ruled by the birds.

Diversity and growth

A city governed by birds might be more comfortable than a city governed by men. But it would not be human, nor would it be great; a city is great only in its human associations, confusing as they may be. The ancient Athenians, true urbanites, delighted in the everyday drama of human encounter. For them, the city was the supreme instrument of civilization, the tool that gave men common traditions and goals, even as it encouraged their diversity and growth. "The men who dwell in the city are my teachers," said Socrates in Plato's *Phaedrus,* "and not the trees or the country." In turn, the city transformed them into something they had not been previously and could not have become without it—men who within a few generations produced more thought and works of beauty and value than the race had ever seen before.

Athens is a living memory of the Western world. Its great militaristic rival, Sparta, is all but forgotten as a center of human culture—and with reason. It is hard to classify as great a city that limits human contact, either through political repression, like Moscow, or through distance, like Los Angeles. It is also hard to imagine a city that is great only during the day. If too many of its occupants retreat to the suburbs to eat and sleep each evening, the place is, in fact, not so much a city as a collection of buildings—the unhappy truth about most American cities.

When nations were smaller than they are today, Athens could be great with 100,000 people, Renaissance Florence with 60,000, Alexandria with 700,000 and ancient Rome with something like 1,000,000—no more than live in metropolitan Indianapolis now. To represent all the diverse elements of much more populous societies—diversity is one essential of greatness—the city must now have a population of several millions. Cincinnati and Phoenix, to cite two typical American provincial cities, may be agreeable places to live in, but they are simply not large enough to contain, as does New York, the wide variety of types and temperaments that form the American character. Americans and foreigners alike call New York the least American of cities. In fact, it is the most American, reflecting as does no other all aspects of national life. Still, great is not synonymous with big. Calcutta and Bombay have more than enough people, but too many of them live in misery for the cities to be considered great.

It is doubtful that any one nation can claim more than one great city at any given time—great, after all, is a word that implies uniqueness. It is doubtful, too, that the world itself can contain more than half a dozen great cities at once. Indeed, a great city cannot exist in an unimportant country, which is why Urban Planner John Friedmann of U.C.L.A. prefers to call great cities "imperial cities." London and Paris are still great cities, but they lost some of their luster when world politics shifted to

Washington, Moscow and Peking—all of which lack at least one ingredient of greatness. Washington may be the political center of the nation, but, except for its superb galleries, cultural life there is as provincial as that of Des Moines or Butte, Mont. Both Mexico City and Rio de Janeiro have an effervescent vitality that suggests the potential of great cities. They may yet fulfill that potential as Mexico and Brazil grow in wealth and influence. After Tokyo, an undeniably great city despite its pedestrian architecture, Hong Kong is the most vibrant metropolis in Asia. It is, however, a city without a country—and therefore lacks greatness. Cairo is the capital of the Moslem world; but it lacks vitality.

Almost by definition, a city can be great only at the expense of other cities that are less than great. If the power, money and creativity that are now centered in London were divided with Birmingham, Birmingham would not become great, but London would be irretrievably lessened. A delight to live in and a joy to behold, Rome has certain qualities of greatness. It is redolent with tradition; it is the center of a universal religion; it has a people with character and a lively sense of politics. But it does not quite make the first rank of cities today, if only because Milan—cold but confident—controls too much of Italy's wealth and industrial power. The U.S., which is rich in both money and people, ought to be able to support two great cities, perhaps one on either coast, but it does not. A half-century ago, San Francisco looked as if it might become the great city of the West. Instead, it has remained a charming, eccentric and physically beguiling minor metropolis. Los Angeles, in the unlikely event that it ever should overcome its centrifugal forces, may yet become the Western collossus. Though it has many parts of greatness, Chicago, on the other hand, has always thought of itself as the "second city"—and so it always will be, if not third or forth. Even without the political power that resides in a national capital—one of the usual prerequisites for civic greatness—New York, the cultural, financial and commercial capital, is thus the only truly great city in the U.S.

Pleasures and vices

A city does not have to be comfortable to be great, but it nonetheless must have the ameni-ties to make life tolerable. Misery should not force thousands to live on the streets, as it does in the big cities of India; residents must be able to move from one place to another without undue strain or great delay; the conditions of life, ranging from prices to climate, cannot be totally oppressive. A great city also must have within its boundaries a large leisured class to pay for the culture and pleasure that are the outward signs of its pre-eminence. Money cannot buy a great city, but a great city must have money. The late Ian Fleming's definition of a "thrilling city," which emphasized girls and food, was adolescent, but he was not altogether wrong. A great city is always tolerant, even permissive, and provides outlets for a wide range of human pleasures and vices.

Whatever else it may possess or lack, a great city cannot be dull. It must have a sense of place and a feeling all its own, and its citizens must be different from and more vital than those who live elsewhere. The difference does not even have to be in their favor. The native Parisian, for instance, is born with an ineradicable hauteur that others define as rudeness, and the native New Yorker knows the meaning of avarice before he can spell the word. So strong is the trait that a century ago, Anthony Trollope waspishly noted that every New Yorker "worships the dollar and is down before his shrine from morning to night." To preserve the spirit of the place, he suggested, every man walking down Fifth Avenue should have affixed to his forehead a label declaring his net worth. No such label is really needed: a Parisian is a Parisian and a New Yorker a New Yorker, with no mistake possible. But a man who lives in Detroit or Cleveland is not necessarily identifiable as a Detroiter or a Clevelander.

First wild promise

The city was a place of worship before it was a fortress or trading center, with a magical attraction for men who had always lived in wandering groups or in villages. Prudence might have dictated other sites, but men returned, again and again, to the cities they remembered. Troy was destroyed and rebuilt so many times that archaeologists classify their discoveries as Troy I through IX; Troy VIIA was the "Ilios, city of magnificent houses," as Homer called it, that fell to the duplicity of Greeks. Leveled by the

Romans, Carthage returned to life to become the third city of the Empire; in the Middle Ages, Frederick Barbarossa poured salt on the blackened ruins of Milan, but neither fire nor salt could stop the city's resurgence.

The great city retains the ancient magic even today. Men do not always love it; often, indeed, they hate it. More often still, they hate it and love it by turns. Yet once caught by it, they cannot forget or long leave it. "If you are lucky enough to have lived in Paris as a young man," wrote Ernest Hemingway, who did love Paris, "then wherever you go for the rest of your life, it stays with you, for Paris is a moveable feast." New York, wrote Thomas Wolfe, who did not always love it, "lays hand upon a man's bowels; he grows drunk with ecstasy; he grows young

and full of glory; he feels that he can never die."

Like all magic, the attraction of the great city is, in the end, beyond analysis and beyond definition. Marshall McLuhan and the late Frank Lloyd Wright may have been right in arguing that the city should be replaced by smaller communities. But men, alas and thank God, are never strictly practical. Until people are known by numbers alone, the great city will continue to exist. F. Scott Fitzgerald was speaking of Manhattan, but he might just as well have been talking of London or Paris—or Nebuchadnezzar's Babylon or Justinian's Constantinople. Looking at it from afar, he said, was always to see it "in its first wild promise of all the mystery and beauty in the world."

Mathematics, ecology, and a piece of land

46

ALFRED G. ETTER

Among geographers, the men who call themselves cultural geographers are frequently characterized as the last hold-outs from quantification. With the exception of studies in locational analysis, which also involve facets of culture and hence cultural geography, this mathematical tool has been little utilized in the positing and solving of problems germane to cultural geography. Alfred Etter in this article from Landscape *clearly points out the reason for this aversion to mathematics and abstraction in cultural and ecological fields. Etter's case is built with a nice discussion of sequent occupance of a "noncomformist tree," a blackjack oak. The discussion of culture history and a plea for continuing subjectivity in matters of the landscape make this a significant article in the education of anyone concerned with cultural geography.*

Alfred G. Etter, "Mathematics, Ecology, and a Piece of Land," *Landscape*, XII, No. 3 (Spring 1963), pp. 28–31.

Several years ago I read an article called "Mathematical Systematization of Environment, Organism, and Habitat," by Edward Haskell. It was one of the first of many pleas for greater precision of terms in the study of ecology. The author claimed the predictability of the science was nil, and would remain so until it could be developed in a manner comparable to the physico-chemical sciences. The first prerequisite was a series of mathematical definitions. He then defined environment, habitat and organism, three essential concepts, in mathematical terms.

This seemed reasonable, for obviously the very foundation of all life is multiplication from a single cell, or even from a single substance; and the individual bird, corn plant or tree is the product. Within this product are contained all the millions of individual multiplications that produce growth. Animal and plant populations are only an extension of this same process. Environment is full of variables that can be measured, plotted and columned and so lend themselves to the methods of the punched card and the electronic brain. We are often told that there is nothing mathematics cannot do. Is there any reason why earth processes and living things could not be resolved into systems of data that could be fed to computers to produce a more predictable world?

I took this question with me for a walk one warm March day. I entered a woods where gaunt fallen trunks with tangled roots lay gathering leaves. It was a peaceful place; where could I put the question to a better test than here?

The nonconformist tree

Before me was a blackjack oak with wide-spreading limbs. At best a blackjack is a sort of home-made tree, patched together with crooked branches and leathery duck-foot-shaped leaves. Scrubby specimens cover the rocky hills of southern Missouri, but here on the windblown soil near the Mississippi this one had had the time and food to become a giant. I tried to reach around it, but could reach only halfway. A blackjack twelve feet around might be two-and-a-half centuries old. I took a cold mathematical look at it. Formulate as I might, it presented problems. It was too old, too eccentric. It had the jack-oak leaf, but there its conformity ended. It was neither integer nor fraction, even nor odd. It was an individual acorn that had fallen into the grass, and it had seen all the environment that Missouri had had to offer for two hundred and fifty years. John Donne has said "there is not so poor a creature but may be thy glass to see God in." I suspected that by looking at the blackjack carefully I might see not only some celestial light but considerable reflection from the mundane world as well. Whether this light could be focused to yield an equation was another question.

In 1764 when a group of Frenchmen founded the village of Saint Louis 12 miles southeast of the oak, they recorded that much of the land around was covered with prairie grass. In 1775, a small French settlement a few miles northwest was named Florissant, from the prairie flowers that surrounded it. In 1817 a party of surveyors was ordered into the field to block out the land between the two towns into sections. The big blackjack, after a century of living in an un-

charted wilderness, ended up in the middle of section twelve. As the surveyor scanned the land along the north section line he made an entry in his field notes: "Prairie, good soil, scattering blackjacks and hickories." On the east side, however, he remarked, "Soil rich and good for farming, thickly covered with oak and hickory."

Section twelve lay in that broad transition zone where forest met prairie. A traveler of the day, making a trip from St. Louis to Florissant, described the country thus: "I had my first view of the unfenced fields of flowers and trees. It was like a ride through a garden or the private land on a gentleman's estate."

I returned to the woods and found several big spreading black oaks and a single oak or two that must have been contemporaries of the blackjack judging from their size and open-grown habit, but this old confederacy was all but lost in an imposing forest of tall straight oaks and hickories of uniform age. Where had they come from? A few of them had recently been cut for fence posts, and I counted the rings. Without exception, they had begun to grow between 1815 and 1830.

I could only conjecture how they had suddenly intruded on the prairie, but I later discovered some observations which had a bearing on the matter. In 1819, R. W. Wells, one of the same surveyors who had blocked out the land, had published a note in the first volume of *The American Journal of Science*. He was discussing the origin of prairies.

"I have seen, in the country between the Missouri and Mississippi Rivers after unusually dry seasons, more than one hundred acres of woodland converted (by fire) into prairie. And again, where the grass has been prevented from burning by accidental causes, or the prairie has been depastured by large herds of domestic cattle, it will assume in a few years the appearance of a young forest . . . All the old French inhabitants (of St. Louis and Saint Charles, a nearby town) will tell you that the prairies formerly came immediately up to those places. Now the surrounding country for several miles is covered with a growth of trees of four or five inches diameter near the towns where the burning first ceased, and gradually diminishing in size as you recede, until you at length gain the open prairies." Here were data that had the ring of fact. Could they be punched on a card?

The first man to own the big oak, according

to old property records, was a certain John Engel who received it with a grant of 800 *arpens* of land in 1799 from the Spanish Governor of the Louisiana Territory. In five years, he built a house, cleared ten acres of land and put it under fence. The invasion had begun.

Prairie into forest

When Engel sold out for a dollar an acre in 1804, Simon Wood moved in to stay for sixteen years. The activities he engaged in are not recorded, but it can scarcely be doubted that he found the prairies and parklands an easy place to pasture stock. Paths and clearings began to intercept the prairie fires. Sprouts survived that should have died. Weak places in the sod caused by gnawing and treading of stock provided beds for the seeds of elms, snakeroot, milkweed, mullein and thistle. They in turn provided lighting places for birds that in their brief visits cast seeds, ready-scarified and acid treated, into the soil. Hackberries, wild cherries, mulberries, dogwoods and sassafras gained footholds this way.

Mice and squirrels planted treasures they never uncovered. 'Possum, coon and fox dropped blackberry, grape, persimmon and plum seeds along their routes. Hundreds of other seeds found ways to be spread into the grass; some had been waiting in the sod many years for a chance to grow. This transition zone belonged to anybody and man had unwittingly favored brush and trees. The reign of scattered oaks and flowering prairie had reached an end. Though ranging stock might consume or trample many plants and so help somewhat to stem the tide, they could never develop the efficiency or appetite of a prairie fire.

In 1820 Simon Wood had to sell his land to a speculator who then allowed it to lie idle. Wood received $3 an acre for his farm. In 30 years it would sell for $50 an acre. Here were some statistics, but what changes in habitat, environment and organism were measured by them?

A study of the ages of the tall straight trees in the woods showed that the invasion of the prairie by new oaks and hickories reached a peak shortly after this transaction, and then ceased as the vegetation closed over and shaded the ground. In this way changes of ownership have probably been subtly recorded on our landscapes more often than we suspect.

Looking down on this upwelling of new life around it, the blackjack was obliged to accept some of the responsibility for the crowd of trees, for many of them were little blackjacks. While it had flowered profusely in times past and shed its mast year after year, the fires and thick sod of the prairie had served as a sort of birth control. Now that the fires were gone, the oak became prodigiously fertile.

So it happens with living things. Life does not regard each acorn as sacred. A goodly share of them are assigned to destruction. Those that survive do so by time's or man's manipulation of the environment. Some few appear to have a destiny, as did this oak. One may bemoan the smothering of the individual by an irruption of sprouts, but that would seem to be an oft-repeated theme in nature. Man himself is not immune; take away the searing fire and even he floods the earth with himself.

The silent revolution

When nature makes a change it is thorough. This new colonization was a complex reorganization of species and environments. As grass yielded to brush and brush yielded to sprouts of hickory and oak, dickcissel, meadowlark and prairie chicken moved away. Indigo bunting and towhee and chat moved in. A revolution occurred in the soil as the organic matter of the prairie became available to new micro-organisms. Molds and fungi flourished, and new empires of insects were established.

Where environments interfinger, these changes can proceed with great rapidity. Surplus insects, woodpeckers, squirrels and quail periodically leave their ancestral home for unoccupied areas. Most of them fail and die, but when a large and uniformly usable territory suddenly becomes available they will move in and increase at tremendous rates. Likewise, these irruptions are often terminated by catastrophes, for uniformity in plant or animal societies carries with it a predisposition for sudden change.

The struggle for existence among plants is fairly predictable. The blackberries and elderberries and hazel become unproductive as the shade increases and the tap roots of trees drain the soil. Sassafras and persimmons fade, elms become spindly and die, and hickories and oaks begin their advance. On good soils blackjacks thin out as more vigorous trees take advantage of the fertility. Perhaps with the proper symbolism these successional data could be fitted into a progression of some kind.

A very placid, but unmathematical, view of these changes was painted by Edmund Flagg in a journal of a trip he made through the outskirts of St. Louis in 1836:

"The face of the country is neither uniform nor broken, but undulates imperceptibly away, clothed in dense forests of blackjack oak, interspersed with thickets of the wild plum, crabapple and the hazel. Thirty years ago the broad plain was a treeless, shrubless waste without a solitary farmhouse to break the monotony. But the annual fires were stopped, a young forest sprang into existence, and delightful villas and country seats are now gleaming from the dark foliage in all directions."

Fifteen years later, the old blackjack was sinking in the rising sea of trees when James H. LaMotte, a West Point major, acquired the land and revealed his dream of settling down in the country when his service in the army was completed. Envisioning a stable of horses he wrote his wife urging her to "make the man at the farm put in timothy, even if we have to furnish the grain." A new element had been added to the equation.

The long-looked-for day came in 1856 when the Major retired, but his plans were soon interrupted by the Civil War. When it was over, LaMotte resumed his goal of clearing more land and building his home at the edge of a woods. In November of 1867, young Frank LaMotte wrote his father, then traveling in the east, "We are well and comfortably fixed at Wildwood, plenty to eat, drink and smoke. Carpets down, potatoes all in, fences up, etc." Finally the farm had a name, Wildwood, a happy choice that reflected the owner's love for the woodland at his door. In time, because of this love, a tradition developed that no trees should be cut and so the woods and the old blackjack continued to thrive.

Wildwood

The fields produced, the woods grew, and the La Motte's Wildwood home became well known for beauty and hospitality. Then in 1892 the Major died. His wife lived on for twenty years at the old mansion, and in 1911

died at the age of 92. No heirs claimed the property.

Wildwood gathered ghostliness. Swifts flew in and out of the many chimneys and groundhogs heaped dirt about the summer house. Fringed carriages and riding equipment grew grey with dust and spider webs. The woods breathed on. Boys shot squirrels out of its hickories in August. Families wandered into the edges of the woods for autumn picnics. Some came, as did I, in search of an island in quietness, whatever the season.

I well remember the last time I visited the woods. I walked up the hill to the Mansion. Hidden among old locust trees it was a beautiful remnant, lingering like the blackjack, and the grey barns in the valley. Soon the green twilight descended, encompassing all the mystery and truth that lived within the woods and about the home. I climbed the stile and went down the dim road. I had found so much time hidden away that I was breathless trying to encompass it, and ill prepared to face even the most trivial evidence of the 20th Century—much less to consider seriously how this amazing place might be pictured or defined mathematically.

Wildwood was finally killed by a bright yellow machine. The blackjack was tough. It gave the bulldozer a good fight, but its death was really instantaneous when compared to its two hundred and fifty years of living. The fallen trees were pushed into a few big pyramids and a raging fire consumed the last evidences of LaMotte's beloved woods and the blackjack oak.

Part of the big hole on the horizon left by Wildwood was filled by a sign—*Forestwood—A Planned Community of 600 Homes*. The irony of the name *Forestwood* was continued in the street markers: Meadowcrest, Pondview, Oakwood, Hickory Lane. The Mansion still stood, but its Wildwood was gone, and its farm was gone. It suddenly became apparent to me how it is possible to make the muddle of ecology into a predictable science. Simplify the environment until there is nothing left but space!

Formula for a tree

Admittedly the world is built with multiplications. Environment, habitat, and organism bear a cause and effect relationship. The stuff called life may be resolvable into chemicals, patterns and bonds; but what formula could be drafted that would allow for all the adventures of the blackjack, what equation could predict the events of a single day in the woods? The woods was a symbol of the intractable, the inexpressible. Its beauty and order were the product of freedom, of millions of small decisions, of the meshing of infinite phenomena aided by tradition, tropism, instinct, intelligence and desire.

This complexity is confusing to man, hence his desire to reduce nature to something on paper so that every man on the street can claim to understand it. Because of some simple discoveries in this field it is man's idea that all life is mathematically designed, and that he can therefore control it.

The ecologist's role

This is a dangerous assumption. As it becomes evident that nature cannot be made to fit into his calculations, he increasingly resorts to the same solution as that used in Wildwood, where the environment and the life upon it were remade so that they *could* be described with a mathematical vocabulary. The end product of thinking mathematically is to want to think more mathematically, to wish for an earth where everything is predictable, neat, efficient and numbered. The wish, we were long ago reminded, is father to the thought. So the thought appears today as Edward Teller, in his plea for greater freedom to use his nuclear toys, has offered us the grand vision of a world reshaped by man to suit himself.

This is folly, and ecologists should be the first to say so. Man is hard put to it to design portable systems of productivity for space. Putting algae and men in a goldfish bowl is one thing. Building man an earth is something else. The truth of the matter is that man *has* an earth. He was born into it. He is a product of it. He cannot now decide that it is not to his liking, and change it willy-nilly.

It is the role of the ecologist to speak of this while others go about their simpler talks of planning ways of blowing the biota to bits. Aldo Leopold has said that an ecologist (and he referred to the kind with an ecological conscience) "lives alone in a world of wounds." Precious few ecologists today so martyr themselves. Hiding behind a veil of mathematics, they have joined Haskell's parade to punch cards and feed computers—in short, to produce from the beauty and complexity of Wildwood, a numbered and rootless *Forestwood* of the future.

Ecologists and all those of similar heart and mind have a responsibility to speak out concerning the limitations of mathematics and the impossibility of a completely predictable world. They should teach us to rejoice in complexity rather than simplicity, to object to a world already simplified to the point of boredom and ugliness and instability. Who is more aware than the ecologist of the intangible values of the landscape which make life dedicated to it? Who knows better that time is the only thing that can fashion an environment to suit a living thing, unless that living thing be caged? Who knows better that man is not, and never shall be, able to design a world for men—unless they too be caged?

Empty land, full land, poor folk, rich folk

DANIEL B. LUTEN

47

Man has clearly become proficient in his ability to modify environment. He is not, however, equally able to recognize the ramifications of his acts. Only within the last decade has man begun to show a general alarm at the magnitude of the modifications wrought through mobility, husbandry, and spatial organization. This recent awareness has been growing in crescendo fashion, and we are sure to witness a decade of interest, fright, crisis, and legislation.

Daniel Luten provides some illustrative comment on how man in the United States has stumbled into this role of despoiler. In tracing the process of change from nonconcern to nonchalance to angry alarm, Luten shows how our behavior is predicated upon the primacy of the economic world. His analysis concludes not only with a call for nonmonetary values for society, but with a specific call to geographers to concern themselves with the deteriorating environment. It is the geographer, and others who are concerned with the cultural landscape, who should use this perception of landscape evolution to restrain those who would continue to exploit the environment as though we continued to be poor people in an empty land.

My thesis is simplicity itself. We came, poor people, into an empty continent. We devised resource management policies for an empty land and for poor people. Now the land is full and we are rich beyond earthly precedent. Our needs have changed and, ever faster, still change. But we have failed to abandon, to adapt, to invent resource policies to keep up. And so we stretch, warp, patch, wire up, lick and promise. But it won't work.

Daniel B. Luten, "Empty Land, Full Land, Poor Folk, Rich Folk," *Yearbook of the Association of Pacific Coast Geographers*, Vol. 31 (1969), pp. 79–89.

Now let me pick up a little about "systems" from an earlier paper.[1] A system is simply some object of interest, a nucleus together with its significant environment. Its significant environment is what influences it, what constrains it, what guides it on its course through time.

In natural resources inquiry the inescapable nucleus of the system is man. But, try as we may, the task of understanding this system is beyond us. We must turn, and it is a token of defeat to do this, to subordinate systems, to resource systems. In such subsystems the nucleus may be the resource itself—a few dozen whooping cranes, a Douglas-fir forest, a salmon population, the North Cascades wild-lands.

The boundaries of the system will have to include all of the environment which is significant and should exclude that which is not. Perhaps a major part of the significant environment will be human influences and perhaps it will help if we categorize many of these under the heading of "disturbance." What we are largely concerned with is disturbance, existing or proposed, and the response to disturbance. The test of significance is whether it influences the future within the degree of precision sought or attainable. The overwhelming task of resources inquiry is to decide what must be included and what may be excluded. Here is where genius takes the high road and pedestrians the low.

But why say all of this, that everyone knows, in words less easily understood? Using such phrasing does not simplify the problem. True

[1] D. B. Luten, "Resource Quality and Value of the Landscape," in S. V. Ciriacy-Wantrup and James J. Parsons, eds., *Natural Resources—Quality and Quantity*, (Berkeley: University of California Press, 1967), pp. 19–34. Article is based on a paper read at the 31st annual meeting of the Association.

enough, but let me try now to fit some rough patterns into this machinery.

Without going into detailed history, accept my proposition that in three centuries the United States has changed from an empty land to a quite full land. Once if we wanted work done, we dammed a rill and diverted its water. Once if we wanted to get rid of anything, we threw it in the river, confident that it would never be seen again. Once if the passenger pigeons nested nearby, we harvested as many as we could. If ever anything was in infinite supply, it was passenger pigeons. Once if we plowed up and down the hill and our cropland washed away, we moved on to new land. When men wanted land, we gave it to them. If the effete east, becoming crowded earlier, had doubts and restricted the gift of land, we in the west subverted their rules. Our policy was to occupy and develop. If *we* had not, others willing to occupy would have appeared.

These things that we did bothered no one else. It was a land of infinite resources. On this all agreed. Stuart Chase said in a book from a generation ago, *Rich Land, Poor Land,* "The whole system is wrong. . . . It started under the American concept of infinity."[2]

---

2 Stuart Chase, *Rich Land, Poor Land,* (New York: McGraw-Hill, 1936), p. 130.

In recalling that period, think, please, in terms of systems of widely dispersed families and settlements. One man's actions did not disturb his neighbors; he was not a part of his neighbors' significant environment. The boundaries of their systems did not overlap.

The symbol on the map of this era is Yellowstone Park (Figure 1). To define the boundaries of the Park took eight lines:

> . . . *commencing at the junction of Gardiner's river with the Yellowstone river, and running east to the meridian passing ten miles to the eastward of the most eastern point of Yellowstone lake; thence south along said meridian to the parallel of latitude passing ten miles south of the most southern point of Yellowstone lake; thence west along said parallel to the meridian passing fifteen miles west of the most western point of Madison lake; thence north along said meridian to the latitude of the junction of the Yellowstone and Gardiner's rivers; thence east to the place of beginning.*[3]

That is all. No one knew what else was there; no competing demands existed; no one cared.

But times change. Our technological capacity to change the face of the earth grew beyond all

---

3 17 Stat. 32 (S. 392, H. R. 464, 42 Cong. 2 Sess.)

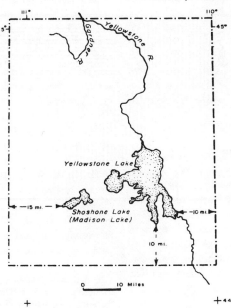

Figure 1. Yellowstone National Park in northwestern Wyoming.

precedent. Our numbers, too! We began to rub against each other. Cattlemen quarreled with sheepmen for a place on the range—that once infinite range. One man's sewage becomes another man's drink. Water developments now are focused on great dams with "forebays," "afterbays," "fishways," recreational development, flood control criteria, and must conform to demands for irrigation water, must be integrated as peaking units in great power systems.

We found that if we permitted free access to the natural wealth of the land, someone, always someone else, would take more than his reasonable share. We began to develop a legal code constraining what might lawfully be done to the landscape. It can be said with both fairness and bitterness that we locked stables already well robbed. Thus, Stuart Chase continued: "By the time the theory of forest inexhaustibility became clearly fallacious . . . America's magnificent forest [had fallen] before an economic system which had no philosophy of conserving natural wealth."[4] We finally demanded replanting of timberlands. We denied access to the market place of virtually all inland wildlife; we imposed inefficiencies on the harvesting of marine wildlife. We devised legislative hearings

---

[4] Chase, *loc. cit.*

so voluminous that it is asked whether we will one day cut our forests to provide the paper which records the Congressional hearings on their fate.

This simply says that in a full land what one man does affects his neighbors. Each man is now a part of his neighbors' significant environment. The subsystem boundaries overlap endlessly. The entire resource system seems to encompass all activities, to be continent-wide.

The symbol on the map today is the proposed North Cascades National Park (Figure 2). A century ago the significant environment would have included little but the geographic neighborhood and the boundaries of the system could have encircled the mountains in any fashion. Today every section line is a quarrel. Every man has different plans for every valley. Wilderness as unwanted and unknown land is gone. Influences of remote places are manifestly significant: the prospective price of copper, of lumber, of electricity, the remote fortunes of Congressional politics, the population of hunters and of the North Cascades Conservation Council and its friends. All of these may affect the future of the North Cascades.

But we continue to act as if we had an empty land to fill. In the arid southwest we came to call this "reclamation." But also we came to

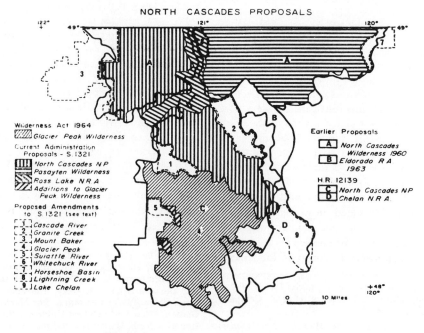

Figure 2.

have qualms over our record of giving away our natural wealth in support of development. We had given land to all comers; we had condoned, perhaps encouraged, widespread fraud in the sale of timberlands. Perhaps our moral sense in those times can be expressed by a paraphrase of a rhyme by Ogden Nash, ". . . robbing is a crime, unless you rob the Government ten million at a time." So finally we felt obliged to demonstrate that development was beneficial and accordingly we began to calculate benefits to prove to skeptics that such undertakings would promote the general welfare.

But we quite ignored reasonable notions of a system and tended to define the significant environment as that region in which benefits could be shown, not as the region significantly influencing or influenced by the activity. To take as homely an example as I can coin, a new recreational lake can be argued to be beneficial because sales of beer at it will go up. But perhaps church contributions nearby will go down, the money having been spent on beer. Who is to say which is the more beneficial? Carefully, though, we do not ask such questions, even though we could turn for help to Housman's couplet:

For malt does more than Milton can
To justify God's ways to man.[5]

It was a policy for an empty land; can it possibly be germane to a full land? Is it wise to load the southwest corner of the nation with people? The land is already tilting!

So much for the empty versus the full land. How about the poor versus the rich society? In our early days on this continent we were poor, not as poor as most of the people of the earth, but poor by today's standards. We agreed on what we wanted from a tree: we wanted to burn it to keep warm, to build something from it, or to sell it. It seemed unlikely that we, or any of the world's people would want more from it. J. B. Say stated, in a premise to Say's Law, the proposition that human wants are infinite and can never be satisfied.[6]

But in the nineteenth century in the Atlantic community signs of a change appeared. The combination of the raw materials and markets of new worlds, of land to absorb population growth, of an explosive technology, of declining birth rates led to an affluence more widespread than ever envisioned. And so today we hear of the "man who has everything." While he is not common, neither is he royalty. Even though many still want, more and more we hear, "I have enough." More and more we see a rejection of the scramble for a place on the ladder of conforming achievement. Our attitudes are influenced by such people. Say's premise is not dead, but it is dying.

Ambivalence in human ambitions is not new. The church made demands at odds with economics. Charles Dickens, concerned throughout with the nineteenth century factory economy, brought the matter clearly to light in *A Christmas Carol*. Even Scrooge, the symbol of the pure economic individual, flinched when brought face to face with the issue. But American affluence today, unlike earlier societies, is not directed toward the greater glory of God, neither toward hedonism. Americans in their search for a national identity have made much of nature and of the idea of wilderness.[7] The demands of the nineteenth century geologists for more time than the Bible could grant may have helped, as certainly did Darwin's unification of man with the rest of life.

But just now let me recall Thoreau's "some things are more to be admired than used." Here is the signpost to two roads. Gifford Pinchot took one and brought forth a conservation movement dedicated to the proposition that natural resources should be saved because they are useful. John Muir, with a splinter of the conservation movement, took the other road with the proposition that the landscape should be saved because it is beautiful.

Efforts persist to nullify the difference by arguing that beauty is valuable and therefore useful. You can usually stir up a quarrel by asserting that the value of beauty is not adequately measured by its price. Thus the Mona

---

[5] "Shropshire Lad," in *The Collected Poems of A. E. Housman,* (New York: Henry Holt & Company, 1924), LXII, p. 88.

[6] Robert Heilbroner, *The Worldly Philosophers,* (New York: Simon and Schuster, 1953), pp. 80–81.

[7] George Perkins Marsh, *Man and Nature,* David Lowenthal, ed., (Cambridge, Massachusetts: Harvard University Press, 1965); Hans Huth, *Nature and the American,* (Berkeley: University of California Press, 1957): Leo Marx, *The Machine in the Garden,* (New York: Oxford University Press, 1964); Roderick Nash, *Wilderness and the American Mind,* (New Haven: Yale University Press, 1967).

Lisa is said to be beautiful and is worth five million dollars. How beautiful is my $5 print of the Mona Lisa? One-millionth as beautiful? Only to a connoisseur of dollars, not of art. In fact the quality of beauty stands apart from the quality of usefulness. Thoreau's distinction has merit.

We try to gloss over other distinctions in quality by putting dollar values on them. But it won't work. Does the man who goes to the beach in a Cadillac have twice as much fun as he who goes in a Volkswagen? It costs him twice as much. Is our wildlife resource valued because we spend 20 billion dollars annually on services and facilities for hunting and fishing? If so, how valuable is the cotton boll weevil, on which we spend a half billion dollars annually? Whose answer will you prefer, the pesticide manufacturer's, the cotton grower's, or the man who pays the taxes for cotton price support?

Let me try one more example: Recently a beautiful old eucalyptus tree on the Berkeley campus took ill. It was argued that a small new parking lot nearby was responsible although general campus unrest was just as likely a cause. At any rate the parking lot was removed and the soil surface restored. It was then argued, since replacement of the parking spaces at going rates would have cost $30,000, that this

shows the tree was worth at least $30,000. None of this argument stands close inspection. The alternative lot was not built so no one spent $30,000. The effect on parking was, in a sense, that the few people who parked in the lot instead must park at the outer limit of campus parking a half-mile away. More realistically, a good many people must park one space farther away. Further, they don't know they are parking farther away and haven't been asked if they prefer this hardship rather than the tree. The tree died anyway.

In a subsequent tree controversy also on the Campus, some handsome quite sizable redwoods were threatened by a road relocation. An alternative existed, but it would have cost $60,000 and would have come out of the University's budget. The budget people thought it preferable to remove the trees. Were the redwoods less beautiful than the eucalyptus?

I want to suggest now that usefulness and admirability are, in fact, incommensurable quantities. In Figure 3 I have shown several pairs of antitheses: "Used" versus "admired," "quantity" versus "quality," and so on. On the vertical scale in the simple vector diagrams are measured changes in what broadly may be called economic attributes; on the horizontal scale, changes in aesthetic attributes. Only posi-

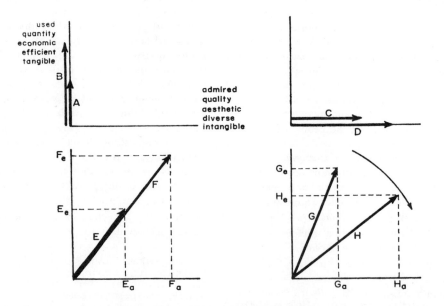

Figure 3. Incommensurability of disturbances.

tive values appear in this quadrant; negative values would appear in the three unused quadrants. In the first diagram, of two proposals to disturb the landscape which do not change its beauty but which increase its usefulness in different degree, B, the larger, is preferred. In the second diagram, of two proposals to disturb the landscape which do not change its usefulness, but which change its beauty in different degree, D, the larger, is preferred. In the third diagram, of two proposals to disturb the landscape which increase its beauty and usefulness in equal degrees, F, the larger, is preferred. Thus far the matter is trivially simple. What, though, is the decision when one proposal leads to greater usefulness but less beauty than its alternate: Which of G and H is preferred?

No unequivocal answer can be given; however, as a society becomes richer, it will tend to prefer H over G. As affluence increases, preference in this quadrant rotates clockwise. Perhaps, given a bit of mystical license, I can say, "This is the clock of progress."

One final comment on this symbolism: rather than two incommensurable attributes as suggested in the figure, in fact a host of incommensurables must be envisioned. The present versus the future is a notable example. The practical question which will not cease to plague us is: How many of these are significant?

Another phrasing of the situation is that the economist works in economic space, the modern conservationist in aesthetic space, and that someone had better come along soon who can work in a manifold of such spaces.

When we were poor and the land was empty, the economic criteria for decision were reasonable. The market is a fine device for making small decisions on allocation of sparse means. It has not proved its merit with great decisions, neither for disposal of abundant means. And on the available evidence the economists again working with baling wire, tire patches, and paint are not succeeding brilliantly. And yet in the field of resources management, society has given them the ball, the rules, and the referee, and has let them come up with "externalities," "opportunity cost," "shadow pricing," and "benefit cost analysis."

The schemes of benefit cost analysis used to evaluate major resource disturbance proposals combine qualities so grossly incommensurable that they have no meaning. Answers rest on irrational assumptions. Anyone who works backward from the desired answers to the necessary assumptions is no more honest than he should be; anyone who does not is no wiser than he should be. Any prestidigital computer, any numbersmith, can take an intricate mess of unsound data, run them through a host of calculations until the idiocy of their birth has disappeared, and come out with impressive results fully and predictably capable of convincing legislators. The legislators, after all, simply want to be able to say they did what the calculations said was wise. This was not invented with fancy electronic computers; they only make the act more impressive. The basic computer warning still holds: "GIGO, garbage in, garbage out." If you put in lies and junk, you will get out, in silk and satin, lies and junk. A better way must exist. And yet Wilbur Zelinsky recently wrote: "It is abundantly clear that neither ecologist, economist, geographer, planner, nor any other professional has really bothered himself about the global wholeness of our emergent North America, and, from the evidence . . . that they don't yet know how. (I like to daydream about my fellow geographers heroically marching into a breach that seems providentially designed for them; but I know better.)"[8]

Again, George Macinko has recently written, "Were America dependent on the university alone for the ethical and aesthetic vision necessary to the establishment of a conservation attitude things would be in a sorry state."[9]

Traditionally the teaching of conservation has fallen to the geographer. Yet today the geographer has recoiled from his task and prefers to look backward to easier times when the patterns on the land were leaden rather than mercurial.

Meanwhile, proceeding without help from the university, proceeding in defiance of the dicta of the resource economists, a conservation movement based on the thesis that beauty cannot be reduced to dollars has come on the stage. Still only a shadow, it grows in strength perhaps more rapidly than any directing element in our

8 *Landscape*, Volume 17, Number 2, Winter 1967–68, pp. 38–39.

9 *The Biologist*, Volume 50, Numbers 1 and 2, January 1968, pp. 1–19.

society and soon will shape the face of the land.

The geographer's rejection of a directing role in and failure to study this movement may end up merely hurting geography. Is the day nearing when geographers will peer, surprised, on a landscape which has been molded by forces under their very nose, forces which they preferred to ignore; and all because geographers failed to march into this "breach that seems providentially designed for them"?

Where is science taking us?

F. RAYMOND FOSBERG

48

This selection by Raymond Fosberg has been chosen to close this anthology because of the clarity with which he states man's likely choices for the future. If man continues to create his distinctive cultural landscapes like a pioneer, then his future on earth can be only chaotic and tragic. Even if man does not eliminate himself through his exploitive overuse of the earth, he will evolve to "be harder, and the gentler traits that we now admire, as well as the appreciation of and need for the beauty of nature, will be bred out of him."

As has been made apparent in this anthology, man has gained a truly frightening capacity for modifying his environment. The combination of this ability with rapidly increasing populations in environments which they deplete of natural resources at a destructive rate bodes no good for man. Pioneer-species characteristics, when found in animal populations, result in short-term destruction of a habitat and great reduction in the size of the pioneer group. Fosberg draws a timely parallel between such patterns and man's activities on earth.

The thrust of Fosberg's article, and in fact of this section of the anthology, is simple. The power which man has developed to create a distinctive and productive cultural landscape must be immediately comprehended so that continuing modifications of the earthscape may be

F. Raymond Fosberg, "Where Is Science Taking Us?", *Saturday Review*, November 14, 1959, pp. 72–73. Copyright 1959, Saturday Review, Inc.

made in closer harmony with our environment, our emotional needs, and the earth as a whole.

Most organisms occupy a very definite, usually rather restricted position on a scale ranging from the *pioneer* types that inhabit raw newly-available habitats to the so-called *climax* organisms, those of mature stable communities. An important distinction separating these types is the duration of their occupancy of habitat. The *pioneer* exerts a strong effect on its environment and tends to change the environment relatively rapidly, soon rendering its own further occupancy unsuitable. The *climax* organism, on the contrary, does not bring about or further such change, but lives in adjustment with its environment and may even tend to stabilize the environment and maintain equilibrium.

Good examples of *pioneer* organisms are the army worm and the migratory locust, which swarm over open cultivated fields devouring everything green and are forced to move on, hunting for other forage, or perish from starvation.

The gray squirrel may exemplify a *climax* organism. It lives in the stable oak-hickory forest, eating the surplus acorns, but, incidentally and unintentionally, in the course of storing acorns for winter use, planting enough of them to assure ample reproduction of the oaks on which it depends.

The physiology of most organisms determines

their patterns of ecological behavior and only changes in the organisms' genetic makeup can alter these patterns. In man the emergence of the faculty of intelligence makes possible self-determination or choice of type of ecological behavior, probably for the first time in the course of organic evolution. Man, as a species, has it within his power to fulfill the role of a *pioneer* (but in all probability temporary) member of the world biotic community, or the role of a permanent *climax* species.

Modern man seems clearly to be following the role of a *pioneer* species. His numbers are increasing geometrically. His ability to modify his environment is likewise growing geometrically and is being used without restraint. His rate of consumption of the resources of his environment naturally follows the curve of the products of the two factors just mentioned.

Two points in this picture are of especial concern here.

First, most or all of the resources essential to man's life or well-being are definitely limited in amount and some are already in short supply. Most of these shortages are not yet so apparent in the United States, especially as we are financially able to buy abroad what we do not have here. But in many countries raw materials for industry such as petroleum, coal, iron ore, and bauxite, potash and phosphate for fertilizers, and even basic foods, are in desperately short supply. Fertile agricultural land is no longer to be had for the asking. In large areas of the Earth lack of water is a specter always in sight.

In the United States, an attempt to invade the Porcupine Mountains State Park in Michigan for its low-grade copper ore has just been averted. Here it was proposed to sacrifice needed recreational resources to satisfy a need for minerals. Forced choices of this sort will become more and more frequent. Space, as a resource, has become important almost overnight. Bitter fights are already being waged over the location of super-highways, because of differences of opinion on the relative importance of the use of the same land for highways versus residence or recreation. In the western United States a contest of giants is going on over what areas are to use the waters of the Colorado River drainage. If the upper Colorado states win, as now seems to be the case, California and Arizona will have much less water, and water is a limiting factor in their

development. Such problems were scarcely imagined fifty years ago.

Secondly, man was physically and emotionally evolved to fit a particular range of habitats. Early fossil man is known principally from such warm areas as Indonesia. Before he discovered the use of fire and skin clothing to keep himself warm he was confined to climates where artificial warmth or protection were unnecessary. He was also very likely restricted to forest edges, stream sides, and coastal sites where he could, without implements, secure fruits, seeds, and shellfish for food. Little is known about the exact habitat range of man prior to his discovery of fire, but we may be sure that with this discovery and that of weapons he was able to spread to colder regions and places where food was harder to get. This was the beginning of technology. By means of modern technology he has managed to increase vastly his habitat range. Physically little changed, he has spread into most of the natural environments on the Earth's land surface and into a great diversity of those of his own making.

Technologically, it is probably feasible to modify almost any environment to accommodate human occupation physically. This will be true, as long as resources hold out, of all except, perhaps, habitats highly contaminated with radioactive materials. Man's physiology is reasonably well understood and his physical requirements are the preoccupation of most of the constructive efforts of applied science.

The adjustment between man's emotional and nervous makeup and these profound changes in his environment is a more immediately serious matter. Failure of the nervous system, the sensory and communications apparatus of the human organism, is not merely equivalent to, but, from the point of view of society, worse than, complete failure of the whole organism, or death. Neither the physiology of the nervous system nor the functioning of the human mind and emotions is understood nearly as well as are the physical requirements of man. His nervous system and its product, the mind, have shown themselves to be very resilient and have adapted to an amazing amount of change from the situations they were evolved to meet. But instincts are an essential part of the organism, evolved along with its physical attributes and adaptations, to assure survival in the natural environment. It seems clear enough that conflict between instincts and the natural environment would not exist, and that such conflict would arise and increase as the environment became modified.

It is entirely possible, even probable, that this is the modern form assumed by natural selection in the continued evolution of man. If so, this means that the surviving portion of the human race will be different from man as we know him now. He will be harder, and the gentler traits that we now admire, as well as the appreciation of and need for the beauty of nature, will be bred out of him.

It is entirely possible that man will not survive the changed environment that he is creating, either because of failure of resources, war over their dwindling supply, or failure of his nervous system to evolve as rapidly as the change in environment will require. Or he may survive only in small numbers, suffering the drastic reduction that is periodically the lot of *pioneer* species, or he may change beyond our recognition. All of these alternatives have plenty of precedent among *pioneer* plant and animal species.

The fossil record is replete with species of plants and animals that have not survived environmental change. Witness the whole order of the dinosaurs, the giant plants of the coal periods, and the widespread sabre-tooth tigers.

Modern *pioneers* that build up large populations when new open habitats are available and which suffer drastic reduction when their habitats become modified have been mentioned above. The army worm and migratory locust are plagues in open grasslands and cultivated areas, not in undisturbed forests. Every forest fire scar and every abandoned cultivated field provide equally striking examples of *pioneer* weeds, coming in, increasing by thousands for two or three years, changing the environment, and dying down to mere stragglers that persist under the changed conditions till another opportunity arises.

Change in the characteristics of species as environments change is one of the normal patterns of evolution. The classic example is the gradual evolution of the horse from a tiny primitive five-toed denizen of the forest to the highly specialized one-toed inhabitant of open plains that we know today. This took place with increasing prevalence of plains conditions during the later geological epochs.

If the foregoing fates are not palatable to man, the possibility of assuming another role than that of the *pioneer* species may still be open to him. If this is true, it will be the part of the sciences of ecology and geography, especially the former, to show the way. These two, alone, have as a principal function the building up of knowledge and understanding of the environment as such. The extent and nature of the change in man's treatment of his environment necessary to the establishment of a permanent equilibrium with it can only be formulated through a broad ecological approach.

I have suggested elsewhere that any community, at whatever level, from town to nation, might profitably have on its staff of public servants a community ecologist. We now regard it as normal to employ engineers to supervise our highway, water, and sewer activities. It is perhaps even more important to give an influential status to an ecologist. His specific task would be to study all proposals that would result in any modification of the environment to determine if the modification would result in a less satisfactory habitat for man.

Especially at the higher levels of community integration, as in state and national governments, a similar office of community geographer might also be very appropriate. His task would be the same as that of the community ecologist but he would approach it through major geographical patterns. His understanding of the environment would be extensive rather than intensive, but his function would be the same, to keep man from making mistakes that would degrade his environment.

How to achieve a stable biotic community with man as a member is certainly the most important single question ever to face any branch of applied science. No answer is yet available. It must certainly involve some means of stabilizing or even reducing the human population of the world. It will involve the elimination or control of greed and the rational, balanced, use of natural resources. There must be achieved the management and utilization of the environment on a true sustained yield basis. And all this must be accomplished without altering the environment beyond the capacity of the human organism as we know it to live in it.

As the task progresses and basic understanding develops, the human factor will loom larger and larger. As the physical and biological framework is outlined the task of fitting man into it and establishing his role in the new system will become paramount. Even more critical will be the educational problem of influencing man to assume this role. Whether as a scientific community we are sufficiently interested, far-sighted, and courageous to attack such a problem may well determine the future of man on Earth.

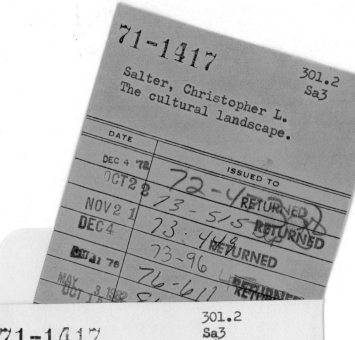